ULTIMATE
SPORTS
FACT & QUIZ BOOK

PAUL DREW

Cartoons By
PETER COUPE

STOPWATCH

Published by
Stopwatch Publishing Limited
1-7 Shand Street
London SE1 2ES

For Bookmart Limited
Desford Road
Enderby
Leicester LE9 5AD

This edition published 2000

The views and opinions expressed in this book are not
necessarily those of Bass Brewers Limited

ISBN 1 900032 19 8

Printed and bound in Finland

FOREWORD

Any self-respecting sports lover will be able to tell you which team won the 1996 World Cup in football or who ran the first sub-four minute mile. But you'll have to go to the true trivia professional if you want to know jockey Willie Carson's middle names, or find out how many contestants entered the 1899 British Open golf tournament. This book contains both the easy and the hard questions, with plenty of middle ground, so whatever your level of skill, you're bound to score. Whether your interest is in being the most respected member of your local pub quiz team or the world's foremost expert on football, all the answers are here, as are most of the questions!

At any time, dip into the facts section to refresh your memory on some of the golden years and glorious highlights of your favourite sports or simply improve and widen your knowledge from the pool of sports facts. The Carling Ultimate Sports Fact and Quiz Book is a testament to the individuals and the teams whose performances have marked the world of competitive games.

CONTENTS

THE QUIZZES

QUIZ CONTENTS

THE ULTIMATE SPORTS FACT AND QUIZ BOOK

FOOTBALL CRAZY!

THE ULTIMATE SPORTS FACT AND QUIZ BOOK

Quiz 01   FOOTBALL CRAZY!

1. Who is England's third most prolific goalscorer after Charlton and Lineker?

2. Who refereed the 1994 F.A. Cup Final between Manchester United and Chelsea?

3. How many full England caps did Peter Osgood win?

4. Who was African Footballer of the Year in 1991 & '92?

5. At which London club was England's 1993 U-21 fixture versus Poland played?

6. Who was South American Player of the Year from 1974-76?

7. Who scored four goals for England in their 9-2 win versus Northern Ireland in the 1949/50 season?

8. Who was top scorer in Division Two in 1990/91?

9. Against which country did Malcolm MacDonald score all five goals for England in a 1974/5 fixture at Wembley?

10. By what score did Nottingham Forest beat West Ham in the 1990/91 F.A. Cup?

11. Who won the 1994 F.A. Challenge Trophy?

12. Which Celtic player was top scorer in the Scottish Premier League in 1990/91?

13. By what aggregate score did Leeds United beat Manchester United in the 1993 F.A. Youth Challenge Cup?

14. By what aggregate score did Rangers beat Valetta in the 1990/91 European Cup?

15. To which club did Blackburn Rovers sell Colin Hendry in 1989?

ANSWERS 1. Jimmy Greaves 2. David Elleray 3. 4 4. Abedi Pele 5. Millwall 6. Elias Figueroa 7. Jack Rowley 8. Teddy Sheringham 9. Cyprus 10. 4-0 11. Woking 12. Tommy Coyne 13. 4-1 14. 10-0 15. Manchester City.

Quiz 02 FOOTBALL CRAZY!

1. How many goals did Geoff Hurst score for England?

2. Diego Maradona won the South American Player of the Year in 1979 & '80 whilst playing for which two clubs?

3. Who scored a hat-trick for England in their 1962/63 8-1 win versus Switzerland?

4. Who won the 1990/91 Third Division Championship?

5. How many full England caps did Norman Hunter win?

6. Who defeated Chelsea in the semi-finals of the 1990/91 Rumbelows League Cup?

7. Which club sold Mark Lawrenson to Liverpool in 1981?

8. In which Italian city was England's 1994 World Cup qualifier away fixture versus San Marino played?

9. By what aggregate score did Aberdeen beat Famagusta in the 1990/91 European Cup Winners' Cup?

10. In the 1952/53 season who scored in five out of his eight games for England?

11. Who were Italian Serie A champions in 1990/91?

12. Against which country did Bryan Robson score a hat-trick for England in 1984/85?

13. Who were league champions of Portugal in 1990/91?

14. Who won the 1994 F.A. Challenge Vase?

15. Which team won the Scottish First Division in 1990/91?

ANSWERS 1. 24 2. Argentinos Juniors & Boca Juniors 3. Bobby Charlton 4. Cambridge United 5. 28 6. Sheffield Wednesday 7. Brighton & Hove Albion 8. Bologna 9. 5-0 10. Nat Lofthouse 11. Sampdoria 12. Turkey 13. Benfica 14. Diss Town 15. Falkirk.

Quiz 03 FOOTBALL CRAZY!

1. Against which two countries did Gary Lineker score hat-tricks for England in 1985/86?

2. How many goals did Mick Channon score for England?

3. Who was South American Player of the Year in 1989?

4. How many full England caps did Brian Kidd win?

5. Who was Arsenal manager from 1983-86?

6. To which club did Arsenal transfer Ian Ure in 1969?

7. Who scored a hat-trick for England in their 1960/61 9-3 win against Scotland?

8. Who was South American Player of the Year in 1993?

9. Who did Arsenal beat in the 1994 F.A. Youth Challenge Cup?

10. Who finished bottom of the First Division in 1990/91?

11. By what aggregate score did Manchester United beat Wrexham in the 1990/91 European Cup Winners' Cup?

12. Who were Republic of Ireland league champions in 1990/91?

13. Who were Turkish league champions in 1990/91?

14. Who were Second Division champions in 1983/4 and 1988/9?

15. To which Italian club did Werder Bremen sell Karl-Heinz Riedle in 1991?

ANSWERS 1. Portugal and Turkey 2. 21 3. Bebeto 4. 2 5. Don Howe 6. Manchester United 7. Jimmy Greaves 8. Carlos Valderrama 9. Millwall 10. Derby County 11. 5-0 12. Dundalk 13. Besiktas 14. Chelsea 15. Lazio.

Quiz 04   FOOTBALL CRAZY!

1. Who finished bottom of the Premier League in 1993/94?

2. Who finished top scorer in league Division One in 1990/91?

3. From which club did Aston Villa buy Ian Ormondroyd in 1989?

4. How many full England caps did Cyril Knowles win?

5. Who were Belgian league champions in 1990/91?

6. How many goals did Martin Peters score for England?

7. After Aston Villa beat Internazionale 2-0 at home in the 1990/91 UEFA Cup, what was the away leg score?

8. From which German club did Juventus sign Thomas Hässler?

9. Who scored a hat-trick for England in their 4-0 win versus Peru in 1961/2?

10. Who preceded Bill Shankly as Liverpool boss?

11. Which team won the F.A. Youth Challenge Cup from 1953-57?

12. Who did the Greek league and cup double in 1990/91?

13. By how many points did Liverpool win the 1975/76 league title?

14. From which club did Sheffield Wednesday buy David Hirst in 1986?

15. Who was South American Player of the Year in 1995?

ANSWERS 1. Swindon Town 2. Alan Smith 3. Bradford City 4. Four 5. Anderlecht 6. 20 7. 3-0 to Inter 8. Cologne 9. Jimmy Greaves 10. Phil Taylor 11. Manchester United 12. Panathinaikos 13. One 14. Barnsley 15. Enzo Francescoli.

THE ULTIMATE SPORTS FACT AND QUIZ BOOK

Quiz 05 FOOTBALL CRAZY!

1. Which team finished bottom of the First Division in 1993/94?

2. Which team finished bottom of the Second Division in 1990/91?

3. How many goals did Allan Clarke score for England?

4. After Hearts beat Bologna 3-1 at home in the 1990/91 UEFA Cup, what was the score in the away leg?

5. By how many points did Liverpool win the 1976-77 Football League title?

6. How many full England caps did Brian Little win?

7. Who won the 1990/91 Dutch league title?

8. By what score did Swindon defeat Arsenal in the 1969 League Cup Final?

9. Geoff Hurst famously scored a 1966 World Cup Final hat-trick. Who did he hit three against in 1968/9 in an England shirt?

10. To which two teams was goalkeeper Gary Walsh loaned whilst at Manchester United?

11. At which league club did Everton's Dave Watson begin his career?

12. For which international side does Bradford City's Gunnar Halle play?

13. Who were 1997/8 Austrian league champions?

14. Who was African Footballer of the Year in 1996?

15. Who finished third in the First Division in 1990/91?

ANSWERS 1. Peterborough United **2.** Hull City **3.** Ten **4.** 3-0 to Bologna **5.** One **6.** One **7.** PSV Eindhoven **8.** 3-1 **9.** France **10.** Airdrieonians and Oldham **11.** Liverpool **12.** Norway **13.** Sturm Graz **14.** Nwankwo Kanu **15.** Crystal Palace.

Quiz 06   FOOTBALL CRAZY!

1. Who scored a hat-trick for England in 1960/61 in their 8-0 win against Mexico?

2. Which team did the League and Cup double in Croatia in 1997/8?

3. From which club did Leicester buy Steve Walsh?

4. Who were Spanish league champions in 1990/91?

5. How many goals did Jack Charlton score for England?

6. In his three season spell at Lazio, how many league goals did Paul Gascoigne score?

7. Who was PFA Young Player of the Year in 1991?

8. Who was Scottish PFA Young Player of the Year in 1991?

9. How many full England caps did Malcolm MacDonald win?

10. From which Italian club did Juventus sign Roberto Baggio in 1990?

11. Who was African Footballer of the Year in 1994 & '95?

12. Who was sacked as Leicester manager in January 1991?

13. Who scored four for England against San Marino in a 1992/3 fixture?

14. Who was South American Player of the Year in 1996?

15. For what international side does Paulo Wanchope play?

ANSWERS 1. Bobby Charlton 2. Croatia Zagreb 3. Wigan 4. Barcelona 5. Six 6. Six 7. Lee Sharpe 8. Eoin Jess 9. 14 10. Fiorentina 11. George Weah 12. David Pleat 13. David Platt 14. Jose-Luis Chilavert 15. Costa Rica.

Quiz 07 FOOTBALL CRAZY!

1. With which London club did Marcus Gayle begin his career?

2. FC Valetta were league champions of which European country in 1997/8?

3. Who scored 10 goals for Luton Town against Bristol Rovers in a Division 3 (South) fixture in 1936?

4. How many goals did Glenn Hoddle score for England?

5. With which club did Paul Warhurst begin his career?

6. From which Dutch club did Milan sign Ruud Gullit in 1987?

7. Who was sacked as Shrewsbury's manager in January 1991?

8. Against whom did Ted MacDougall score 9 for Bournemouth in the 1st round of the F.A. Cup in November 1971?

9. Who scored nine league hat-tricks for Middlesbrough in Division Two in 1926/27?

10. How many full England caps did Peter Reid win?

11. Which team were league champions in Turkey in 1997/98?

12. Who was South American Player of the Year in 1997?

13. Which club bought Chris Garland from Bristol City in 1971?

14. To which two teams has Tottenham's Ian Walker been loaned in his career?

15. Who scored four goals for England in their 6-1 win versus Norway in 1965/66?

ANSWERS **1.** Brentford **2.** Malta **3.** Joe Payne **4.** 8 **5.** Manchester City **6.** PSV Eindhoven **7.** Asa Hartford **8.** Margate **9.** George Camsell **10.** 13 **11.** Galatasaray **12.** Marcelo Salas **13.** Chelsea **14.** Oxford and Ipswich **15.** Jimmy Greaves.

THE WORLD CUP

1930—1998

Quiz 01 THE WORLD CUP 1930-1998

1. Which teams drew 0-0 in the opening game of the 1970 Finals?

2. Which team placed third in the 1978 Finals?

3. For which Spanish side was West Germany's Bernd Schuster playing at the time of the 1982 Finals?

4. Which Asian team finished bottom of Group A in the 1986 finals?

5. What birthday was Pat Jennings celebrating when Northern Ireland lost 3-0 to Brazil in the 1986 Finals?

6. For which English club was Scotland's David Speedie playing at the time of the 1986 Finals?

7. Who lost all three games in Group A of Italia '90?

8. Who did Yugoslavia beat to qualify for the 1962 Finals?

9. Who lost all three games in Group F of USA '94?

10. How many goals did Italy concede in Group 2 of the 1970 Finals?

11. How many times have Croatia played in the Finals?

12. For which Italian club was Dan Petrescu playing at the time of USA '94?

13. How many times have the Dutch East Indies played in the Finals?

14. For which Dutch side was Belgium's Luc Nilis playing at the time of France '98?

15. By what score did England beat Kuwait in the 1982 Finals?

ANSWERS 1. Russia & Mexico 2. Brazil 3. Barcelona 4. South Korea 5. 41st 6. Chelsea 7. U.S.A. 8. South Korea 9. Morocco 10. None 11. Once 12. Genoa 13. Once 14. PSV Eindhoven 15. 1-0.

THE ULTIMATE SPORTS FACT AND QUIZ BOOK

Quiz 02   THE WORLD CUP 1930-1998

1. Which national side did Ali Parvin & Ghafour Djahani represent at the 1978 Finals?

2. By what score did Argentina beat Peru in the second phase of the 1978 Finals?

3. Which teams opened the 1986 Finals on May 31st with a 1-1 draw?

4. Which team finished bottom of England and Italy's qualifying group for the 1978 Finals?

5. For which Spanish team was goalkeeper Zubizarreta playing at the time of the 1986 Finals?

6. Who scored two for England against France in the 1966 Finals?

7. For which club side were Bruce Rioch and Don Masson playing at the time of the 1978 Finals?

8. Which Asian side lost all three of their Group 8 games in the 1986 Finals?

9. Who beat Argentina in the opening game of Italia '90?

10. Who did Ireland beat in their opening game of USA '94?

11. Who did Mexico beat to qualify for the 1962 Finals?

12. For which French club side was Sweden's Anders Linderoth playing at the time of the 1978 Finals?

13. In their six games in the Finals, how many goals have El Salvador conceded?

14. For which Italian team was Gheorghe Hagi playing at the time of USA '94?

15. Who headed Group 5 of the 1982 Finals?

ANSWERS 1. Iran 2. 6-0 3. Italy & Bulgaria 4. Luxembourg 5. Athletic Bilbao 6. Roger Hunt 7. Derby County 8. Iraq 9. Cameroon 10. Italy 11. Paraguay 12. Marseille 13. 22 14. Brescia 15. Northern Ireland.

THE ULTIMATE SPORTS FACT AND QUIZ BOOK

Quiz 03 THE WORLD CUP 1930-1998

1. Who lost all three of their games in Group 6 of the 1982 finals?

2. How many goals did Canada score in the 1986 Finals?

3. Who lost all three of their Group C games in Italia '90?

4. Which two teams won all three second phase group games in the 1974 Finals?

5. How many of the 12 teams won both their games in phase two of the 1982 Finals?

6. Which Spanish side was Romario playing for at the time of USA '94?

7. Who coached Saudi Arabia in France '98?

8. Of Denmark's 22 at the 1998 Finals, how many played for English clubs?

9. Who did Brazil beat to qualify for the 1958 Finals?

10. Which team did Luis Hernandez represent in France '98?

11. How many English club players were in Holland's France '98 squad?

12. Who scored the Republic of Ireland's goal in their 2-1 defeat against Mexico in USA '94?

13. How many goals did the U.A.E. concede in Group D of Italia '90?

14. For which club was Pelé playing at the time of the 1970 Finals?

15. Which African side did Northern Ireland play in the 1986 Finals?

Quiz 04 THE WORLD CUP 1930-1998

1. By what score did West Germany beat France on penalties in the 1982 semi-finals?

2. Which Asian team lost all three games in Group E of Italia '90?

3. For which club was Gordon Banks playing at the time of the 1970 Finals?

4. Who did Mexico beat to qualify for the 1958 Finals?

5. Which team did Hans Krankl & Kurt Welzl represent in the 1982 Finals?

6. How many times have Algeria played in the Finals?

7. Which were the only two sides with maximum points after Round 1 of the 1986 Finals?

8. How many times have Canada played in the Finals?

9. Who coached Scotland in France '98?

10. Of France's 22 at France '98, how many were playing for English league clubs?

11. Who beat Costa Rica in the second round of Italia '90?

12. For which Italian side was Germany's Christian Ziege playing at the time of France '98?

13. Who did Wales beat to qualify for the 1958 Finals?

14. What was the aggregate score between Iran & Australia in the 1998 Asia-Oceania play-off for France '98?

15. How many times have Cuba played in the World Cup Finals?

ANSWERS 1. 5-4 2. South Korea 3. Stoke City 4. Costa Rica 5. Austria 6. Two 7. Brazil & Denmark 8. Once 9. Craig Brown 10. Four 11. Czechoslovakia 12. Milan 13. Israel 14. 3-3 15. Once.

Quiz 05 THE WORLD CUP 1930-1998

1. For which Italian club was Dino Zoff playing at the time of the 1970 Finals?

2. With which side did Scotland draw 0-0 in Group E of the 1986 Finals?

3. For which Italian club was Brazil's Falção playing at the time of the 1982 Finals?

4. Who headed Group F after the first phase of Italia '90?

5. Which Spanish side was Bebeto playing for at the time of USA '94?

6. Who coached Spain in France '98?

7. Who did Italy beat to qualify for the 1962 Finals?

8. Which team did Jerzy Gorgon & Robert Gadocha represent in the 1974 Finals?

9. How many goals did Mexico concede in Group 1 of the 1970 Finals?

10. Who did Germany beat in the opening game of USA '94?

11. Who was West Germany's trainer in the 1974 Finals?

12. Which two of the Home Countries qualified for the 1954 Finals?

13. For which German team was Tony Woodcock playing at the time of the 1982 Finals?

14. Who scored Scotland's goal in their 1986 2-1 defeat against West Germany?

15. Who lost all eight games in the 1982 World Cup qualifying group headed by Belgium?

ANSWERS 1. Napoli 2. Uruguay 3. Roma 4. England 5. Deportivo La Coruña 6. Javier Clemente 7. Israel 8. Poland 9. None 10. Bolivia 11. Helmut Schön 12. England & Scotland 13. Cologne 14. Gordon Strachan 15. Cyprus.

Quiz 06 THE WORLD CUP 1930-1998

1. Which club was Scotland's David Hay with at the time of the 1974 Finals?

2. How many goals did Cameroon concede in Group B of USA '94?

3. For which French club side was Michel Platini playing at the time of the 1978 Finals?

4. Who did Austria beat to qualify for the 1954 Finals?

5. With which two teams did Morocco draw 0-0 in the 1986 Finals?

6. Who scored Scotland's goal in their 1998 2-1 defeat against Brazil?

7. For which French club side was Colombia's Carlos Valderrama playing at the time of Italia '90?

8. In which year did Morocco first appear in the Finals?

9. For which English team was Ludek Miklosko playing at the time of Italia '90?

10. For which English club was Peter Shilton playing at the time of Italia '90?

11. How many times have New Zealand appeared in the Finals?

12. For which English club was Ray Houghton playing at the time of USA '94?

13. Which German club side was Sweden's Roland Sandberg with at the time of the 1974 Finals?

14. Who was Kevin Keegan playing for at the time of the 1982 Finals?

15. How many goals did El Salvador score in the 1970 Finals?

ANSWERS 1. Celtic 2. 11 3. Nantes 4. Portugal 5. England & Poland 6. John Collins 7. Montpellier 8. 1970 9. West Ham 10. Derby County 11. One 12. Aston Villa 13. Kaiserslautern 14. Southampton 15. None.

Quiz 07 THE WORLD CUP 1930-1998

1. For which Spanish club was West Germany's Günther Netzer playing at the time of the 1974 Finals?

2. By what score did Belgium defeat USSR in the 1986 Finals?

3. Who lost all three games of Group D in USA '94?

4. Who did Turkey beat to qualify for the 1954 Finals?

5. For which French club was Holland's Johnny Rep playing at the time of the 1978 Finals?

6. Who did Portugal defeat in the 1966 World Cup quarter-finals?

7. For which team was Terry Butcher playing at the time of Italia '90?

8. How many times have Portugal appeared in the finals?

9. For which Italian team was Ruud Gullit playing at the time of Italia '90?

10. Who has appeared more often in the finals - England or Scotland?

11. Which team did Augustine Okocha play for in the 1998 Finals?

12. For which English club was Kevin Moran playing at the time of Italia '90?

13. Which team did Vicente Pereda & Aaron Padilla represent in the 1970 Finals?

14. For which Italian club side was Gianluca Vialli playing at the time of Italia '90?

15. Who knocked Romania out of USA '94 on penalties?

Quiz 08 THE WORLD CUP 1930-1998

1. Who coached Italy in France '98?

2. How many goals did Zaire concede in Group 2 of the 1974 Finals?

3. For which Spanish side was Brazil's Rivaldo playing at the time of France '98?

4. How many goals did Haiti concede in Group 4 of the 1974 Finals?

5. Of Norway's 22 at the 1998 Finals how many were playing club football in England at the time?

6. For which club side were Paolo Rossi & Marco Tardelli playing at the time of the 1982 Finals?

7. Which country did Taher El Khalej represent in France '98?

8. By what score did England beat Paraguay in the 1986 Finals?

9. Who did Italy beat to qualify for the 1954 Finals?

10. For which English club side was Scotland's Stuart McCall playing during Italia '90?

11. For which German club side was Austria's Anton Polster playing at the time of France '98?

12. Which Italian side was Argentina's Batistuta playing for at the time of USA '94?

13. Who scored Jamaica's first goal in the 1998 Finals?

14. At the time of France '98, which Italian club was South Africa's Phil Masinga playing for?

15. For which French club side was Mick McCarthy playing at the time of USA '94?

ANSWERS 1. Cesare Maldini 2. 14 3. Barcelona 4. 14 5. 11 6. Juventus 7. Morocco 8. 3-0 9. Egypt 10. Everton 11. Cologne 12. Fiorentina 13. Robbie Earle 14. Bari 15. Lyon.

Quiz 09 THE WORLD CUP 1930-1998

1. Which South American side finished bottom of Group 3 in the 1974 Finals?

2. For which German side was Brazil's Dunga playing at the time of USA '94?

3. Who coached Norway in France '98?

4. Which team did goalkeeper Luis Rubiños represent in the 1970 Finals?

5. Which country did Rigobert Song represent in France '98?

6. Who lost all eight of their qualifying games for the 1982 Finals in the group headed by Yugoslavia?

7. Of Scotland's 22 at the 1998 Finals, how many played for English clubs?

8. Who did South Korea beat to qualify for the 1954 Finals?

9. For which Dutch club was Swede Ove Kindvall playing at the time of Mexico '70?

10. By what score did West Germany beat Mexico on penalties in a 1986 World Cup quarter-final?

11. For which Italian side was Rudi Völler playing at the time of Italia '90?

12. For which Turkish team was Bulgaria's Zlatko Yankov playing at the time of the 1998 Finals?

13. Which team finished second to Argentina in the South American qualifying group for France '98?

14. Who scored Scotland's goal against Norway in the 1998 Finals?

15. For which English side was Andy Townsend playing at the time of Italia '90?

Quiz 10 THE WORLD CUP 1930-1998

1. Who lost all three games in Group 3 of the 1970 Finals?

2. Who did the Republic of Ireland beat on penalties in Round 2 of Italia '90?

3. For which Spanish club was Ruben Ayala playing at the time of München '74?

4. How many teams won all three of their group games in USA '94?

5. Who drew 0-0 in the opening game of the 1978 Finals?

6. Who coached France in France '98?

7. For which Belgian team was Poland's Lato playing at the time of the 1982 Finals?

8. Which Italian club was Chile's Ivan Zamorano playing for at the time of España '82?

9. How old was Alan Hansen when Scotland's 1982 Finals was over?

10. Which country did the USA beat to qualify for the 1934 Finals?

11. For which Spanish club was West Germany's Ulrich Stielike playing at the time of the 1982 Finals?

12. How many times have Turkey appeared in the Finals?

13. For which English club was Eddie McGoldrick playing at the time of USA '94?

14. Which team did Jean-Claude Desir & Philippe Vorbe represent in the 1974 Finals?

15. For which French team was Argentinian Jorge Luis Burruchaga playing at the time of the 1986 Finals?

ANSWERS 1. Czechoslovakia 2. Romania 3. Atletico Madrid 4. None 5. West Germany & Poland 6. Aime Jacquet 7. Lokeren 8. Internazionale 9. 27 10. Mexico 11. Real Madrid 12. One 13. Arsenal 14. Haiti 15. Nantes.

Quiz 11 THE WORLD CUP 1930-1998

1. How many goals did Mexico concede in Group 2 of the 1978 Finals?

2. Who won all three games in Group 3 of the 1970 Finals?

3. By what score did Argentina beat Yugoslavia on penalties in the quarter-final of Italia '90?

4. Which club side did East Germany's Peter Ducke & Bernd Bransch represent at the time of the 1974 Finals?

5. Who knocked the Republic of Ireland out of USA '94?

6. Who did Scotland draw 1-1 with in the 1978 Finals?

7. Of Italy's 22 at the 1998 Finals how many were playing with English clubs at the time?

8. For which club was Asa Hartford playing at the time of the 1982 Finals?

9. Which country did Egypt beat to qualify for the 1934 Finals?

10. What were the scores of both semi-finals in Italia '90?

11. Which Italian club was Brazil's Junior playing for at the time of Mexico '86?

12. In which year did Tunisia first appear in the finals?

13. Which Italian side was West Germany's Hans-Peter Briegel playing for at the time of Mexico '86?

14. Who coached Germany in France '98?

15. Which Spanish club was Johann Cruyff playing for at the time of the 1974 Finals?

ANSWERS 1. 12 **2.** Brazil **3.** 3-2 **4.** Carl Zeiss Jena **5.** Holland **6.** Iran **7.** One **8.** Everton **9.** Palestine **10.** 1-1 **11.** Torino **12.** 1978 **13.** Verona **14.** Berti Vogts **15.** Barcelona.

THE ULTIMATE SPORTS FACT AND QUIZ BOOK

Quiz 12 THE WORLD CUP 1930-1998

1. Which European side headed Group 3 of the 1978 Finals?

2. Which Italian club was Brazil's Edinho playing for at the time of the 1986 Finals?

3. For which Italian club was Ray Wilkins playing at the time of the 1986 Finals?

4. For which Spanish side was Argentina's Jorge da Silva playing at the time of the 1986 Finals?

5. Who drew 0-0 in Group A in Phase 2 of the 1978 Finals?

6. Which World Cup hosts played the fewest games in a tournament?

7. Who was Uruguay's first choice goalkeeper at Mexico '70 - to many the world's No. 1 'keeper at the time?

8. Who coached Argentina in France '98?

9. For which Spanish side was Hristo Stoichkov playing at the time of USA '94?

10. Which country did Spain beat to qualify for the 1934 Finals?

11. Which country did Sami al Jaber represent in USA '94?

12. Who headed Group 1 of the 1974 World Cup Finals?

13. Who scored Scotland's goal in their 1974 1-1 draw with Yugoslavia?

14. For which Italian side was Swede Tomas Brolin playing at the time of USA '94?

15. Who scored Wales's first goal in the 1958 Finals?

ANSWERS 1. Austria 2. Udinese 3. Milan 4. Atletico Madrid 5. Italy & West Germany 6. France (2 in 1938) 7. Ladislao Mazurkiewicz 8. Daniel Passarella 9. Barcelona 10. Portugal 11. Saudi Arabia 12. East Germany 13. Joe Jordan 14. Parma 15. John Charles.

Quiz 13 THE WORLD CUP 1930-1998

1. Who lost 1-0 in the opening game of the 1982 Finals?

2. For which Italian side was Maradona playing at the time of Italia '90?

3. Which teams drew 0-0 in the opening game of the 1974 Finals?

4. For which club were Sepp Maier and Gerd Müller playing at the time of Mexico '70?

5. Which country did Daniel Amokachi represent in USA '94?

6. Who coached Brazil in France '98?

7. Of the six games in Group 1 of España '82, how many finished goalless?

8. For which Portuguese side was Brazil's Aldair playing at the time of Italia '90?

9. Who beat El Salvador 10-1 in the 1982 Finals but still didn't qualify for phase 2?

10. Which country did Hungary beat to qualify for the 1938 Finals?

11. For which Italian side was Jürgen Kohler playing at the time of USA '94?

12. Who scored Scotland's goal in their 3-1 defeat by Peru in 1978?

13. For which Spanish team was USA's Tab Ramos playing at the time of USA '94?

14. By what score did Brazil beat Wales in the 1958 Finals?

15. For which Italian team was Joe Jordan playing at the time of the 1982 Finals?

Juventus 12. Joe Jordan 13. Real Betis 14. 1-0 15. Milan.
11. Greece 10. Hungary 9. Benfica 8. Three 7. Mario Zagallo 6. Nigeria 5.
Munich 4. Bayern 3. Brazil & Yugoslavia 2. Napoli 1. Argentina ANSWERS

Quiz 14 THE WORLD CUP 1930-1998

1. How many goals did Australia score in the 1974 World Cup Finals?

2. For which Dutch side was Romario playing at the time of Italia '90?

3. Which South American teams drew 0-0 in Group B in Phase 2 of the 1978 Finals?

4. Whose squad featured 'keeper Joseph-Antoine Bell in Italia '90?

5. Who did Bo Johansson coach in France '98?

6. For which Italian side was Stefan Effenberg playing at the time of USA '94?

7. Which country did Czechoslovakia beat to qualify for the 1938 Finals?

8. For which Spanish club was 'keeper Zubizarreta playing at the time of France '98?

9. For which Spanish club was Argentinian Daniel Carnevali playing at the time of the 1974 Finals?

10. Who knocked Nigeria out of USA '94?

11. Who won all three of their Group 1 games in the 1978 Finals?

12. Which country did Yugoslavia beat to qualify for the 1950 Finals?

13. Who won all three games in Group 4 of the 1970 Finals?

14. How many times have Australia played in the World Cup Finals?

15. For which Spanish club was Mexican Hugo Sanchez playing at the time of the 1986 Finals?

ANSWERS 1. None 2. PSV Eindhoven 3. Argentina & Brazil 4. Cameroon 5. Denmark 6. Fiorentina 7. Bulgaria 8. Valencia 9. Las Palmas 10. Italy 11. Italy 12. France 13. West Germany 14. One 15. Real Madrid.

THE ULTIMATE SPORTS FACT AND QUIZ BOOK

Quiz 15 THE WORLD CUP 1930-1998

1. For which Spanish club was Mario Kempes playing at the time of the 1978 Finals?

2. For which country did Cyrille Makanaky play in Italia '90?

3. For which club side was Northern Ireland's Sammy McIlroy playing at the time of the 1982 Finals?

4. What was the score in both of the 1986 World Cup semi-finals?

5. For which Italian club was Mark Hateley playing at the time of the 1986 Finals?

6. Who knocked Argentina out of USA '94?

7. Which country did Switzerland beat to qualify for the 1950 Finals?

8. Who did Italy beat 4-1 in the quarter-finals of Mexico '70?

9. Which country did Roland Hattenberger & Kurt Jara represent in the 1978 Finals?

10. For which English club was Sammy McIlroy playing at the time of the 1986 Finals?

11. In their six games in the World Cup Finals, against which team did Bolivia achieve their best result - a 0-0 draw?

12. Of South Africa's 22 at the 1998 Finals, how many were playing for English clubs?

13. How many times have Greece appeared in the Finals?

14. For which French team was Jürgen Klinsmann playing at the time of USA '94?

15. Who scored both of Haiti's goals in München '74?

ANSWERS 1. Valencia 2. Cameroon 3. Stoke City 4. 2-0 5. Milan 6. Romania 7. Luxembourg 8. Mexico 9. Austria 10. Manchester City 11. South Korea 12. Three 13. Once 14. Monaco 15. Emmanuel Sanon.

Quiz 16 THE WORLD CUP 1930-1998

1. Who did West Germany beat for third place in the 1970 Finals?

2. For which French club was Argentinian Hugo Bargas playing at the time of the 1974 Finals?

3. Who knocked Belgium out of USA '94?

4. For which Spanish club did Brazilian Luis Pereira play at the time of the 1978 Finals?

5. For which French side was Cameroon's Andre Kana-Biyik playing at the time of Italia '90?

6. For which side was N. Ireland's Billy Hamilton playing at the time of the 1982 Finals?

7. In which World Cup Finals did Honduras take part?

8. Which national side did Joel Bats represent in Mexico '86?

9. For which club side was N. Ireland's Mal Donaghy playing at the time of Mexico '86?

10. In which World Cup Finals did Israel play?

11. For which Italian team was Holland's Bryan Roy playing at the time of USA '94?

12. Which country did Spain beat to qualify for the 1950 Finals?

13. For which club was Brazil's Gerson playing at the time of the 1970 Finals?

14. For which club was N. Ireland's Sammy Nelson playing at the time of España '82?

15. Who lost all three games in Group 2 in the 1982 Finals?

ANSWERS 1. Uruguay 2. Nantes 3. Germany 4. Atlético Madrid 5. Metz 6. Burnley 7. 1982 8. France 9. Luton Town 10. 1970 11. Foggia 12. Portugal 13. São Paulo 14. Brighton & Hove Albion 15. Chile.

THE ULTIMATE SPORTS FACT AND QUIZ BOOK

Quiz 17 THE WORLD CUP 1930-1998

1. Which five countries bid for the first World Cup?

2. What was the opening game of the 1962 World Cup?

3. At which grounds were the Group 4 matches for the 1966 Finals held?

4. Who scored England's only goal against Czechoslovakia in the 1970 Finals?

5. Who scored a hat-trick for Holland against Iran in 1978?

6. Which three countries were in the running to stage the 1994 World Cup?

7. Who scored the first goal for Croatia against Germany in 1998?

8. Who was England's goalkeeper against U.S.A. in 1950?

9. Who was the Brazil's goalkeeper in the 1994 World Cup Final?

10. How many games did Gary Lineker take to score his six goals in 1986?

11. For which team did Morlock and Eckel play in 1954?

12. Approximately how high in inches is the FIFA World Cup Trophy, first presented in 1974?

13. Who were England's first opponents in the 1970 Finals?

14. Where were the 1970 Finals originally intended to be held?

15. What nationality was the referee in the 1966 Final?

ANSWERS 1. Holland, Spain, Italy, Sweden & Uruguay 2. Chile vs. Switzerland 3. Roker Park & Ayresome Park 4. Allan Clarke 5. Rob Rensenbrink 6. U.S.A., Mexico & Brazil 7. Robert Jarni 8. Bert Williams 9. Taffarel 10. Five 11. West Germany 12. 20 13. Romania 14. Argentina 15. Swiss.

TRUE OR FALSE?

Quiz 01   TRUE OR FALSE?

1. Selborne Boome won the 1899 Grand National.

2. Gaffie du Toit won the first Prix de l'Arc de Triomphe.

3. Northampton released striker Ian Atkins because he was more interested in fishing.

4. Pop group The Trammps appeared before the 1998 Ipswich vs. Birmingham game dressed in Ipswich shirts.

5. Greg Norman's company is called Great White Shark Enterprises.

6. The Mitsubishi Shogun Tingle Creek Chase is a rallying competition.

7. Ram Muay is a Thai boxing ritual.

8. Rick Lips won the 1974 Greyhound Derby.

9. Kinder Bologna is an Italian tourist agency's advertising slogan.

10. Boxer François Botha's sporting hero as a child was ice skater John Curry.

11. The Pelican Strand is a golf course in Florida.

12. Dick Pound was head of the six-member I.O.C. team that investigated the Salt Lake City winning bid for the 2002 Winter Olympics.

13. Dennis Mitchell, Olympic athlete, escaped a doping ban by claiming he had sex three times the night before the drug test.

14. Gloucester cricketer M.G.N. Windows's second name is Glass.

15. Baroni, Moscardi and Cristofoletto are all ski resorts in the Alps.

ANSWERS **1.** False. He's a rugby union player. **2.** False. He's a rugby union player **3.** False. It was golf. **4.** True. **5.** True. **6.** False. It was a horse race at Sandown in 1998 **7.** True. **8.** False. He's a rugby union player. **9.** False. It's a basketball team. **10.** False. It was Muhammad Ali. **11.** True. **12.** True. **13.** False. He claimed to have had sex four times. **14.** False. It is Guy. **15.** False. They are Italian rugby players.

THE ULTIMATE SPORTS FACT AND QUIZ BOOK

Quiz 02   TRUE OR FALSE?

1. Hamlet Williams is an England basketball player.

2. Iztok Cop is a Slovenian rower.

3. Gay Brewer won the 1970 Grand National.

4. Fred Funk won the 1998 Deposit Guaranty Classic in golf.

5. El Prat is a Barcelona golf course.

6. Golfer Jarmo Sandelin has a cobbler who makes up his golf shoes from crocodile skin.

7. Charlton Eagle is a soccer fanzine.

8. Footballer Ted Drake's nickname was 'D.A.'

9. Tennis player Pat Rafter played 'Puck' in a school Shakespeare production.

10. Tennis player Fred Perry was once engaged to actress Barbara Stanwyck.

11. Dan Luger plays rugby union for Harlequins.

12. Maurice Minor plays rugby union for Leicester.

13. There is an annual bog snorkelling championship held in Wales.

14. Galveston Gnus are an American Football team.

15. Orlando Thunder American Football team play at the Citrus Bowl stadium.

ANSWERS 1. False. Yorick Williams however is 2. True 3. False. It was Gay Trip. Gay Brewer is a golfer 4. True. 5. True 6. True 7. False. He's a tennis coach 8. False 9. False. 10. False 11. True 12. False. Austin Healey however does 13. True 14. False 15. True.

Quiz 03

TRUE OR FALSE?

1. Bristol Rovers once sacked their half-time announcer for saying of a rival Bristol City player -"Here comes Junior Bent. I bet he is."

2. Hull City won the First F.A. Cup Final at Wembley.

3. Film director Spike Lee was once a quarter-back for the Miami Dolphins.

4. Hugo Maradona, Diego's brother, used to play for Rapid Vienna.

5. Blackburn football player Damien Duff was born in Trieste.

6. 1995 world angling champion Paul Jean is a professional wall of death rider.

7. 1992 Olympic men's archery champion Sébastien Flute studied at Harrow.

8. Greco-Roman wrestling was once included in the Olympic pentathlon competition.

9. Golfer John Daly was once a much-sought after children's entertainer.

10. Erik Lemming was a Swedish Olympic champion.

11. Blind Man's Buff was suggested as a potential Olympic event for the Stockholm Games.

12. The team from Djibouti won the 1985 I.A.A.F. men's world cup marathon.

13. The surnames of the first three athletes to finish in the men's 400m at the 1990 European Championships were Black, White and Brown.

14. Former Cameroon footballer Roger Milla was presented by the Cameroon president with a prize water melon on returning from the 1990 World Cup Finals.

15. Adelaide Crows are an Australian Rules Football team.

ANSWERS 1. True 2. False 3. False 4. True 5. False 6. False 7. False 8. True 9. False 10. True 11. False 12. True 13. False 14. False 15. True.

Quiz 04 TRUE OR FALSE?

1. The game of badminton was once known as Shut le Dore.

2. Sue Egypt is an international women's hockey player.

3. Chesterfield football team once played in a Union Jack shirt.

4. Phoenix Bessemer are an American minor league baseball team.

5. Future Cutlet won the 1933 Greyhound Derby.

6. Boxer Primo Carnera appeared in the film 'A Kid for Two Farthings'.

7. Jockey George Stevens rode in fifteen Grand Nationals and never fell.

8. J.F. Mitchell wore a hearing aid in the 1922 F.A. Cup Final.

9. Culture Vulture won the 1991 Greyhound Derby.

10. Ian Botham once appeared in the pantomime 'Jack and the Beanstalk'.

11. The New York Giants played the New York Yankees in the 1936 World Series.

12. Nottingham Forest were once called Moses Hosiery.

13. Norwegian international footballer Bjorn Otto Bragstad has won six league titles with Rosenborg.

14. Chelsea scored 99 league goals in Division One in 1960/61.

15. Crewe Alexandra were named after Princess Alexandra.

ANSWERS 1. False 2. False 3. True 4. False. They were an English football team 5. True 6. True 7. True 8. False. He did however wear spectacles 9. False. It is a horse 10. True 11. True 12. True 13. True 14. False. It was 98 15. True.

Quiz 05 TRUE OR FALSE?

1. The Chicago Bears were once known as the Chicago Teddy Bears.

2. Canadian film director David Cronenberg once played ice hockey for his country.

3. Ron Harris made 666 appearances for Chelsea from 1962-80.

4. Newcastle United's previous football grounds include South Byker.

5. Tristram Speaker was a U.S. baseball player.

6. Jelena Dokic beat Martina Hingis 2-6, 6-2, 6-0 at Wimbledon in 1999.

7. No England batsmen featured in the Top 20 batting averages for the 1999 Cricket World Cup.

8. No England bowler featured in the Top 20 bowling averages for the 1999 Cricket World Cup.

9. Boxer Angel Firpo's nickname was 'The Gaucho with the Oucho'.

10. Paulie Ayala beat Johnny Tapia to win the W.B.A. featherweight title.

11. Boxer Aldo Rios is Canadian.

12. Eddie Plank was a U.S. baseball player.

13. Queens Park Rangers were named after Scottish football clubs Queens Park and Rangers.

14. Boxer Napoleon Tagoe is Nigerian.

15. Cornish boxer Bob Fitzsimmons moved to New Zealand at the age of five.

Quiz 06   TRUE OR FALSE?

1. Manchester United defender Jaap Stam was often mistaken in Holland for actor Pete Postlethwaite.

2. Liverpool boxer Shay Neary won the W.B.U. light-heavyweight championship.

3. Liverpool used only 15 players to win the 1965/6 Football League.

4. Formula 1 driver Jarno Trulli is Norwegian.

5. Aaron Slight is a 500 c.c. motorcyclist.

6. Johnny Herbert won the 1995 British F1 Grand Prix.

7. Arsenal were once known as Dial Square.

8. Eyal Berkovic signed for Celtic from West Ham in 1999 under the Bosman ruling.

9. Jesper Parnevik led after the first round of the 1999 Standard Life Loch Lomond golf tournament.

10. Mario Cipollini won the fourth stage of the 1999 Tour De France.

11. Mario Cipollini finished last in the fifth stage of the 1999 Tour De France.

12. Michael Douglas played an American marathon runner in the 1979 film 'Running'.

13. Racing driver Damon Hill played a cameo part as a cab-driver in an episode of sitcom 'Father Ted'.

14. Footballer Teddy Sheringham cultivates orchids as a hobby.

15. Tennis player Jimmy Connors is now a qualified speech therapist.

ANSWERS **1.** False **2.** False. He won the light-welterweight championship **3.** False. They used 14 **4.** False. He's Italian **5.** True **6.** True **7.** True **8.** False. He cost £5.5m **9.** False. He led after the second **10.** True **11.** False. He won it **12.** True **13.** False **14.** False **15.** False.

Quiz 07   TRUE OR FALSE?

1. The word billiards is a derivative of 'billart' meaning playing cue.

2. Footballer Eric Cantona appeared as a toad in a 1998 French radio drama.

3. The first world chess champion was a Mr. Knight.

4. World flyweight boxing champion Pancho Villa died of blood poisoning.

5. Film actress Demi Moore was once an Olympic skier.

6. The declaration in cricket was first permitted in 1889.

7. Southport F.C. were once known as Southport Vulcans.

8. Seven brothers of the Forster family played cricket for Worcestershire.

9. Footballer Robert Fleck played one season with Partick Thistle.

10. W.H. Denton, who played county cricket, lost a leg in World War I.

11. Footballer Kevin Francis is 6ft 8 inches tall.

12. Wicketkeepers' gloves were originally yellow in colour.

13. Tennis player Jo Durie is the ex-wife of footballer Gordon Durie.

14. India withdrew from football's World Cup when FIFA refused to allow them to play in bare feet.

15. Tiger Woods and Lee Westwood both scored 286 in the 1997 U.S. Open.

ANSWERS 1. True 2. False 3. False 4. True 5. False 6. True 7. True 8. True 9. True 10. True 11. False. He is 6ft 7 inches tall 12. True 13. False 14. True 15. True.

Quiz 08   TRUE OR FALSE?

1. Bradford City played 11 F.A. Cup ties between 1910-12 without conceding a goal.

2. Tom Steels won the first stage of the 1999 Tour De France.

3. England footballers A.M. and P.M. Walters were nicknamed Morning and Afternoon.

4. Indian women's cricketer Anjum Chopra scored 100 for India against England in a one-day Test on July 9th, 1999.

5. Latvia won the 1935 European men's basketball championship.

6. Cricketer Bob Willis's nickname was 'Kitten'.

7. The oldest English bowling green dates back to Southampton in 1299.

8. Tennis player Pat Cash made a rock album called 'Highly Strung Racket'.

9. Former world middleweight boxing champion Stanley Ketchell died in 1997 at the age of 105.

10. Goal nets were invented in 1890.

11. Football pundit Jimmy Hill once took out a patent on superglue.

12. In their 1920 season, Derbyshire cricket team lost 17 out of 18 games, the other being abandoned.

13. Film director Alfred Hitchcock was a former world amateur billiards semi-finalist.

14. England footballer W. Howell lived in a cave.

15. A dog called Gyp once scored in a professional football game.

Quiz 09   TRUE OR FALSE?

1. World bantamweight champion Mario d'Agata was a deaf and dumb mute.

2. Cricketer W.E. Hollies of Warwickshire was out for nought 200 times.

3. Chelsea F.C. were formed in a pub.

4. Golfer Ernie Els won the 1997 U.S. Masters.

5. Sunderland football manager Peter Reid once recorded a version of the pop song *Bright Eyes* for charity.

6. In 1898, a league game between Sheffield Wednesday and Aston Villa was abandoned, the remaining 11 minutes being played the following year.

7. Ice skater Robin Cousins starred on Broadway in *The Rocky Horror Show*.

8. Former tennis star Sue Barker has written a book on aromatherapy.

9. Football manager Graham Taylor has had a variety of cabbage named after him.

10. Boxer Tiger Flowers became a priest after quitting the ring.

11. West Ham footballer Julian Dicks was born in Cyprus.

12. The game of curling was originally called shufflestone.

13. Randy Bigfoot was 1981 A.B.C. Masters Bowling champion in the U.S.

14. Boxer Henry Cooper once rode in the Grand National.

15. Author Lord Archer once appeared in a wrestling bout under the name of 'The Peckham Throttler'.

THE ULTIMATE SPORTS FACT AND QUIZ BOOK

Quiz 10 TRUE OR FALSE?

1. The original name of basketball was 'Hoopla!'.

2. Robert Dazla scored a goal for the Old Etonians in the 1881 F.A. Cup Final.

3. The word dressage comes from the French word dresser, meaning 'to stiffen'.

4. Odd Socks won the 1900 Epsom Derby.

5. Boxer Lou Nova's real first name was Lee.

6. Crow won the 1976 St. Leger.

7. The cost of a season ticket to West Bromwich Albion in 1886 was three shillings.

8. Olivier Peslier won the 1996 Coronation Stakes on Shake the Yoke.

9. Boxer Randolph Turpin was once mistakenly billed as Randall Turnip.

10. Frank Bruno once played a genie in pantomime.

11. The wicketkeepers in the 1920/1 Test series between England and Australia were called Dolphin and Whale.

12. Nick Faldo was the highest earner in British sport in 1990.

13. The Pilgrim Fathers played darts aboard the Mayflower.

14. Barry McGuigan was known as 'The Cones Hotline'.

15. Lithuania won the 1939 European men's basketball championship.

ANSWERS 1. False 2. False 3. False 4. False 5. False 6. True 7. True 8. True 9. False 10. True 11. False. Dolphin and Carter 12. False. It was Nigel Mansell 13. True 14. False 15. True.

Quiz 11   TRUE OR FALSE?

1. Barry McGuigan was once in pantomime at Catford.

2. Werder Wüdhaus won the German First Division in 1992.

3. Split Hares are a Yugoslav athletics club.

4. The horses which won the Coronation Cup from 1995-8 all began with the letter S.

5. When the town of Clevedon won the 1957 Rinks championship of the E.B.A. in bowling, the team was made up of two pairs of fathers and sons.

6. The Brine Northern League is a lacrosse championship.

7. Bend Over Backwards won the 1898 Epsom Derby.

8. Cricketer W.R. Endean of South Africa was given out for handling the ball in a 1956/7 Test match against England.

9. Hugo's Dare won the 1937 Greyhound Derby.

10. Tom Stare was men's European Open judo champion in 1981.

11. The world's first cycling club was called 'The Pickwick Club'.

12. Pony Express won the 1967 Cheltenham Gold Cup.

13. Archie Moore was 51 years old when he last won the world heavyweight boxing championship.

14. Sharpo won the 1982 July Cup at Newmarket.

15. Painter Pablo Picasso was once on the books of Real Madrid.

ANSWERS 1. True 2. False 3. False 4. True 5. True 6. True 7. False 8. True 9. False 10. False 11. True 12. False 13. False. He was however in his late forties 14. True 15. False.

Quiz 12 TRUE OR FALSE?

1. Footballer Mick Harford played one season with Newcastle United.

2. Runner-up to Sally Little in the 1988 Du Maurier golf classic was Betsy Large.

3. Boxer 'Kid' McCoy was married ten times.

4. U.S. athlete Mary Decker was 1983 Sports Illustrated Sportswoman of the Year.

5. Footballer Marcus Gayle played one season for Torquay United.

6. Cricketer Nicholas Felix invented a bowling machine called the Catapulter.

7. Gary Lineker was 1986 B.B.C. Sports Personality of the Year.

8. Motor cyclist Wayne Gardner was the highest earner in Australian sport in 1990.

9. Ho Lin-Won was 1999 Thailand Masters golf champion.

10. Cult author Jake Arnott races pigeons in his spare time.

11. Dolphin are an Irish rugby union team.

12. Tabard are an English rugby union team.

13. University of Wales won the Temple Challenge Cup at Henley Regatta in 1998.

14. Damon Hill won the 1998 Italian F1 Grand Prix.

15. Frankie Dettori rode over 200 winners in the 1994 flat race season.

ANSWERS 1. True 2. False 3. True 4. True 5. False 6. True 7. False. Nigel Mansell out-personalitied him 8. False. Greg Norman was 9. False 10. False 11. True 12. True 13. True 14. False 15. True.

Quiz 13   TRUE OR FALSE?

1. The 1904 first-class fixture between Yorkshire and Kent at Scarborough was held up for twenty minutes on the second day when a freak shower of eels fell from the sky.

2. Harleston Magpies are a national league hockey team.

3. Sweden won the 1998 men's European handball championships.

4. Portsmouth Penguins are an Express Cup ice hockey team.

5. Jason Beaver is a leading flat race jockey.

6. Scott Verplank is a U.S. golfer.

7. Marion Sutton came third in the 1998 Flora London Marathon.

8. Leicester City football club were once called O'Donnells Hand Stitchers.

9. Match Me Sidney won the 1938 Preakness Stakes.

10. Oceania finished last in both men and women's events in the 1998 Athletics World Cup.

11. Bill Rogers was 1979 World Matchplay golf champion.

12. Soling, Finn and Tornado are all sailing classes.

13. Fatima Whitbread was a former winner of Miss Pears beautiful child competition.

14. Marco Van Basten learnt to speak Mandarin at night school in Italy.

15. Ludger Beerbaum are a German Third Division football team.

ANSWERS 1. False 2. True 3. True 4. False 5. False. Jason Weaver is however 6. True 7. False, she finished tenth 8. False 9. False 10. True 11. True 12. True 13. False 14. False 15. False.

MOTOR SPORTS

THE ULTIMATE SPORTS FACT AND QUIZ BOOK

Quiz 01   MOTOR SPORTS

1. In which month of 1998 was the first Formula 1 Grand Prix?

2. What nationality was F1 driver Joakim Bonnier?

3. For which team did Rubens Barichello drive in the 1998 F1 season?

4. Which moto-cross champion was awarded the M.B.E. in 1970?

5. For which team did Jackie Stewart race in his 1969 F1 championship year?

6. How many times did Peter Collins win the world pairs title in speedway?

7. In which year was F1 driver Shinji Nakano born?

8. Which pair won the 1972 R.A.C. Rally?

9. Which London-born racing driver won the Le Mans 24-hour race from 1928-30?

10. Which team won the constructors' cup in F1 from 1988-91?

11. Which Briton won the 1959 French & German F1 Grand Prix?

12. What is the colour of the flag in Formula 1 used to indicate a race has been stopped?

13. Which driver's only F1 win was the 1961 French Grand Prix?

14. At which F1 Grand Prix in 1997 did Olivier Panis break his legs?

15. Which Irish motorcyclist won the senior T.T. on the Isle of Man in 1922, '24 & '27?

ANSWERS 1. March 2. Swiss 3. Stewart Ford 4. Jeff Smith 5. Matra 6. Four Tony Brooks 12. Red 13. Giancarlo Baghetti 14. Canadian 15. Alec Bennett. 7. 1971 8. Roger Clark and Tony Mason 9. Woolf Barnato 10. McLaren 11.

Quiz 02
MOTOR SPORTS

1. How many drivers won more than one Formula 1 motor racing Grand Prix in 1998?

2. In which year did Peter Craven win the second of his two individual world speedway titles?

3. Which trio won the 1986 & '87 Le Mans 24-hour race?

4. Which German won the 1961 F1 Grand Prix?

5. For which team did Eddie Irvine drive in the 1998 F1 season?

6. In which year did Geoff Duke win his first senior T.T. on the Isle of Man?

7. By how many points did Carl Fogarty win the 1998 world superbike championship?

8. In which year was Michael Schumacher born?

9. Which motorcycle rider won the 1998 British Grand Prix at 500 c.c.?

10. Which Scottish driver's only F1 win was 1961's U.S. Grand Prix?

11. In which Italian city was F1 driver Alex Zanardi born?

12. What nationality is motorcyclist Pierfrancesco Chili?

13. Which driver's only F1 win was the 1964 Austrian Grand Prix?

14. Which motorcyclist was voted B.B.C. Sports Personality of the year in 1959?

15. Which pair won the 1968 Monte Carlo Rally?

ANSWERS 1. Two 2. 1962 3. Derek Bell, Hans Stuck & Al Holbert 4. Wolfgang von Trips 5. Ferrari 6. 1950 7. 4.5 8. 1969 9. Simon Crafar 10. Innes Ireland 11. Bologna 12. Italian 13. Lorenzo Bandini 14. John Surtees 15. Vic Elford & David Stone.

Quiz 03   MOTOR SPORTS

1. Who finished second in the 1998 Formula 1 Australian Grand Prix?

2. For which team did Jos Verstappen drive in the 1994 F1 season?

3. What nationality is F1 driver Jacky Ickx?

4. Which Grand Prix saw the biggest win margin in the 1998 F1 season?

5. Who was 500 c.c. moto-cross world champion in 1985 & '86?

6. Which Leeds-born speedway rider lost in a run-off to Lionel Van Praag in the first world individual champiosnhip?

7. In how many of the 16 races in F1 in 1998 did David Coulthard race the fastest lap?

8. Which Swiss driver won the 1968 British Grand Prix in F1?

9. Which make of bike took first three places in the 1998 500 c.c. German Grand Prix?

10. Of the 151 Grand Prix he raced by the end of F1 1998, how many had Jean Alesi won?

11. Which driver's only F1 win was the 1972 Monaco Grand Prix?

12. Which F1 driver holds the record for most Grand Prix raced?

13. Who was Isle of Man senior T.T. winner in 1985?

14. Which Cornish driver won the 1931 Monte Carlo rally?

15. At the end of the 1998 F1 season, how many drivers had scored more than 500 points in their career?

ANSWERS **1.** David Coulthard **2.** Benetton Ford **3.** Belgian **4.** Italian **5.** Dave Thorpe **6.** Eric Langton **7.** Three **8.** Jo Siffert **9.** Honda **10.** One **11.** Jean-Pierre Beltoise **12.** Riccardo Patrese **13.** Joey Dunlop **14.** Donald Healey **15.** Three.

Quiz 04   MOTOR SPORTS

1. Which Cambridge-born rider was 1980 world individual speedway champion?

2. Who drove the fastest lap in the 1998 Brazilian Formula 1 Grand Prix?

3. Which country hosted the last of the 1998 world superbike races?

4. Which Irish motorcyclist won the junior T.T. on the Isle of Man in 1923?

5. For which team did Jean Alesi drive in the 1998 F1 season?

6. Where was the last motorcycling Grand Prix of the 1998 season on October 25?

7. Which team won the constructors cup in F1 from 1975-77?

8. Before the 1999 season, who was the last F1 driver since 1989 to win the first race but not the championship?

9. Which two drivers in the 1998 F1 season did not compete in the 1997 season?

10. Which trio won the 1998 Le Mans 24-hour race?

11. Which driver won the 1998 Network Q R.A.C. Rally?

12. What age was Juan Fangio when he won the 1957 F1 world championship?

13. Who came second in the 1998 world rallying championship?

14. Which driver's only F1 win was the 1975 Austrian Grand Prix?

15. Who, in 1949, became the first motorcycle rider to be awarded the O.B.E.?

Quiz 05   MOTOR SPORTS

1. Who was runner-up in the 1949 world individual speedway championships?

2. Which pair won the 1964 Monte Carlo Rally?

3. Which Spaniard won the 1998 500 c.c. motorcycle Spanish Grand Prix?

4. Who drove the fastest lap in the 1998 Argentinian Formula 1 Grand Prix?

5. Which F1 driver had a hat-trick of wins in 1998 at the Canadian, French and British Grand Prix?

6. Who was Isle of Man senior T.T. winner in 1990?

7. What nationality is rally driver Didier Auriol?

8. Which driver was the youngest ever winner of the F1 world championship?

9. Which Australian won the 1998 500 c.c. motorcycle Australian Grand Prix?

10. Which team won the constructors' cup in F1 from 1992-94?

11. By how many points did Tommi Makinen win the 1998 world rallying championship?

12. In which year was driver Johnny Herbert born?

13. Before 1998, when had Kazuto Sakata last won the 125 c.c. motorcycling Grand Prix championship?

14. At which Grand Prix did Jochen Mass have his only F1 win, in 1975?

15. Who was runner-up in the 1998 Belgian F1 Grand Prix?

Quiz 06

MOTOR SPORTS

1. Who was runner-up in the 1998 Formula 1 San Marino Grand Prix?

2. Who won the Isle of Man senior T.T. in 1934 & '36?

3. Which country hosted the first of the 1998 world superbike races?

4. Who won the 1952 125 c.c. motorcycling Grand Prix championship?

5. A flag of half-black, half-white separated by a diagonal indicates what in Formula 1 motor racing?

6. When did Rod Gould win the 250 c.c. motorcycling Grand Prix championship?

7. At which track did Gilles Villeneuve die in practice in 1982?

8. How many laps are completed to win the Indy 500 race?

9. When did Alessandro Nannini win the F1 Japanese Grand Prix?

10. For which F1 team did Heinz-Harald Frentzen drive in his opening season in 1994?

11. Which F1 world championship winner later won the 1993 CART championship series in the U.S.?

12. Which Irish motorcyclist won the 1932 & '33 senior T.T. on the Isle of Man?

13. Where in Britain did Arrows open a $10m technical centre in 1989?

14. In F1 what do the initials of the BAR team stand for?

15. Which London-born speedway rider was runner-up in the 1951 and '53 world individual championships?

ANSWERS 1. Michael Schumacher 2. Jimmy Guthrie 3. Australia 4. Cecil Sandford 5. Unsportsmanlike behaviour 6. 1970 7. Zolder 8. 200 9. 1989 10. Sauber Mercedes 11. Nigel Mansell 12. Stanley Woods 13. Milton Keynes 14. British American Racing 15. Split Waterman.

Quiz 07 MOTOR SPORTS

1. Over how many laps is the Monaco Grand Prix in Formula 1 raced?

2. How many of the 23 drivers in the 1998 FIA drivers championship failed to score?

3. Which Italian won the 125 c.c. motorcycling Grand Prix championship from 1958-60?

4. Which two Brazilian drivers won the world F1 championship three times?

5. Who won both races at the 1998 British world superbike meeting at Donington?

6. How many times did Nigel Mansell win the British F1 Grand Prix?

7. What nationality was Walter Villa, winner of the 250 c.c. motorcycling Grand Prix championship from 1974-76?

8. Who in 1949 became the first English individual world speedway champion?

9. How many times did Mario Andretti win the CART championship series in the U.S.?

10. In which city was Mike Hailwood born?

11. Which Brazilian F1 driver had his only success at the 1977 Brazilian Grand Prix?

12. How many drivers called Hill have won the F1 world championship?

13. What was the last year in which the winner of the 500 c.c. motorcycling Grand Prix championship was from neither the U.S. or Australia?

14. For which F1 team did Jean Alesi drive in his opening season in 1989?

15. Which American won the 1997 superbikes world championship?

THE ULTIMATE SPORTS FACT AND QUIZ BOOK

Quiz 08 MOTOR SPORTS

1. Which Briton won the 1994 R.A.C. Rally?

2. Which Formula 1 driver holds the record for the most world championship points with 768.5?

3. Who was runner-up in the 1954 F1 world championship?

4. How many F1 Grand Prix wins did John Watson achieve?

5. Who won the 1997 500 c.c. motocross world championship?

6. For which F1 team did Rubens Barrichello drive in his opening season in 1993?

7. What is the Indianapolis Motor Speedway Track also called?

8. Which U.S. driver won the 1973 British F1 Grand Prix?

9. Which F1 world champion won the 1995 Indianapolis 500?

10. Which Italian driver's only F1 win was the 1966 Italian Grand Prix?

11. Who won the 1997 & '98 CART championship series in the U.S.?

12. Where was the European world superbike meeting held on August 2, 1998?

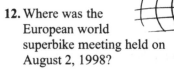
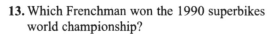

13. Which Frenchman won the 1990 superbikes world championship?

14. How many cars started the 1998 Indianapolis 500 race?

15. Who won the 1998 Indianapolis 500 race?

Quiz 09   MOTOR SPORTS

1. How many Formula 1 Grand Prix wins did Stirling Moss achieve in his career?

2. Which motorcyclist won the Isle of Man senior T.T. in 1989?

3. Which American won the 1996 superbikes world championship?

4. For which F1 team did Pedro Diniz drive in his opening season in 1995?

5. Which F1 world champion earlier won the 1995 CART championship series?

6. Who holds the record with nine successive F1 Grand Prix wins?

7. In which year did the championship series, now conducted by CART, begin in the U.S.?

8. Who was the highest placed British motorcyclist in the 1998 500 c.c. world riders' championship?

9. Who was runner-up in the 1961 F1 world championship?

10. In which year was Benetton Formula 1 established?

11. How many Britons finished in the Top Ten of the final standings of the 1997 world superbike championship?

12. How many F1 motor racing Grand Prix did Brands Hatch host from 1964-86?

13. Who won the 1997 & '98 125 c.c. motocross world championships?

14. In which year was Ferrari's first F1 victory?

15. At which circuit was the 1991 U.S. Grand Prix held - its last to date?

Quiz 10   MOTOR SPORTS

1. What is the name of the Spanish Grand Prix circuit N.E. of Barcelona?

2. By how many points did Kazuto Sakata win the 1998 125 c.c. world riders' championship in motorcycling?

3. In his 129 Grand Prix to the end of the 1998 F1 season, how many had Johnny Herbert won?

4. Who was runner-up in the 1971 F1 world championship?

5. Of the 23 drivers who competed in F1 1998, how many competed in F1 1994?

6. Who won the 1991 Indianapolis 500 race?

7. Which British motorcyclist was killed in 1969 whilst practicing for the East German Grand Prix?

8. Who was the highest placed Briton in the 1984 world F1 championship?

9. Which American won the 1991 & '92 superbikes world championship?

10. Who won the first four races of the 1991 F1 season?

11. Who finished second in the 1997 500 c.c. motorcycle world championships?

12. Which F1 world champion won the 1993 Indianapolis 500?

13. What, in the U.S., does NASCAR stand for?

14. Why was the Daytona 24-hour race shortened in 1972?

15. How many laps of the 1998 F1 season were led by Eddie Irvine?

Quiz 11 MOTOR SPORTS

1. What flag in Formula One signals the end of a race?

2. Who finished second in the 1998 F1 Monaco Grand Prix?

3. Which Welshman won the 1950 & '53 world individual speedway title?

4. In how many F1 Grands Prix did Alain Prost take part?

5. Who won the 1989 Indianapolis 500?

6. Which Scottish motorcyclist won the 1957 Isle of Man senior T.T.?

7. Who was runner-up in the 1974 F1 world championship?

8. Which Kent motorcyclist was nicknamed 'The Mint'?

9. Who had a hat-trick of wins at France, Britain and Germany in the 1991 F1 season?

10. What make of car did Arie Luyendyk, Didier Theys & Mauro Baldi drive to win the 1998 Daytona 24-hour race?

11. In motorcycling, the top nine riders in the 125 c.c. world championship came from which two countries?

12. Who finished second in the 1997 250 c.c. motor cycling world championships?

13. Who won the 1969 Indianapolis 500 and a later F1 world championship?

14. Since 1960, how many drivers have won three out of the four top NASCAR events?

15. In which year was Jordan Formula 1 formed?

Quiz 12

MOTOR SPORTS

1. Which 1991 Formula 1 Grand Prix saw the narrowest winning margin?

2. Which Ulsterman finished third in the 1998 Canadian Grand Prix at Montreal?

3. Who won the 1998 250 c.c. world riders' championship in motorcycling?

4. Who was runner-up in the 1985 F1 world championship?

5. Who scored more world championship points in their F1 career - Nigel Mansell or Niki Lauda?

6. By how many points did Mick Doohan win the 1997 500 c.c. world motorcycle championship?

7. Who was the highest placed Briton in the 1998 250 c.c. world motorcycle riders' championship?

8. How many F1 Grand Prix wins did Ayrton Senna achieve?

9. Who was runner-up in the 1997 world superbikes championship?

10. How many times did Jim Clark win the F1 British Grand Prix?

11. Which F1 motor racing driver world champion won the 1966 Indianapolis 500?

12. At what track did Jochen Rindt die in practice in 1970?

13. Which circuit has hosted the Brazilian Grand Prix in F1 since 1991?

14. For which team did Damon Hill drive in the 1997 F1 season?

15. Which Luton-born motorcyclist won the 1977 Isle of Man senior T.T.?

THE ULTIMATE SPORTS FACT AND QUIZ BOOK

Quiz 13   MOTOR SPORTS

1. Over how many laps was the 1998 Formula 1 Grand Prix in France held?

2. Which make of bike did the first five riders in the 1997 500 c.c. world championship ride?

3. When did Melbourne host its first F1 Grand Prix?

4. Which Brazilian driver did not qualify for the 1998 German Grand Prix in F1?

5. Which is the longest of the four top NASCAR events in the U.S.?

6. How many F1 Grand Prix wins did Jackie Stewart achieve?

7. Which make of car won the 1998 Le Mans 24-hour race?

8. Which Essex-born driver won the 1959 Le Mans 24-hour race with Carroll Shelby?

9. Who won the F1 championship and Indianapolis 500 in 1965?

10. Of the 15 races in the 1997 world 500 c.c. motorcycle championship, how many did Mick Doohan win?

11. Which London-born motorcyclist was awarded the M.B.E. in 1978?

12. Who was runner-up in the 1997 F1 world championship?

13. For which F1 team did Mika Hakkinen drive in his opening season in 1991?

14. By how many points did Mick Doohan win the 1998 500 c.c. riders' championship in motorcycling?

15. Where was the 1998 F1 British Grand Prix held?

ANSWERS 1. 71 2. Honda 3. 1996 4. Ricardo Rosset 5. World 600 6. 27 7. Porsche 8. Roy Salvadori 9. Jim Clark 10. 12 11. Barry Sheene 12. Heinz-Harald Frentzen 13. Lotus Judd 14. 52 15. Silverstone.

HORSE RACING

Quiz 01 HORSE RACING

1. Which horse won the 1958 Prix de l'Arc de Triomphe?

2. Which jockey won the 1997 & '98 2,000 Guineas?

3. At which course was the English Derby run from 1940-5?

4. Which horse won the 1957 Preakness Stakes?

5. Which was the first of Willie Carson's Epsom Derby wins?

6. What links the names of the Epsom Derby winners from 1993 to 1997?

7. At which course is the Sussex Stakes run?

8. In which year was the Irish 2,000 Guineas first run?

9. Who was flat race champion jockey in 1992?

10. Which horse was beaten by a short head by Nimbus in the 1949 2,000 Guineas?

11. Who was champion flat race jockey in 1997 & '98?

12. In which month is the Prix de l'Arc de Triomphe run?

13. Who won the 1995 Cheltenham Gold Cup on Master Oats?

14. At which course is the Whitbread Gold Cup run?

15. Which horse was leading U.S. money earner in 1995 & '96?

ANSWERS 1. Ballymoss 2. Michael Kinane 3. Newmarket 4. Bold Ruler 5. Troy 6. They each featured consecutive repeated letters 7. Goodwood 8. 1921 9. Michael Roberts 10. Abernant 11. Kieren Fallon 12. October 13. Norman Williamson 14. Sandown Park 15. Cigar.

Quiz 02   HORSE RACING

1. Which jockey won the 1975 & '76 2,000 Guineas?

2. Which horse won the 1863 Epsom Derby?

3. Which was the first filly to win the Epsom Derby?

4. Which was the last of Lester Piggott's nine Epsom Derby wins?

5. At which course is the Yorkshire Oaks run?

6. In which year was the Irish 1,000 Guineas first run?

7. Which horse won the 1971 2,000 Guineas?

8. Which horse won the Champion Hurdle at Cheltenham from 1949-51?

9. Over how many furlongs is the Derby run?

10. At which course is the Murphy's Gold Cup run?

11. Which jockey had a hat-trick of wins in the Prix de l'Arc de Triomphe from 1985-7?

12. In which month is Australia's Melbourne Cup held?

13. Which horse won the 1974 & '75 King George VI Chase?

14. Which horse won the 1996 Dubai World Cup?

15. Which jockey has won the Oaks most times?

ANSWERS 1. Gianfranco Dettori 2. Macaroni 3. Eleanor 4. Teenoso 5. York 6. 1922 7. Brigadier Gerard 8. Hatton's Grace 9. Twelve 10. Haydock Park 11. Pat Eddery 12. November 13. Captain Christy 14. Cigar 15. Frank Buckle.

Quiz 03   HORSE RACING

1. At which course is the Fillies Mile run in September?

2. At which English course is a Hennessy Cognac Gold Cup run?

3. Which horse won the 1958 St. Leger?

4. In which year was the Irish Oaks first run?

5. Who trained 1986 Epsom Derby winner Shahrastani?

6. Who was champion flat race trainer from 1963-65?

7. Who was champion flat race apprentice jockey in 1950 & '51?

8. Where was the 1989 St. Leger run?

9. At which course is the Coronation Stakes run?

10. Which jockey won the 1997 & '98 Irish Oaks?

11. The Poule d'Essai des Poulains is the French equivalent of which English classic?

12. Which leg of the U.S. Triple Crown did Silver Charm fail to win in 1997?

13. Who rode Sundew to victory in the 1957 Grand National?

14. Who rode Gay Trip to victory in the 1970 Grand National?

15. Over what distance is the Ascot Gold Cup run?

Quiz 04   HORSE RACING

1. Who trained 1989 Grand National winner Little Polveir?

2. Which jockey has ridden nine St. Leger winners?

3. Which horse won the Prix de l'Arc de Triomphe in 1977 & '78?

4. At which course is the July Cup run?

5. Which jockey rode 1991 Epsom Derby winner Generous?

6. Which horse won the 1997 & '98 King George VI & Queen Elizabeth Diamond Stakes?

7. Which was Lester Piggott's last victory, in 1984, in the Oaks?

8. On which day is the King George VI Chase traditionally run?

9. Which horse won the Champion Hurdle at Cheltenham from 1952-54?

10. Which trainer's first classic win was Fair Salinia in the 1978 Oaks?

11. Who was French champion jockey 15 times between 1959-83?

12. Who was the leading N.H. trainer in 1966/7?

13. In which year was jockey and trainer Stan Mellor born?

14. Which horse won the 1939 Epsom Derby?

15. Which horse won the 1939 Grand National?

Quiz 05 HORSE RACING

1. Who was champion flat race apprentice jockey in 1952 & '53?

2. Which horse won the 1974 Prix de l'Arc de Triomphe?

3. Which jockey won the 1989 Oaks in 1990?

4. At which course is the Eclipse Stakes run?

5. In which year was the Irish St. leger first run?

6. On which Irish course is a Hennessy Cognac Gold Cup run?

7. Which leg of the U.S. Triple Crown did Real Quiet fail to win in 1998?

8. Which horse won the 1987 Grand National?

9. Which horse won the U.S. Triple Crown in 1948?

10. Which horse won the King George VI and Queen Elizabeth Stakes in 1986?

11. In which year was the Jockey Club formed?

12. Which horse won the 1989 2,000 Guineas and Epsom Derby?

13. At which course is the Queen Elizabeth II Stakes run?

14. Which jockey rode Pilsudski to win the 1997 Japan Cup?

15. Which horse won the 1997 Dubai World Cup?

ANSWERS 1. Joe Mercer 2. Allez France 3. Steve Cauthen (His mount Snow Bride was belatedly promoted to winner following the disqualification of Aliysa) 4. Sandown 5. 1915 6. Leopardstown 7. Belmont Stakes 8. Maori Venture 9. Citation 10. Dancing Brave 11. 1750 12. Nashwan 13. Ascot 14. Michael Kinane 15. Singspiel.

Quiz 06 HORSE RACING

1. Which horse won the Cheltenham Gold Cup from 1932-36?

2. Which 1986 Cheltenham Gold Cup-winning horse died later in the year?

3. Which race is the first classic of the English season?

4. Where was the St. Leger run in 1945?

5. Which horse won the 1975 Epsom Derby & Irish Derby?

6. At which course is the Cheveley Park Stakes run?

7. Which horse won the 1990 1,000 Guineas and the Oaks?

8. Which leg of the U.S. Triple Crown did Tabasco Cat fail to win in 1994?

9. Which horse won the 1840 Grand National?

10. Which horse won the Champion Hurdle at Cheltenham from 1968-70?

11. Which horse won the 1850 & '51 Grand National?

12. Which horse won the 1998 St. James's Palace Stakes?

13. Who finished as leading jockey at Royal Ascot in 1998?

14. Which horse won the 1998 Tote Ebor handicap?

15. Which horse won the 1977 U.S. Triple Crown?

ANSWERS 1. Golden Miller 2. Dawn Run 3. 1,000 Guineas 4. York 5. Grundy 6. Newmarket 7. Salsabil 8. Kentucky Derby 9. Jerry 10. Persian War 11. Abd-el-kader 12. Dr. Fong 13. Frankie Dettori 14. Tuning 15. Seattle Slew.

Quiz 07   HORSE RACING

1. Which horses were the sire and dam of Desert Orchid?

2. Which jockey has won the 1,000 Guineas seven times?

3. Which horse won the Cheltenham Gold Cup from 1948-50?

4. At which course is the Middle Park Stakes run?

5. Which horse won the 1989 Belmont Stakes?

6. Which jockey rode Singspiel to win the 1996 Japan Cup?

7. Which horse won the U.S. Triple Crown in 1930?

8. Who was the leading jockey at the May, 1998 Cheltenham Festival?

9. Which horse won the 1987 Epsom Derby & St. Leger?

10. Which horse was runner-up in the 1998 Grand National?

11. Which horse won the 1998 Tote Cesarewitch?

12. Which horse was runner-up in the 1997 Grand National?

13. Which horse won the U.S. Triple Crown in 1943?

14. Which is the oldest of the five classics?

15. Which horse won the 1933 Epsom Derby & St. Leger?

ANSWERS 1. Grey Mirage and Flower Child 2. George Fordham 3. Cottake Rake 4. Newmarket 5. Easy Goer 6. Frankie Dettori 7. Gallant Fox 8. Tony McCoy 9. Reference Point 10. Suny Bay 11. Spirit of Love 12. Suny Bay 13. Count Fleet 14. St. Leger 15. Hyperion.

Quiz 08 HORSE RACING

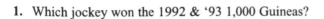

1. Which jockey won the 1992 & '93 1,000 Guineas?

2. Which horse won the 1986 1,000 Guineas and the Oaks?

3. At which course is the Racing Post Trophy run?

4. Which horse won the 1985 1,000 Guineas, the Oaks and St. Leger?

5. What three races comprise the English Triple Crown?

6. The Prix de Diane Hermès is the French equivalent of the Oaks. At which course is it run?

7. Who was champion flat race apprentice jockey in 1964 & '65?

8. In which year was the Prix de l'Arc de Triomphe first run?

9. In which year did Bob Davies and Terry Biddlecombe tie as champion National Hunt jockey?

10. Which leg of the U.S. Triple Crown did Thunder Gulch fail to win in 1995?

11. Which jockey won the Breeders' Cup Classic from 1993-95?

12. Which horse was the first to win the U.S. Triple Crown?

13. Who was leading jockey at the May, 1997 Cheltenham Festival?

14. Who was leading jockey in 1997 at Royal Ascot?

15. Which of the three U.S. Triple Crown races is the shortest?

ANSWERS 1. Walter Swinburn 2. Midway Lady 3. Doncaster 4. Oh So Sharp 5. 2,000 Guineas, Derby & St. Leger 6. Chantilly 7. Paul Cook 8. 1920 9. 1969 10. Preakness Stakes 11. Jerry Bailey 12. Sir Barton 13. Richard Dunwoody 14. Frankie Dettori 15. Preakness Stakes.

Quiz 09   HORSE RACING

1. Which of the three races in the U.S. Triple Crown is the longest?

2. Which horse won the 1983 Oaks and St. Leger?

3. Which jockey rode 1915 Triple Crown winner Pommern?

4. Which jockey has won the 2,000 Guineas most times?

5. Where was the St. Leger run in 1940?

6. In which Irish county is the Curragh?

7. Which of the three legs of the U.S. Triple Crown did Laffit Pincay, Jr. win from 1982-84?

8. Which horse won the 1995 Breeders' Cup Classic?

9. Which horse won the 1997 Cheveley Park Stakes?

10. Which horse finished second in the 1997 Epsom Derby?

11. Which jockey rode Victory Gallop to victory in the 130th Belmost Stakes in 1998?

12. Which U.S. horse won the Eclipse Award for Horse of the Year in 1997?

13. In which month is Tokyo's Japan Cup run?

14. Who was leading National Hunt trainer in 1975/6?

15. Which horse won the 1997 Coronation Stakes?

ANSWERS 1. Belmont Stakes 2. Sun Princess 3. Steve Donoghue 4. Jem Robinson 5. Thirsk 6. County Kildare 7. Belmont Stakes 8. Cigar 9. Embassy 10. Silver Patriarch 11. Gary Stevens 12. Favourite Track 13. November 14. Fred Rimell 15. Rebecca Sharp.

THE ULTIMATE SPORTS FACT AND QUIZ BOOK

Quiz 10   HORSE RACING

1. Which jockey rode the 1978 U.S. Triple Crown winner Affirmed?

2. Which Ascot Gold Cup winner was the sire of Alcide?

3. Which horse won the 1957 Epsom Derby & 2,000 Guineas?

4. Which jockey rode Triple Crown winner Nijinsky?

5. What starting price was 1985 Grand National winner Last Suspect?

6. Who trained 1985 Epsom Derby winner Slip Anchor?

7. In which of his eight consecutive seasons as flat race champion jockey from 1964-71 did Lester Piggott ride 191 winners?

8. Of his 40 classic wins as trainer how many of John Scott's victories came in the St. Leger?

9. What in England is the Fillies Triple Crown?

10. At which course is the Coronation Cup run?

11. Which two horses finished in a dead heat in the 1988 Irish Oaks?

12. Which horse won the Champion Hurdle at Cheltenham from 1985-87?

13. In which country was jockey Laffit Pincay, Jr. born?

14. Which jockey rode Pilsudski to win the 1996 Breeders' Cup Turf?

15. In the six years from 1967-72, how many St. Leger wins did Lester Piggott have?

Quiz 11   HORSE RACING

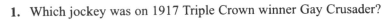

1. Which jockey was on 1917 Triple Crown winner Gay Crusader?

2. Who trained 1982 Epsom Derby winner Golden Fleece?

3. Which horse came second in 1978 in all three legs of the U.S. Triple Crown?

4. In which year did John Francome and Peter Scudamore tie as champion National Hunt jockey?

5. Which was the last of Willie Carson's St. Leger wins, in 1988?

6. In which year did Arkle die?

7. How many classics did Willie Carson ride?

8. At which course is the St. James's Palace Stakes run?

9. The Poule d'Essai des Pouliches is the French equivalent of which English classic?

10. Which horse won the 1998 Dubai World Cup?

11. Who rode the horse Conrad in the 1839 Grand National?

12. Which horse was runner-up in the 1998 Epsom Derby?

13. At which course is the Nunthorpe Stakes run in August?

14. Which horse won the 1998 Coronation Stakes?

15. Which horse won the King George VI & Queen Elizabeth Stakes in 1973 & '74?

ANSWERS 1. Steve Donoghue **2.** Vincent O'Brien **3.** Alydar **4.** 1982 **5.** Minster Son **6.** 1970 **7.** 17 **8.** Royal Ascot **9.** 1,000 Guineas **10.** Silver Charm **11.** Captain Becher **12.** City Honours **13.** York **14.** Exclusive **15.** Dahlia.

GOLF

Quiz 01

GOLF

1. Who was runner-up in the 1996 US PGA tournament?

2. Which two Australians tied on second place in the 1989 British Open?

3. By how many shots did Nick Faldo win the 1992 British Open?

4. What nationality is golfer Richard Zokol?

5. Who finished runner-up with Ernie Els to Tom Lehman in the 1996 British Open?

6. By how many shots did Larry Nelson win the 1981 US PGA?

7. Who did Hale Irwin beat at the 1st extra hole of the 1990 U.S. Open after an 18 hole play-off was tied?

8. Which two majors did Jack Nicklaus win in 1980?

9. Which country does Dennis Watson, a 1985 U.S. Open runner-up, represent?

10. Who low-scored in the third and fourth rounds of the 1983 U.S. Open to win by one shot over Tom Watson?

11. What nationality was Flory van Donck, a runner-up at the 1956 & '59 British Open?

12. In which year did Peter Thomson win his fifth and last British Open tournament?

13. Which Italian was runner-up in the 1953 US PGA (Matchplay) championship?

14. How much in sterling did Seve Ballesteros win in taking the 1979 British Open?

15. Who hit a low-score 63 in the 2nd Round of the 1984 US PGA but finished four shots behind eventual winner Lee Trevino?

ANSWERS **1.** Kenny Perry **2.** Wayne Grady & Greg Norman **3.** One **4.** American **5.** Mark McCumber **6.** Four **7.** Mike Donald **8.** U.S. Open & US PGA **9.** Zimbabwe **10.** Larry Nelson **11.** Belgian **12.** 1965 **13.** Felice Torza **14.** £15,000 **15.** Gary Player.

Quiz 02

GOLF

1. Who led after 54 holes of the 1996 U.S. Masters before losing out to Nick Faldo?

2. In which year did the U.S. Open celebrate its centennial?

3. Who led the first three rounds of the 1972 US PGA but finished behind Nick Price?

4. Which Swede finished equal 12th in the 1991 British Open?

5. In which year did Seve Ballesteros win the U.S. Masters for the second time?

6. Who did Nick Faldo defeat in play-offs to win the 1989 & '90 U.S. Masters?

7. Which Spaniard finished 6th equal in the 1965 U.S. Masters?

8. Which was Bill Rogers's only win in a major?

9. How much in sterling did Tom Watson win in taking the 1980 British Open?

10. The winner of the 1989 U.S. Open also had the lowest score of the tournament. Who was it?

11. Which American was runner-up of the 1973 U.S. Open?

12. Which American, five times winner of the British Open, finished second equal in the 1984 tournament?

13. What nationality is golfer Peter Senior?

14. Who led the first three rounds of the 1969 U.S. Masters to lose by one shot to George Archer?

15. Which golfer's only major win was the 1969 U.S. Open?

ANSWERS 1. Greg Norman 2. 1995 3. Gene Sauers 4. Magnus Sunesson 5. 1983 6. Scott Hoch ('89) & Ray Floyd ('90) 7. Ramon Sota 8. 1981 British Open 9. £25,000 10. Curtis Strange 11. John Schlee 12. Tom Watson 13. Australian 14. Billy Casper 15. Orville Moody.

THE ULTIMATE SPORTS FACT AND QUIZ BOOK

Quiz 03

GOLF

1. Who led the first three rounds of the 1992 U.S. Open before hitting 81 on the last day to finish in joint 13th?

2. Who did David Graham beat in a play-off for the 1979 US PGA title?

3. What nationality was Sewsunker Sewgolum, well placed in the 1963 British Open?

4. Which American golfer's best result in a major was joint runner-up in the 1980 U.S. Masters?

5. At what extra hole did Steve Elkington beat Colin Montgomerie in a play-off for the 1995 US PGA?

6. Which four Europeans won the U.S. Masters in the '80's?

7. How much in dollars did Ian Woosnam pick up for winning the 1991 U.S. Masters?

8. Who led the first three rounds of the 1986 US PGA but hit five over on the last day to end as runner-up?

9. Whose second major was the 1985 US PGA?

10. How much in dollars did the winner of each of the three U.S. majors get in 1989?

11. What nationality is golfer Eduardo Romero?

12. The 1988 U.S. Open was held at the Country Club, Brookline. In which state is it?

13. Which American won the 1935 US PGA title?

14. Where was golfer Chi Chi Rodriguez from?

15. Who led the first two rounds of the 1994 U.S. Masters?

Quiz 04

GOLF

1. Which Taiwanese player led the first three rounds of the 1985 U.S. Open?

2. Which was Ted Ray's first major, in 1912?

3. Which two majors did Gary Player win in 1974?

4. Who beat Jerry Pate and Tom Watson in a play-off to win the 1978 US PGA?

5. Before 1994, when was the previous three-way play-off for the U.S. Open?

6. Whose first major was the 1992 U.S. Masters?

7. What nationality is Brett Ogle?

8. How many players beat par over the 72 holes at the 1976 US PGA?

9. Which of the four days in the British Open in 1988 was a washout?

10. Which American finished runner-up to Hale Irwin in the 1974 U.S. Open?

11. Which two Americans tied as runner-up in the 1981 U.S. Open?

12. What was Tommy Aaron's only win in the Majors?

13. Who led the first three rounds of the 1972 U.S. Masters and ended up three shots clear at the finish?

14. How much in sterling did Lee Trevino net for winning the 1972 British Open?

15. Which Scot won the 1985 British Open?

ANSWERS **1.** Tze-Chung Chen **2.** British Open **3.** U.S. Masters and British Open **4.** John Mahaffey **5.** 1963 **6.** Fred Couples **7.** Australian **8.** None **9.** Third **10.** Forrest Fezler **11.** Bill Rogers & George Burns **12.** 1973 U.S. Masters **13.** Jack Nicklaus **14.** £5,500 **15.** Sandy Lyle.

THE ULTIMATE SPORTS FACT AND QUIZ BOOK

Quiz 05

GOLF

1. Who ended 1994 at the head of the Sony World Rankings?

2. At which two of the majors in 1991 were spectators killed by lightning?

3. Which was Charles Coody's only majors win?

4. Who led the first three rounds of the 1989 US PGA but finished joint second after a double-bogey on the 17th on the last day?

5. Who did Lee Trevino beat in a play-off to win the 1971 U.S. Open?

6. Which Taiwan golfer was runner-up in the 1971 British Open?

7. At which course was the 1970 US PGA held?

8. Who hit the lowest round score, 64, in the 1988 US PGA?

9. In which year did Ben Crenshaw win his second U.S. Masters?

10. Who was the highest placed European in the 1987 U.S. Open?

11. Who hit the lowest round score, 63, in the 1993 US PGA to equal the record?

12. Who did Larry Nelson beat in a play-off to take the 1987 US PGA?

13. Who finished 2nd in the 1991 U.S. Open, beaten in a play-off by Payne Stewart?

14. How old was Greg Norman when he won the 1986 British Open?

15. At which course was the 1983 British Open held?

Quiz 06

GOLF

1. How much in dollars did Corey Pavin win for his 1995 U.S. Open victory?

2. Which two majors did Nick Price win in 1994?

3. By how many shots did Tom Watson beat Jack Nicklaus in the 1982 U.S. Open?

4. Who in 1981 became the first Australian to win the U.S. Open?

5. Which American won the US PGA in 1970 & '76?

6. Who led the 1993 U.S. Open after round two and stayed on to win first prize?

7. How old was Seve Ballesteros when he tied 2nd place in the 1976 British Open?

8. Leading after round three of the 1986 U.S. Open, what did Greg Norman score in the par 70 fourth round to end up in joint 12th?

9. Which two Americans tied 2nd spot behind Jerry Pate in the 1976 U.S. Open?

10. What happened to Richard Boxhall on the third tee of round three in the 1991 British Open?

11. Which English player led after round one of the 1975 British Open?

12. Which course hosted the 1983 US PGA - its first major since 1948?

13. Which American golfer's best major result was runner-up at the 1979 U.S. Masters after a play-off?

14. In which year did Lee Trevino win his first US PGA?

15. Who did John Daly defeat in a play-off for the 1995 British Open

ANSWERS 1. $350,000 2. British Open & US PGA 3. Two 4. David Graham 5. Dave Stockton 6. Lee Janzen 7. 19 8. 75 9. Tom Weiskopf & Al Geiberger 10. He broke his leg 11. Peter Oosterhuis 12. Riviera Country Club, California 13. Ed Sneed 14. 1974 15. Costantino Rocca.

Quiz 07

GOLF

1. How much in sterling did Greg Norman get for winning the 1993 British Open?

2. Who were the only two Europeans to finish in the top ten of the 1993 U.S. Masters?

3. How many under par did Ray Floyd finish to win the 1976 U.S. Masters?

4. Which English golfer was joint runner-up in the 1982 British Open?

5. At which course was the 1975 U.S. Open held?

6. At which course was the 1979 U.S. Open held?

7. Who led after the 2nd round in the 1991 US PGA and went on to take the title?

8. How much in sterling did Nick Faldo pick up for winning the 1987 British Open?

9. Who hit a low-score 63 in the second round of the 1975 US PGA?

10. Who was the only player to beat par over 72 holes in the 1974 British Open?

11. Which two Americans tied second place in the 1981 U.S. Masters?

12. How old was Jack Nicklaus when he won the 1986 U.S. Masters?

13. Which Australian won the 1990 US PGA title?

14. How much did Craig Stadler win in dollars for taking the 1982 U.S. Masters?

15. How many under par was Nick Faldo in winning the 1990 British Open?

!? !?

NAMES & NICKNAMES

Quiz 01   NAMES & NICKNAMES

1. Which Premier League goalkeeper is nicknamed 'Calamity James'?

2. Which athlete is 'The Kansas Cannonball'?

3. What in 1999 was 'Lolgate'?

4. Which skier is 'The Hermannator'?

5. What was the nickname of rugby union player W.J.A. Davies?

6. What was the nickname of rugby union player Herbert Waddell?

7. Which cricketer did Steve Waugh refer to as 'The Picasso of the run chase'?

8. Which cricketer did coach Geoff Marsh refer to as 'The Iceman'?

9. Which Australian cricketer was known simply as 'AB'?

10. What are the Australian women's football team known as?

11. What religious name did Stoke City fans have for manager Brian Little in the 1998/99 season?

12. Which horse race gambler is 'The Sundance Kid'?

13. Which professional jockey rode illegally under the names of Angel Jacobs and Carlos Castro?

14. What are Lawrence Dallaglio's middle names?

15. What is rugby referee Fred Howard known as?

Quiz 02   NAMES & NICKNAMES

1. Which boxing venue is known as 'The House That Tex Built'?

2. Which rugby player is Inga the Winger?

3. Which French rugby union player is 'Piglet'?

4. What is rower Ekaterina Khodotovitch simply known as?

5. Which Leeds and England rugby union player is known as 'The Welsh Wizard'?

6. Which tennis player is 'Pistol Pete'?

7. What is basketball star Michael Jordan simply known as?

8. Which baseball manager was 'The Ol' Perfesser'?

9. Which Wimbledon tennis champion was 'The French waiter'?

10. Which boxer is known as 'The Fleetwood Assassin'?

11. What is Swedish golfer Helen Alfredsson known as?

12. Who is 'The Underpant'?

13. Who is 'The Supercoach'?

14. Which Australian cricket captain was 'Big Ship'?

15. What was the nickname of Australian Test cricketer Bill O'Reilly?

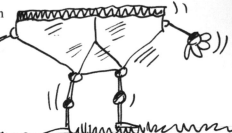

Quiz 03

NAMES & NICKNAMES

1. What is the name of Derbyshire's cricket team in the C.G.U. National League in 1999?

2. Which snooker player is 'The Grinder'?

3. What was snooker commentator Ted Lowe known as?

4. What is baseball star Orlando Hernandez called?

5. Which West Bromwich Albion player is 'The Ginger Ninja'?

6. What was the nickname of Australian bowler R.F. Spofforth?

7. What was the nickname of South African cricketer N.B.F. Mann?

8. What did athlete Voitto Hellsten's first name mean?

9. What was Olympic athlete Edward Jeffreys's nickname?

10. What was the full name of golfer Bobby Jones?

11. What was golfer Harry Cooper's nickname?

12. What were the middle names of tennis player Sidney Wood?

13. What were the middle names of tennis star Mats Wilander?

14. Which Worcester rugby union player is known as 'Spanner'?

15. Which Waterloo rugby union player is known as 'Duke'?

ANSWERS **1.** Derbyshire Scorpions **2.** Cliff Thorburn **3.** Whispering Ted Lowe **4.** El Duque (The Duke) **5.** Lee Hughes **6.** The Demon **7.** Tufty **8.** Victory **9.** Judge **10.** Robert Tyre Jones Jr. **11.** Light Horse **12.** Burr Beardslee **13.** Arne Olof **14.** Spencer Bradley **15.** Paul White.

Quiz 04   NAMES & NICKNAMES

1. Which boxer was the 'Whitechapel Whirlwind'?

2. What was rugby league player Harold Wagstaff's nickname?

3. What was the nickname of basketball Hall-of-Famer Charles Cooper?

4. What was baseball star Arthur Vance known as?

5. Who formed the 'Great Triumvirate' of golf?

6. What was boxer Miguel Angel Canto known as?

7. Which boxer was 'The Casablanca Clouter'?

8. What was South African bowler Hugh Tayfield known as?

9. Which boxer was 'The Cuban Hawk'?

10. Which female swimmer was known as 'Mighty Mouse'?

11. Which boxer was known as 'The Upstate Onion Farmer'?

12. Which billiards player was simply known as 'H.W.'?

13. Which American Football player was called 'The Dodger'?

14. What was baseball player Enos Slaughter known as?

15. Which boxer was known as 'El Terrier'?

ANSWERS 1. Jackie 'Kid' Berg 2. Prince of Centres 3. Tarzan 4. Dazzy 5. John H. Taylor, Harry Vardon and James Braid 6. El Maestro 7. Marcel Cerdan 8. Toey 9. Kid Gavilan 10. Elaine Tanner 11. Carmen Basilio 12. H.W. Stevenson 13. Roger Staubach 14. 'Country' Slaughter 15. Pascual Perez.

Quiz 05   NAMES & NICKNAMES

1. Which boxer was the 'Cincinnati Cobra'?

2. Which horse racing trainer was 'The Emperor of Trainers'?

3. What was boxer Wilfredo Gomez known as?

4. What was baseball player Phil Rizzuto known as?

5. Which boxer was 'The Brockton Blockbuster'?

6. What was baseball star Charles Radbourn known as?

7. What was American Football star Walter Peyton's nickname?

8. What was ice hockey player Lorne Worsley's nickname?

9. Which powerboat racer was 'The Gray Fox'?

10. Which discus thrower was 'Multiple Mac'?

11. What was American Football star Jim Otto known as?

12. What was the nickname of American Football star Randy White?

13. Which Australian cricketer was dubbed 'The New Bradman'?

14. Who was the 'Grand Old Man' of South African cricket?

15. What was American football star Bob Waterfield known as?

ANSWERS 1. Ezzard Charles 2. Robert Robson 3. Bazooka 4. Scooter 5. Rocky Marciano 6. Old Hoss 7. Sweetness 8. Gump 9. Gar Wood 10. Mac Wilkins 11. Double Zero 12. The Manster 13. Norman O'Neill 14. Dave Nourse 15. The Rifle.

THE ULTIMATE SPORTS FACT AND QUIZ BOOK

Quiz 06   NAMES & NICKNAMES

1. Which baseball star was known as 'Little Poison'?

2. What was Spanish motor cyclist Angel Nieto known as?

3. Which boxer was the 'Durable Dane'?

4. What was athlete Renaldo Nehemiah's nickname?

5. What was the nickname of American Football star Lenny Moore?

6. Which footballer was 'The Clown Prince of Soccer'?

7. Which Olympic walker was known as 'The Mighty Mouse'?

8. What is cricketer Fred Trueman's middle name?

9. Which England bowler was known as 'Deadly'?

10. What was cricketer Pelham Warner better known as?

11. What is triathlon star Scott Molina better known as?

12. What was rugby league player Herbert Henry Messenger known as?

13. Which Australian rugby league player is 'Big Mal'?

14. What is Scotland rugby union player Craig Chalmers's middle name?

15. Which female walker's middle name is Undine?

ANSWERS 1. Lloyd Waner 2. El Niño 3. Oscar Nelson 4. Skeets 5. Spats 6. Len Shackleton 7. Don Thompson 8. Sewards 9. Derek Underwood 10. Plum 11. The Terminator 12. Dally 13. Mal Meninga 14. Minto 15. Judy Farr.

Quiz 07

NAMES & NICKNAMES

1. Which boxer was 'The Old Mongoose'?

2. What was American Footballer Johnny McNally known as?

3. Which boxer was 'Terrible Terry'?

4. Which U.S. basketball star was 'Easy Ed'?

5. What was 1961 U.S. Open golf champion Gene Littler known as?

6. What was cyclist Hugo Koblet known as?

7. What was cricketer Jack White known as?

8. Which jockey is 'Stormin' Norman'?

9. What was Sussex bowler John Wisden called?

10. Which jockey was the 'Head Waiter'?

11. What was Scotland rugby union player David Revell Bedell-Sivright known as?

12. What was England rugby union player Jim Brough's middle name?

13. What is show jumper David Broome's middle name?

14. What is American golfer Craig Stadler's nickname?

15. Which Spurs and England footballer is known as 'Sicknote'?

ANSWERS 1. Archie Moore 2. Johnny Blood 3. Terry McGovern 4. Edward Macauley 5. The Machine 6. The Pedaller of Charm 7. 'Farmer' Jack White 8. Norman Williamson 9. The Little Wonder 10. Harry Wragg 11. Darkie 12. Wasdale 13. McPherson 14. The Walrus 15. Darren Anderton.

THE ULTIMATE SPORTS FACT AND QUIZ BOOK

Quiz 08 NAMES & NICKNAMES

1. What was the middle name of Worcestershire cricketer Henry 'Harry' Foster?

2. Which London-born swimmer styled himself 'Amateur Swimming Champion of the World'?

3. What was the nickname of Olympic walker Terence Lloyd Johnson?

4. What was the middle name of Irish rugby union star Maurice 'Moss' Keen?

5. Which British Olympic swimmer's middle name was Bilsland?

6. What is the middle name of rugby league star Martin Offiah?

7. What was the nickname of ice hockey player Yvan Cournoyer?

8. Which baseball manager, who originated the phrase "nice guys finish last", was known as 'Leo the Lip'?

9. What was ice hockey star Phil Esposito's nickname?

10. What was the nickname of baseball player Mark Fidrych?

11. What is the middle name of 1977 British Ladies Open golf champion Vivien Saunders?

12. What was cricketer John Snow's middle name?

13. Yachtsman and aviator Thomas Murdoch Sopwith had an unusual second name - what was it?

14. What was the middle name of Harlequins rugby union player Adrian Stoop?

15. Winner of the 1993 Irish Grand National Charlie Swan has an unusual second name - what is it?

ANSWERS 1. Knollys 2. John Arthur Jarvis 3. Tebbs 4. Ignatius 5. Bobby McGregor 6. Nwokocha 7. The Roadrunner 8. Leo Durocher 9. Espo 10. The Bird 11. Inez 12. Augustine 13. Octave 14. Dura 15. Franan.

Quiz 09 NAMES & NICKNAMES

1. What was the middle name of boxer Randolph Turpin?

2. Which baseball star was 'Hammerin' Hank'?

3. What was the middle name of cricketer Frank Tyson?

4. What was the nickname of handball player Naty Alvarado?

5. What is the middle name of footballer Chris Waddle?

6. What was the nickname of American Footballer Lance Alworth?

7. What is the middle name of Olympic 100m champion Allan Wells?

8. What was basketball's Nate Archibald known as?

9. What was the middle name of footballer William 'Billy' Wright?

10. Which basketball star was 'Mr. Cub'?

11. Which basketball star was 'The Glide'?

12. Which baseball star was 'The Fordham Flash'?

13. Which college basketball coach was known as 'Bighouse'?

14. Which baseball player was 'The Iron Horse'?

15. What was ice hockey goalie Eddie Giacomin's nickname?

ANSWERS **1.** Adolphus **2.** Hank Aaron **3.** Holmes **4.** El Gato (The Cat) **5.** Roland **6.** Bambi **7.** Wipper **8.** Tiny **9.** Ambrose **10.** Ernie Banks **11.** Clyde Drexler **12.** Frankie Frisch **13.** Clarence Gaines **14.** Lou Gehrig **15.** Fast Eddie.

Quiz 10 NAMES & NICKNAMES

1. Who was 'The Black Babe Ruth'?

2. What is the nickname of Waterloo rugby union player Christopher Thompson?

3. What is the nickname of Wakefield rugby union player Mark Beckett?

4. What is Southampton footballer James Beattie known as?

5. What was Aston Villa's Tom Waring known as?

6. What is Kriss Akabusi's full name?

7. What is the middle name of 1968 Olympic Three-Day Event gold winner Derek Allhusen?

8. Which cricketer was 'Barnacle'?

9. Which darts player is 'The Crafty Cockney'?

10. What is the middle name of Sebastian Coe?

11. What is the middle name of Kenny Dalglish?

12. What was jockey John Day, rider of 16 classic winners between 1826-41, sarcastically known as?

13. What is the nickname of new Wimbledon coach Egil Olsen?

14. What was the nickname of cricketer Reginald Erskine Foster?

15. What was W.G. Grace's cricketing brother Edward known as?

ANSWERS 1. Josh Gibson **2.** Physio **3.** Stick **4.** Thunderboots **5.** Pongo **6.** Kriss Kezie Uche Chukwu Duru-Akabusi **7.** Swithin **8.** Trevor Bailey **9.** Eric Bristow **10.** Newbold **11.** Mathieson **12.** 'Honest' John Day **13.** Drillo **14.** Tip **15.** The Coroner.

Quiz 11   NAMES & NICKNAMES

!?   !?

1. Which Liverpool footballer is known as 'God'?

2. Which Waterloo rugby union player is 'Onslow'?

3. What was footballer George Graham's nickname?

4. What was the middle name of Dutch footballer Arnold Muhren?

5. Which Surrey cricketer was 'The Guv'nor'?

6. What was the second name of wicketkeeper Leslie Ames?

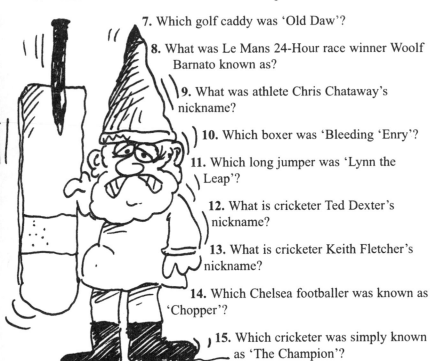

7. Which golf caddy was 'Old Daw'?

8. What was Le Mans 24-Hour race winner Woolf Barnato known as?

9. What was athlete Chris Chataway's nickname?

10. Which boxer was 'Bleeding 'Enry'?

11. Which long jumper was 'Lynn the Leap'?

12. What is cricketer Ted Dexter's nickname?

13. What is cricketer Keith Fletcher's nickname?

14. Which Chelsea footballer was known as 'Chopper'?

15. Which cricketer was simply known as 'The Champion'?

THE ULTIMATE SPORTS FACT AND QUIZ BOOK

!? !?

Quiz 12 — NAMES & NICKNAMES

1. Which Liverpool footballer was known as 'Supersub'?

2. What was the middle name of 1923 British Open golf champion Arthur Havers?

3. What was the nickname of cricketer Jack Hobbs?

4. What was cricket and rugby union international Albert Neilson Hornby's nickname?

5. What was the middle name of Scotland's footballing right winger Alec Jackson?

6. What was the nickname of boxer John Morrissey?

7. Which American Footballer was 'The Galloping Ghost'?

8. Which boxer was known as 'Bendigo'?

9. What was the nickname of basketball player John Havlicek?

10. What was the nickname of boxer Lou Ambers?

11. Which basketball star was 'The World's Greatest Dribbler'?

12. Which fighter was 'The Elongated Panamanian'?

13. Who in ice hockey was 'The Golden Jet'?

14. What was the flowery nickname of boxer Joe Choynski?

15. Which baseball star was 'Big Train'?

ANSWERS 1. David Fairclough 2. Gladstone 3. The Master 4. Monkey 5. Skinner 6. Old Smoke 7. Red Grange 8. William Thompson 9. Hondo 10. The Herkimer Hurricane 11. Marques Haynes 12. Panama Al Brown 13. Bobby Hull 14. Chrysanthemum 15. Walter Johnson.

Quiz 13   NAMES & NICKNAMES

1. What was cricketer Stanley Jackson's nickname?

2. What is the middle name of boxer Lennox Lewis?

3. What was the rather predictable nickname of Birmingham-born athlete Gladys Lunn?

4. Which Scottish rugby union international was known as 'Mighty Mouse'?

5. Which baseball star was 'Tom Terrific'?

6. Which baseball star was 'The Wizard of Oz'?

7. What was the nickname of baseball player Willie Stargell?

8. Which boxer was 'Jack the Giant Killer'?

9. Who in ice hockey is 'Phantom Joe'?

10. What was the ecclesiastical nickname of boxer Tiger Flowers?

11. What was basketball star Pete Maravich known as?

12. Which boxer was 'Ruby Robert'?

13. What was swimmer Mary T. Meagher known as?

14. What was the spooky nickname of boxer Mike Gibbons?

15. What was basketball star Earl Monroe's nickname?

ANSWERS 1. Jacker 2. Claudius 3. Sally 4. Ian McLaughlan 5. Tom Seaver 6. Ozzie Smith 7. Pops 8. Jack Dillon 9. Joe Malone 10. The Georgia Deacon 11. Pistol Pete 12. Bob Fitzsimmons 13. Madame Butterfly 14. Phantom of St. Paul 15. The Pearl.

Quiz 14   NAMES & NICKNAMES

1. What was boxer Alan Minter's nickname?

2. Which cricketer was 'The Lion of Kent'?

3. What was the nickname of jockey Bill Nevett?

4. What is the nickname of footballer and coach Ray Wilkins?

5. What was the nickname of 1930's Arsenal footballer Herbert Roberts?

6. What was the industrial sounding nickname of boxer James J. Jeffries?

7. Which American Footballer was 'Broadway Joe'?

8. Which basketball star was nicknamed 'Moose'?

9. Which tennis player was 'Nasty'?

10. What was the magical nickname of boxer Benny Leonard?

11. Which ice hockey star was 'The Pocket Rocket'?

12. Which boxer was 'The Rockford Sheik'?

13. Which ice hockey star was 'The Rocket'?

14. What was the canine nickname of boxer Mickey Walker?

15. Which basketball star was 'The Big O'?

ANSWERS 1. Boom Boom 2. Alfred Mynn 3. The Cock of the North 4. Butch 5. 'Policeman' Roberts 6. The Boilermaker 7. Joe Namath 8. Edward Krause 9. Ilie Nastase 10. The Ghetto Wizard 11. Henri Richard 12. Sammy Mandell 13. Maurice Richard 14. The Toy Bulldog. 15. Oscar Robertson.

Quiz 15 NAMES & NICKNAMES

1. Which Bradford City footballer is known as 'Bruno'?

2. Which boxer was 'The Pride of the Stockyards'?

3. Which boxer was 'Slapsie Maxie'?

4. What was baseball star Pete Rose's nickname?

5. Which footballer was 'Wor Jackie'?

6. What was the nickname of boxer Jack Delaney?

7. Which tennis player is 'Scud'?

8. Which Wimbledon tennis champion was 'The Praying Mantis'?

9. Which American racehorse trainer was 'Bald Eagle'?

10. Which baseball star was known as 'Sweet Swinging'?

11. Which baseball star was 'The Splendid Splinter'?

12. What was baseball player Carl Yastrzemski known as?

13. Which jockey, who died in 1997, was 'The Master'?

14. Which boxer was 'The King of the Canebrakes'?

15. Which boxer was known as 'The Clutch'?

ANSWERS 1. Darren Moore 2. Packey McFarland 3. Maxie Rosenbloom 4. Charlie Hustle 5. Jackie Milburn 6. Bright Eyes 7. Mark Philippoussis 8. Bob Falkenbu 9. Charles Whittingham 10. Billy Williams 11. Ted Williams 12. Yaz 13. Eddie Arcaro 14. Young Stribling 15. Sammy Angott.

TENNIS

THE ULTIMATE SPORTS FACT AND QUIZ BOOK

Quiz 01   TENNIS

1. To which Swedish qualifier did Thomas Muster lose in the 1998 Australian Open?

2. How many times did Boris Becker win a Grand Slam doubles tournament?

3. Which two players won their first Grand Slam singles titles at the 1977 French Open?

4. In which year did Pete Sampras first reach No. 1 in the world rankings?

5. Who was I.T.F. junior boys' singles world champion in 1978?

6. What nationality is men's player Hicham Arazi?

7. Who is older - Andre Agassi or Richard Fromberg?

8. Which Italian player won the 1998 men's singles at the Grand Prix Hassan II in Casablanca?

9. Cyril Suk is the brother of which women's tennis player?

10. What sport did Lindsay Davenport's father play in the Olympics?

11. Which Argentinian won the 1998 Cerveza Club Colombia Open men's singles title?

12. By what score did Steffi Graf beat Natasha Zvereva in the 1988 French Open singles final?

13. By what score did U.S.A. beat Italy in the 1979 Davis Cup final?

14. What nationality is tennis player Mariano Puerta?

15. To which Frenchman did Michael Chang lose in 1998 Australian Open singles?

ANSWERS **1.** Jan Apell **2.** None **3.** Guillermo Vilas & Mimi Jausovec **4.** 1993 **5.** Ivan Lendl **6.** Moroccan **7.** Fromberg, by a day **8.** Andrea Gaudenzi **9.** Helena Sukova **10.** Volleyball **11.** Mariano Zabaleta **12.** 6-0, 6-0 **13.** 5-0 **14.** Argentinian **15.** Guillaume Raoux.

THE ULTIMATE SPORTS FACT AND QUIZ BOOK

Quiz 02

TENNIS

1. To which Tasmania-born player did Carlos Moya lose in the 1998 Australian Open?

2. How many Grand Slam women's doubles titles did Margaret Court win?

3. Which three males won their first Grand Slam singles title at the French Open in 1982, '83 & '84?

4. Who in 1998 became the first Chilean to reach No. 1 in the men's world rankings?

5. In which year was Serena Williams born?

6. What relation are tennis players Ellis Ferreira & Wayne Ferreira to each other?

7. Who did Sweden beat in the 1987 Davis Cup final?

8. Who was I.T.F. junior girls' singles champion in 1981?

9. Which pair won the 1997 French Open & U.S. Open men's doubles titles?

10. Which tennis player married Barbara Feltus in 1993?

11. How many times did Bill Tilden play for a Davis Cup-winning team?

12. Which Bratislava-born player won the men's singles at the 1998 Internazionali di Tennis di San Marino tournament?

13. Which Italian player holds the record for most Davis Cup appearances?

14. Which country, in 1900, won the first Davis Cup?

15. Which Netherlander beat Goran Ivanisevic in the 1998 Australian Open singles?

ANSWERS **1.** Richard Fromberg **2.** 19 **3.** Mats Wilander, Yannick Noah & Ivan Lendl **4.** Marcelo Rios **5.** 1981 **6.** They are not related **7.** India **8.** Zina Garrison **9.** Daniel Vacek & Yevgeny Kafelnikov **10.** Boris Becker **11.** Seven **12.** Dominik Hrbaty **13.** Nicola Peitrangeli **14.** U.S.A. **15.** Jan Siemerink.

THE ULTIMATE SPORTS FACT AND QUIZ BOOK

Quiz 03   TENNIS

1. How many Grand Slam women's doubles titles did Martina Navratilova win?

2. In which city was Alex Corretja born?

3. Who was I.T.F. junior boys' singles world champion in 1982?

4. Which Australian beat Greg Rusedski in the 1998 Australian Open singles?

5. What nationality is men's singles player Mahesh Bhupathi?

6. Whose only Grand Slam singles win was the 1968 Australian Open men's title?

7. Of his 38 Davis Cup singles games from 1931-6 how many did Fred Perry win?

8. Which two players won their first Grand Slam singles titles at the 1989 French Open?

9. Who was A.T.P. world No. 1 men's player from 29 July, 1974 to 16 August, 1977?

10. After which player is Martina Hingis named?

11. In which round of the 1998 Australian Open singles did the Williams sisters meet?

12. In which year was the Wightman Cup first contested?

13. Which male's first Grand Slam singles win was the 1974 Australian Open?

14. Which country lost the 1981 Davis Cup final to the U.S.A.?

15. Who was Olympic men's singles champion in 1988?

ANSWERS 1. 31 2. Barcelona 3. Guy Forget 4. Todd Woodbridge 5. Indian 6. Bill Bowrey 7. 34 8. Michael Chang & Arantxa Sanchez-Vicario 9. Jimmy Connors 10. Martina Navratilova 11. Second 12. 1923 13. Jimmy Connors 14. Argentina 15. Miroslav Mecir.

THE ULTIMATE SPORTS FACT AND QUIZ BOOK

Quiz 04

TENNIS

1. Prior to Pat Rafter in 1997, who had been the last Australian to win the U.S. Open men's singles title?

2. Which Spaniard beat Andre Agassi in the 1998 Australian Open singles?

3. Who was I.T.F. junior girls' singles world champion in 1984?

4. For which country did Andre Agassi's father box in the 1972 Olympics?

5. What nationality is Tamarine Tanasugarn, victor over Iva Majoli in the 1998 Australian Open singles?

6. Who was 1992 Olympic women's singles champion?

7. Whose first Grand Slam men's singles title was the 1976 Australian Open?

8. Which male holds the records for most doubles titles in a career?

9. Which Romania-born Australian tennis player won the 1998 men's singles title at Coral Springs?

10. Which woman holds the record for most doubles titles in a career?

11. Who has been Jana Novotna's coach since 1990?

12. Which Hungarian was 1947 French Open men's singles tennis champion?

13. Who won his only Wimbledon singles title in 1931?

14. Which three Swedes made the quarter-finals of the 1998 U.S. Open men's singles?

15. In which year did Billie Jean Moffitt become Billie Jean King?

ANSWERS 1. John Newcombe 2. Alberto Berasategui 3. Gabriela Sabatini 4. Iran 5. Thai 6. Jennifer Capriati 7. Mark Edmondson 8. Tom Okker 9. Andrew Ilie 10. Martina Navratilova 11. Hana Mandlikova 12. Joseph Asboth 13. Sid Wood 14. Jonas Bjorkman, Thomas Johansson & Magnus Larsson 15. 1965.

Quiz 05

TENNIS

1. Which players won their first Grand Slam singles title at the 1990 French Open?

2. Who was No. 1 men's seed in the 1998 Australian Open singles?

3. Who was I.T.F. junior boys' singles world champion in 1983?

4. What nationality is Byron Black?

5. What are the names of Arantxa Sanchez-Vicario's two brothers who compete on the men's tour?

6. Who was 1988 Olympic women's singles champion?

7. Who in 1931 became the first German to win the Wimbledon women's title?

8. Which pair won the women's doubles at the 1998 Australian Open?

9. In which year did Venus Williams turn professional?

10. Whose first Grand Slam men's singles title was the January 1977 Australian Open?

11. In which country was Mary Pierce born?

12. What was Martina Navratilova's first Grand Slam singles success?

13. Who won the 1950 Wimbledon & French Open men's singles titles?

14. In which year did Yevgeny Kafelnikov turn professional?

15. How old was Bjorn Borg when he won the 1974 Italian Open?

ANSWERS 1. Andres Gomez & Monica Seles 2. Pete Sampras 3. Stefan Edberg 4. Zimbabwean 5. Emilio & Javier 6. Steffi Graf 7. Cilly Aussem 8. Mirjana Lucic & Martina Hingis 9. 1994 10. Roscoe Tanner 11. Canada 12. Wimbledon 1978 13. Budge Patty 14. 1992 15. 17.

Quiz 06

TENNIS

1. Who in 1987 became the youngest player to compete in the men's singles at the U.S. Open since 1918?

2. Who partnered Justin Gimelstob to win the mixed doubles at the 1998 Australian Open?

3. Who did Andre Agassi marry in 1997?

4. Which two players won their first Grand Slam singles titles at the 1979 U.S. Open?

5. In which year did Conchita Martinez achieve her highest world ranking?

6. At what speed was Greg Rusedski's serve timed at Indian Wells in 1998?

7. Which Frenchman won the 1946 French Open singles title?

8. Who was I.T.F. junior girl's singles world champion in 1994?

9. Which French player became Mrs. Browning in 1975?

10. Who in 1997 became the first Brazilian to break into the men's top 20 rankings?

11. Who won the 1948 Wimbledon men's singles title?

12. Which Spaniards met in the 1998 French Open men's singles final?

13. How did Vitas Gerulaitis die in 1994?

14. Which American pair won the 1988 & '89 Australian Open men's doubles title?

15. Whose first men's singles Grand Slam title was the December 1977 Australian Open?

ANSWERS 1. Michael Chang 2. Venus Williams 3. Brooke Shields 4. John McEnroe & Tracy Austin 5. 1995 6. 149 m.p.h. 7. Marcel Bernard 8. Martina Hingis 9. Francoise Durr 10. Gustavo Kuerten 11. Bob Falkenburg 12. Carlos Moya & Alex Corretja 13. Carbon monoxide poisoning 14. Rick Leach & Jim Pugh 15. Vitas Gerulaitis.

Quiz 07 TENNIS

1. In which city was Dutchman Richard Krajicek born?

2. How are players Albert Costa & Carlos Costa related?

3. In which year was Petr Korda born?

4. Who was president of the Czech Federation from 1994-98?

5. Whose first men's singles Grand Slam title was the 1980 Australian Open?

6. Who was 1981 & '82 Australian Open men's singles champion?

7. In which city was Felix Mantilla born?

8. Which Australian men's player was nicknamed 'Rocket'?

9. In what year did Vic Seixas win the Wimbledon men's singles championship?

10. What nationality was Frew McMillan?

11. Which U.S. pair won the 1992 & '96 Olympic women's doubles title?

12. In which year did Todd Martin turn professional?

13. What nationality is women's tennis player Cara Black?

14. In which year was Steffi Graf born?

15. Which two players won their first Grand Slam singles title at the 1990 U.S. Open?

ANSWERS 1. Rotterdam 2. They aren't 3. 1968 4. Jan Kodes 5. Brian Teacher 6. Johan Kriek 7. Barcelona 8. Rod Laver 9. 1953 10. South African 11. Gigi Fernandez & Mary Joe Fernandez 12. 1990 13. Zimbabwean 14. 1969 15. Pete Sampras and Gabriela Sabatini.

THE ULTIMATE SPORTS FACT AND QUIZ BOOK

Quiz 08

TENNIS

1. Who lost the 1998 French Open women's singles final two weeks after the death of her father?

2. Which German pair won the 1992 Olympic men's doubles title?

3. What was Stefan Edberg's first Grand Slam singles win?

4. In which year did Steffi Graf do the Grand Slam?

5. Who was French women's singles title winner in 1938 & '39?

6. Which Moscow-born player reached the last 16 of the U.S. Open & French Open men's singles in 1998?

7. In which year was Ilie Nastase born?

8. Who in the 1997 French Open singles championship became the first male Belgian to reach a Grand Slam semi-final in the Open era?

9. Who was 1983 French Open men's singles title winner?

10. What is Stan Smith's middle name?

11. Who was 1946 Wimbledon men's singles tennis champion?

12. Which was Jan Kodes's first men's singles Grand Slam title?

13. Which Briton was 1959 French women's singles winner?

14. Which of the Grand Slam singles semi-finals did Andrei Medvedev reach in 1993?

15. What is Fred Stolle's middle name?

Quiz 09   TENNIS

1. Who defeated Pete Sampras in the 1998 French Open men's singles championship?

2. Which Spaniard won the 1972 French Open men's singles title?

3. In which city was Australian Scott Draper born?

4. What is Virginia Wade's first name?

5. What nationality is Leander Paes?

6. Who defeated Switzerland 3-2 in the 1998 Fed Cup final?

7. Which Indonesian lost to Jana Novotna in the 1997 Wimbledon ladies singles quarter finals?

8. In which year did the first prize in the men's singles at Wimbledon reach £100,000?

9. Who did Pete Sampras beat in the 1998 Wimbledon men's singles final?

10. In which year did Thomas Muster turn professional?

11. What was first prize, in sterling, for the 1968 Wimbledon women's singles winner?

12. In which country was Nathalie Tauziat born?

13. Who was U.S. men's singles champion from 1881-87?

14. Which Romanian player was a 1997 French Open ladies singles quarter-finalist?

15. Who was 1967 Australian women's singles winner?

Quiz 10   TENNIS

1. What is the name of Fred Stolle's son, a 1999 U.S. Open title holder?

2. How many Grand Slam doubles titles did Roy Emerson win?

3. In which city was Italian player Silvia Farina born?

4. Who did Marcelo Rios defeat in the 1998 Men's Compaq Grand Slam Cup?

5. In which year was Evonne Cawley born?

6. Which two players won their first Grand Slam singles titles at the 1974 French Open?

7. What was the middle name of Bobby Riggs?

8. Which men's player, born in 1971, has been ranked No. 1 in Morocco since 1990?

9. Which American won the 1951 Wimbledon & Australian men's singles titles?

10. Which Australian won the Kroger St. Jude men's singles title in Memphis in 1998?

11. Who did France defeat in the 1997 Fed Cup final?

12. Which U.S. women's player, born in 1972, reached the Australian Open singles quarter-finals in 1992 & U.S. Open singles quarter-finals in 1995?

13. Of the 61 Wightman Cups held, how many times did Great Britain win?

14. Who did Karen Susman defeat in the 1962 Wimbledon women's singles final?

15. What nationality is women's player Rita Grande?

ANSWERS 1. Sandon 2. 16 3. Milan 4. Andre Agassi 5. 1951 6. Bjorn Borg & Chris Evert 7. Larimore 8. Younes Al Aynaoui 9. Dick Savitt 10. Mark Philippoussis 11. Netherlands 12. Amy Frazier 13. Ten 14. Vera Sukova 15. Italian.

Quiz 11　　TENNIS

1. How many Grand Slam men's doubles titles did John Newcombe win?

2. Which two players won their first and only Grand Slam singles title in the 1976 French Open?

3. Which Frenchman lost the 1997 Wimbledon men's singles final?

4. What nationality is Alexandra Fusai?

5. In which city was Anna Kournikova born?

6. Which German player lost to Monica Seles in the 1996 Australian Open singles final?

7. By what score did the U.S. beat Spain in the 1996 Fed Cup final?

8. Which Australian pair won the 1996 Olympics men's doubles title?

9. Who did Germany beat in the 1998 World Team Cup final?

10. Who did Venus Williams beat in the 1998 Women's Compaq Grand Slam Cup?

11. What was Wimbledon champion Ann Jones's maiden name?

12. What was the first prize in sterling in the 1968 Wimbledon men's singles final?

13. In which year did Sydney-born Bob Hewitt start to represent South Africa?

14. Which American was 1932 Wimbledon men's singles winner?

15. Which American woman won the 1939 Wimbledon singles title?

ANSWERS 1. 17 2. Adriano Panatta & Sue Barker 3. Cédric Pioline 4. French 5. Moscow 6. Anke Huber 7. 5-0 8. Todd Woodbridge & Mark Woodforde 9. Czech Republic 10. Patty Schnyder 11. Haydon 12. £2,000 13. 1967 14. Ellsworth Vines 15. Alice Marble.

SNOOKER

THE ULTIMATE SPORTS FACT AND QUIZ BOOK

Quiz 01 SNOOKER

1. Who in 1927 made a then world record break of 97?

2. Which snooker player was known as 'The Emperor of Pot'?

3. In which city did the 1976 World Championship take place?

4. What prize money did the 1973 World Championship winner Ray Reardon pick up?

5. Who was runner-up in the 1977 World Championships?

6. Where was the 1988 Norwich Union European Grand Prix final held?

7. Which three players represented England in the 1989 snooker World Cup?

8. In which year was Eddie Charlton born?

9. What is Jimmy White's middle name?

10. By what score did Steve Davis beat Doug Mountjoy in the 1981 World Championship final?

11. Which country is Dene O'Kane from?

12. In which year did Ken Doherty turn professional?

13. Who beat Terry Griffiths in the 1982 final of the Welsh championship?

14. From which country does Darren Morgan come?

15. In which year was the Benson and Hedges Masters first staged?

ANSWERS 1. Tom Newman 2. Joe Davis 3. Manchester 4. £2,000 5. Cliff Thorburn 6. Monte Carlo 7. Jimmy White, Neil Foulds & Steve Davis 8. 1929 9. Warren 10. 18-12 11. New Zealand 12. 1990 13. Doug Mountjoy 14. Wales 15. 1975.

Quiz 02

SNOOKER

1. What was the name of the forerunner of snooker employing 15 reds and a white?

2. Which snooker legend was born in 1901 in the coalmining village of Whitwell, Derbyshire?

3. In which city did the first World Championships take place in 1927?

4. How many players contested the 1936 World Championships?

5. Who did Ray Reardon defeat in the 1978 World Championship final?

6. Who beat Terry Griffiths 9-8 in the 1978 Coral U.K. tournament qualifying round after being 8-2 down?

7. Which Canadian made a 142 break in the 1979 World Championship?

8. In which year was Tony Drago born?

9. In which city was Bill Werbeniuk born?

10. Who did Jimmy White beat in the semi-finals of the 1984 World Championships?

11. Which country is Joe Grech from?

12. In what year did Steve Davis turn professional?

13. Which Australian player won the 1988 Australian Championship?

14. In 1988 who did Steve Davis beat in the final of the Everest World Matchplay?

15. In which year did Tony Knowles turn professional?

ANSWERS **1.** Pyramids **2.** Joe Davis **3.** Birmingham **4.** 12 **5.** Perrie Mans **6.** Rex Williams **7.** Bill Werbeniuk **8.** 1965 **9.** Winnipeg **10.** Kirk Stevens **11.** Malta **12.** 1978 **13.** John Campbell **14.** John Parrott **15.** 1980.

Quiz 03
SNOOKER

1. Who in 1937 made the first 'official' total clearance, scoring 133 points?

2. In which year was Mike Hallett born?

3. What is John Virgo's middle name?

4. How many players contested the 1929 World Championships?

5. Which Canadian did Fred Davis beat in a semi-final of the 1950 World Championships?

6. In which year did John Spencer first enter the World Professional Championships?

7. Who did Steve Davis beat in the 1985 Coral U.K. Open final?

8. The 1946 World Championship final was the best of how many frames?

9. Who did Joe Johnson beat in the semi-final of the 1986 World Championships?

10. Who scored a maximum 147 in the 1984 Benson & Hedges Masters semi-final?

11. In which year did Walter Donaldson first enter the World Championships?

12. Which two players contested the 1988 Mercantile Credit Classic final?

13. Who beat Steve Davis 16-15 in the 1983 Coral U.K. final?

14. Who did Jimmy White beat in the second round of the 1988 World Championship?

15. What was Joe Davis's highest break in the World Championship?

THE ULTIMATE SPORTS FACT AND QUIZ BOOK

Quiz 04   SNOOKER

1. Who lost to Joe Davis in the 1928 World Championship?

2. Who was whitewashed 9-0 by Steve Davis in the 1988 Benson and Hedges Masters final?

3. Whose first World Championship win was in 1957?

4. In which year was Alex Higgins born?

5. How many entrants were there in the 1931 World Championships?

6. What is Willie Thorne's middle name?

7. In which year was the World Professional snooker championship held abroad for the first time, in Australia?

8. In which year was the BCE Canadian Masters first staged?

9. How long did the 25 frame tussle between Cliff Thorburn and Terry Griffiths take in the 1983 World Championship?

10. By what score did Steve Davis beat Ray Reardon in the 1985 World Championship final?

11. What was the first prize in the 1987 Mercantile Credit Classic final?

12. Who did Joe Johnson beat in the quarter-finals of the 1987 World Championship?

13. By what score did John Pulman win the 1965 best of 73 World Championship final?

14. In the early 1930's who were the 'Big Four' of snooker?

15. Which brothers met in the 1939 World Championship semi-final?

ANSWERS 1. Fred Lawrence 2. Mike Hallett 3. John Pulman 4. 1949 5. Two 6. Joseph 7. 1970 8. 1985 9. 13 hours 15 minutes 10. 16-5 11. £50,000 12. Stephen Hendry 13. 37-36 14. Joe Davis, Tom Newman, Walter Lindrum & Clark McConachy 15. Joe & Fred Davis.

THE ULTIMATE SPORTS FACT AND QUIZ BOOK

Quiz 05

SNOOKER

1. Who scored the highest break in the first World Championship?

2. In which year was Joe Johnson born?

3. Which Canadian champion entered the 1935 World Championship?

4. In which year was the Dubai Duty Free Classic first staged?

5. Which country is Alain Robidoux from?

6. How many attempts on the final black were made before Dennis Taylor potted it to win the final frame in the 1985 World Championship final?

7. Who beat Stephen Hendry in the 1988 Tennents UK Open final?

8. How many players contested the first World Championship in 1927?

9. Who defeated Jackie Rea to become Irish Professional champion in January 1972?

10. What were the colours of the two extra balls in 'Snooker Plus'?

11. Which two players did Terry Griffiths beat in qualifying rounds of the 1979 World Championship which he eventually won?

12. What is John Parrott's middle name?

13. Who did Willie Thorne beat in the 1985 Mercantile Credit Classic final?

14. What was the frame score in Steve Davis's 1984 World Championship final win over Jimmy White?

15. Who in 1925 made a then world record break of 96?

BRITISH FOOTBALL

Quiz 01 BRITISH FOOTBALL

1. At which club was George Best when he won his last cap for N. Ireland?

2. In which season did Gary Ablett score his first league goal for Liverpool?

3. What age was Jack Charlton when he won his first cap for England?

4. How many league appearances did Joey Beauchamp make for West Ham following his move from Oxford?

5. For which league team did N. Ireland defender Mal Donaghy play from 1992-4?

6. At which club has Francis Benali spent his entire career?

7. Who was Rangers manager from 1978-83?

8. Which was Micky Adams's first league club?

9. Which club did Denis Law join from Huddersfield in 1960?

10. To which club did Manchester United loan David Beckham in the 1994/5 season?

11. Who in October 1936 became the youngest player to score a hat-trick in the English football league?

12. Who was manager of Plymouth Argyle in 1978/79?

13. In which year did Bobby Moore sign as a pro with West Ham?

14. What is the name of Swansea City's ground?

15. From which club did Dele Adebola join Birmingham?

ANSWERS 1. Fulham **2.** 1986/87 **3.** 29 **4.** None **5.** Chelsea **6.** Southampton **7.** John Greig **8.** Gillingham **9.** Manchester City **10.** Preston North End **11.** Tommy Lawton **12.** Malcolm Allison **13.** 1958 **14.** Vetch Field **15.** Crewe Alexandra.

THE ULTIMATE SPORTS FACT AND QUIZ BOOK

Quiz 02 BRITISH FOOTBALL

1. In which year did Glenn Hoddle take over as Swindon boss?

2. To which club did John Beresford move from Newcastle United?

3. In which year were Portsmouth formed?

4. What is the name of Torquay United's ground?

5. Who was Tottenham Hotspur's manager from 1984-86?

6. Which club did Frank Worthington boss from 1985-87?

7. Who scored four goals for England against Portugal on his debut in 1947?

8. Which club did Alan Buckley manage from 1982-86?

9. Who was captain of Ipswich in their 1978 F.A. Cup victory?

10. Who was West Bromwich Albion manager from 1978-81?

11. For which league club did Francis Lee make his debut at the age of 16?

12. Which team won the 1997/98 Football Conference?

13. From which club did Liverpool sign Alan Hansen in 1977?

14. Which Premier League team had the lowest average gate in 1997/98?

15. From which N. Ireland club did Portsmouth sign Derek Dougan in 1957?

ANSWERS 1. 1991 **2.** Southampton **3.** 1898 **4.** Plainmoor **5.** Peter Shreeves **6.** Tranmere Rovers **7.** Stan Mortensen **8.** Walsall **9.** Mick Mills **10.** Ron Atkinson **11.** Bolton Wanderers **12.** Halifax Town **13.** Partick Thistle **14.** Southampton **15.** Distillery.

THE ULTIMATE SPORTS FACT AND QUIZ BOOK

Quiz 03 — BRITISH FOOTBALL

1. What was Steve Perryman's first league club as a manager?

2. What is Martin Chivers's middle name?

3. In which year was Arsenal's Lee Dixon born?

4. Which two national sides did Billy Bingham manage?

5. How many caps did Gordon Banks win for England?

6. From which club did Sunderland sign Kevin Ball?

7. In which year did Sir Matt Busby die?

8. What are the names of the Brightwells who played for Manchester City in the 1980's & '90's?

9. From which club did Manchester United sign Pat Crerand in 1963?

10. In which year was Everton's Michael Branch born?

11. For which league club did Ron Flowers play from 1951-66?

12. Which former Leeds United player was manager of Scunthorpe from 1983-4?

13. Who in 1967 became the first substitute to win an F.A. Cup winners medal?

14. Which team won the 1997/8 Unibond League?

15. How many full England caps did Howard Kendall win?

ANSWERS 1. Brentford **2.** Harcourt **3.** 1964 **4.** Northern Ireland & Greece **5.** 73 **6.** Portsmouth **7.** 1994 **8.** Ian & David **9.** Celtic **10.** 1978 **11.** Wolves **12.** Allan Clarke **13.** Cliff Jones **14.** Barrow **15.** None.

Quiz 04 BRITISH FOOTBALL

1. Which league club play at Bramall Lane?

2. For which English team did David McCreery play after his spell with Tulsa Roughnecks?

3. Which team won the 1997/8 F.A. Umbro Trophy?

4. Which club did Paul McGrath join from Manchester United in 1989?

5. Which team won the 1997/8 F.A. Youth Cup?

6. In which year was Everton's Michael Ball born?

7. Which football Premier League side had the lowest attendance in 1997/8 of 7,688?

8. How many league games did Nick Barmby play for Middlesbrough from 1995-97?

9. In which year was Dwight Yorke born?

10. From which Welsh non-league side did Port Vale sign Mark Bright?

11. Which club play at Portman Road?

12. From which club did Leeds United buy David Hopkin?

13. For which Scottish club did Danny McGrain play his entire career?

14. To which club did Southampton sell Nicky Banger?

15. To which club did Joey Jones move from Chelsea in 1985?

Quiz 05 — BRITISH FOOTBALL

1. Which team won the F.A. Carlsberg Vase in 1997/8?

2. Which former Welsh international became manager of Wrexham in 1989?

3. Which 1st Division team had the lowest average gate in 1997/98?

4. Whose record of 41 England caps was beaten by Billy Wright in 1952?

5. In which year was Ashley Ward born?

6. With which two English clubs was Terry Butcher player-manager after leaving Rangers?

7. From which club did Leicester buy Robbie Savage?

8. For which English club did Belfast-born Joe Bambrick sign in 1934?

9. How many caps did Peter Beardsley win for England?

10. From which club did Gillingham sign Ade Akinbiyi?

11. How many caps did John Charles, the 'Gentle Giant', win for Wales?

12. From which club did Southampton buy Mark Wright in 1982?

13. With which club did Tommy Docherty begin his playing career?

14. Which club did Mark Lawrenson manage from 1989-90?

15. With which club did George Graham sign as a pro in 1961?

ANSWERS 1. Tiverton Town 2. Brian Flynn 3. Crewe Alexandra 4. Bob Crompton 5. 1970 6. Coventry & Sunderland 7. Crewe Alexandra 8. Chelsea 9. 59 10. Norwich City 11. 38 12. Oxford United 13. Celtic 14. Peterborough 15. Aston Villa.

Quiz 06   BRITISH FOOTBALL

1. Who was manager of Sheffield United from 1981-86?

2. Who scored a hat-trick for Scotland's 'Wembley Wizards' in their 5-1 victory over England in 1928?

3. What are the three Devon league teams?

4. In which year was John Aloisi born?

5. Which league club play at Edgeley Park?

6. Which team won the 1997/98 League of Wales?

7. How many points clear were Celtic when they beat Rangers to the 1997/98 league title?

8. In which Scottish town do St. Mirren play?

9. Which team had the highest average gate in Division 1 in 1997/98?

10. Which former England caretaker manager died on his birthday in 1990?

11. Which club did Alan Durban manage from 1978-81?

12. For which club did Wilf Mannion play in 1955 after leaving Middlesbrough?

13. From which club did Oxford United sign John Aldridge?

14. Which England international led Blackpool to three F.A. Cup finals between 1948-53?

15. From which club did Birmingham buy Paul Furlong?

Quiz 07 BRITISH FOOTBALL

1. From which club did Tottenham Hotspur sign Pat Jennings?

2. Before joining Sunderland as boss in 1987, which club had Denis Smith previously managed?

3. Which club did Jimmy Greaves join on leaving Spurs in 1970?

4. Which team won the 1997/8 Smirnoff Irish League?

5. In which country was Scotland international Richard Gough born?

6. In which Scottish city do St. Johnstone play?

7. From which club did Blackburn buy Jeff Kenna?

8. For which club did Jimmy Dickinson make 764 league appearances from 1943-65?

9. Which club play at Sincil Bank?

10. Which club did Bobby Charlton manage after leaving Manchester United?

11. From which club did Liverpool buy David James?

12. From which club did Manchester City sign Colin Bell in 1966?

13. For which club did Alan Ball sign as an amateur in 1961?

14. From which league club did Leeds United sign Lee Bowyer?

15. Which club side was Ron Burgess with when he won 32 caps for Wales?

ANSWERS 1. Watford 2. York City 3. West Ham 4. Cliftonville 5. Sweden 6. Perth 7. Southampton 8. Portsmouth 9. Lincoln 10. Preston North End 11. Watford 12. Bury 13. Blackpool 14. Charlton Athletic 15. Tottenham Hotspur.

THE ULTIMATE SPORTS FACT AND QUIZ BOOK

Quiz 08 BRITISH FOOTBALL

1. Which club did Terry Venables manage from 1980-84?

2. What age was Leslie Compton when he made his England debut in 1950?

3. Which player/manager replaced Ian Porterfield as manager of Reading in 1991?

4. Which football club did Alex Ferguson join in 1957?

5. Which former Leeds United player managed Rochdale from 1986-88?

6. In which year did Paul Ince move from West Ham to Manchester United?

7. Who was Tottenham Hotspur manager from 1987-91?

8. Which player was the first five figure signing in British football?

9. From which club did Bradford City buy Jamie Lawrence?

10. Against which team did Nat Lofthouse score twice on his England debut in 1950?

11. Which London club did Paul Bracewell join from Sunderland in 1997/8?

12. Which Liverpool manager won an F.A. Amateur Cup winners' medal with Bishop Auckland in 1939?

13. Which team play at Kenilworth Road?

14. From which club did Everton sign Earl Barrett in the 1994/5 season?

15. Who was Manchester City's top league goalscorer in 1997/8?

ANSWERS 1. Q.P.R. **2.** 38 **3.** Mark McGhee **4.** Queen's Park **5.** Eddie Gray **6.** 1989 **7.** Terry Venables **8.** David Jack **9.** Leicester City **10.** Yugoslavia **11.** Fulham **12.** Bob Paisley **13.** Luton Town **14.** Aston Villa **15.** Paul Dickov.

Quiz 09   BRITISH FOOTBALL

1. Which team play at Millmoor?

2. Who was Newcastle United's top league scorer in 1997/8?

3. Which team play at Carrow Road?

4. From which club did Stuart Pearce join Nottingham Forest in 1985?

5. Who was Sheffield United's top league goalscorer in 1997/98?

6. With which English club did Ally McCoist play from 1981-3?

7. In which year was Aston Villa player Gareth Barry born?

8. With which league club did N. Ireland international Sam Irving end his career?

9. Who is manager of Southampton F.C.?

10. How many goals did Tom Finney score for England?

11. What is the name of Sunderland's stadium?

12. What age was Steve Coppell when he became Crystal Palace manager in 1984?

13. From which team did Spurs buy Jose Dominguez?

14. How many league clubs did Trevor Brooking play for in his career?

15. Who was West Bromwich Albion's highest league goalscorer in 1997/98?

ANSWERS 1. Rotherham United **2.** John Barnes **3.** Norwich City **4.** Coventry City **5.** Brian Deane **6.** Sunderland **7.** 1981 **8.** Bristol Rovers **9.** Dave Jones **10.** 30 **11.** Stadium of Light **12.** 29 **13.** Birmingham City **14.** One **15.** Lee Hughes.

Quiz 10 — BRITISH FOOTBALL

1. From which Northern Ireland club did Tottenham Hotspur sign Gerry Armstrong?

2. Who in 1930 became the then youngest-ever F.A. Cup finalist at Wembley?

3. From which club did Oxford sign midfielder Mark Angel?

4. For which club did Herbert Chapman sign as a professional in 1901?

5. At which league club did Coventry's David Burrows begin his career?

6. For which club did Scotland and Manchester United player Jimmy Delaney end his career?

7. Which club did Pat Crerand manage from 1976-77?

8. Who in 1991 became the youngest ever to play for Wales?

9. In which year did Notts County form?

10. Who held the Liverpool league scoring record of 245 goals until surpassed by Ian Rush?

11. What was Tottenham Hotspur's worst final league position under Bill Nicholson?

12. Against which team did Geoff Hurst make his international debut?

13. Who was manager of Norwich City from 1973-80?

14. Which Scot captained the 'Wembley Wizards' in 1928?

15. In which Scottish town do Raith Rovers play?

ANSWERS 1. Bangor **2.** Cliff Bastin **3.** Sunderland **4.** Northampton **5.** West Bromwich Albion **6.** Elgin City **7.** Northampton Town **8.** Ryan Giggs **9.** 1862 **10.** Roger Hunt **11.** Eleventh **12.** West Germany **13.** John Bond **14.** Jimmy McMullan **15.** Kirkcaldy.

Quiz 11 BRITISH FOOTBALL

1. In which city was Leeds United manager David O'Leary born?

2. Which Scottish team play at Dens Park?

3. How many league goals did Brett Angell score in his Everton career?

4. From which club did Derby County sign Deon Burton?

5. From which club did Bradford City buy keeper Gary Walsh?

6. In which city was Everton's Danny Cadamarteri born?

7. From which club did Chelsea buy Dan Petrescu?

8. Which club did Jimmy Frizell manage from 1970-82?

9. Who was Sheffield Wednesday's top league goalscorer in 1997/98?

10. Which club did Martin O'Neill join from Norwich in 1983?

11. In which season did Neil Ardley make his first appearance for Wimbledon?

12. From which club did Frank McLintock join Arsenal in 1964?

13. At which London club did Kevin Campbell begin his career?

14. Who captained Newcastle in their 1985 F.A. Youth Cup win?

15. In which year was Sol Campbell born?

ANSWERS 1. London 2. Dundee 3. One 4. Portsmouth 5. Middlesbrough 6. Bradford 7. Sheffield Wednesday 8. Oldham 9. Paolo Di Canio 10. Notts County 11. 1990-91 12. Leicester City 13. Arsenal 14. Paul Gascoigne 15. 1974.

THE ULTIMATE SPORTS FACT AND QUIZ BOOK

Quiz 12   BRITISH FOOTBALL

1. From which club did Dixie Dean join Everton in 1925?

2. In which Scottish town do Queen of the South play?

3. With which club did Mick Channon end his career?

4. In which year was Dennis Wise born?

5. With which club did midfielder Jim Baxter end his career?

6. For which club did Jimmy Armfield sign as an amateur in 1951?

7. From which club did Nottingham Forest buy Chris Bart-Williams?

8. Which Manchester City player scored two in six minutes for England versus Italy at Highbury in 1934?

9. Which club did Kingsley Black join from Nottingham Forest?

10. Which English third division club did Bobby Collins join in 1967?

11. With which Welsh club did Nathan Blake first play league football?

12. For which club did Emlyn Hughes win a League Cup winners' medal in 1980?

13. How many league games did Mark Bosnich play for Manchester United in his first spell there?

14. Billy Liddell signed for Liverpool in 1939. In which year did he make his league debut?

15. How many league goals did Matt Carbon score whilst at Derby?

Quiz 13 — BRITISH FOOTBALL

1. Peter Nicholas earned the last of his 73 caps for Wales whilst at which club?

2. At which league club did Franz Carr begin as an apprentice?

3. How many caps did Jimmy Nicholl win for Northern Ireland?

4. To which club did Arsenal sell Jimmy Carter in 1995?

5. At which league club did Warren Barton begin his career?

6. For how much did Millwall sell Tony Cascarino to Aston Villa in 1990?

7. How many league goals did David Batty score in his first spell at Leeds United?

8. From which club did Andy Booth join Sheffield Wednesday?

9. Of which club was Gordon Lee manager from 1975-77?

10. In which year was Gary Lineker awarded the O.B.E.?

11. From which club did Arsenal sign goalkeeper Vince Bartram?

12. Which Arsenal and Huddersfield player appeared in a then record five Wembley F.A. Cup finals from 1927-38?

13. Which club did Clayton Blackmore join from Manchester United?

14. For which two teams did Mark Hughes play on 11th November, 1987?

15. At which league club did Steve Bould begin his league career?

ANSWERS 1. Watford **2.** Blackburn **3.** 73 **4.** Portsmouth **5.** Maidstone United **6.** £1m **7.** Four **8.** Huddersfield Town **9.** Newcastle United **10.** 1992 **11.** Bournemouth **12.** Joe Hulme **13.** Middlesbrough **14.** Wales & Bayern Munich **15.** Stoke City.

THE ULTIMATE SPORTS FACT AND QUIZ BOOK

Quiz 14   BRITISH FOOTBALL

1. Which club did Scotland international Bobby Evans join as player-manager after leaving Chelsea in 1961?

2. At which Midlands club did Gary Charles start as a trainee?

3. Who scored the winning goal for Stoke City in the 1972 League Cup final?

4. At which ground do Coventry City play?

5. Who moved from Sunderland to Middlesbrough for £1,000 in 1905?

6. From whom did West Ham buy Paul Kitson?

7. In which year did Billy Bremner make his debut for Leeds United?

8. In which year was Wimbledon's Robbie Earle born?

9. Which Spanish club did John Aldridge join after leaving Liverpool?

10. On which island was John Barnes born?

11. At which Welsh club did Tottenham Hotspur's Chris Armstrong start his career?

12. Which former Sunderland captain was manager of Middlesbrough from 1963-6?

13. At which London club did Phil Babb start his career?

14. Which three managers have won the English championship with more than one club?

15. In which year was Manchester United's Wes Brown born?

Quiz 15 — BRITISH FOOTBALL

1. What age was Gerry Francis when he took over the England captaincy in 1975?

2. At which league club did Steve Bruce begin his career?

3. From which club did Liverpool sign Ray Houghton in 1987?

4. Who was manager of Manchester United from 1971-72?

5. Which N. Ireland international was Oldham manager from 1966-68?

6. In which year were Mansfield Town formed?

7. Who was manager of Coventry City from 1993-95?

8. Which former Everton manager was boss at Preston North End from 1975-77?

9. Which club did Neil Aspin join from Leeds?

10. Which Q.P.R. player made 514 league appearances for the club from 1950-63?

11. At which league club did Wolverhampton's Steve Bull begin his career?

12. At which two clubs was Dave Bassett manager before joining Sheffield United in 1988?

13. How many full international caps did Trevor Francis win for England?

14. Which club play at Roots Hall?

15. At which ground do Derby County play?

Quiz 16 BRITISH FOOTBALL

1. Against whom in 1968 was England player Alan Mullery sent off?

2. Who was Middlesbrough manager from 1970-77?

3. For which team did Dave Mackay become player-manager in 1971?

4. In which year was Ian Branfoot appointed manager of Southampton?

5. Who earned 25 caps as a goalkeeper for England from 1929-36, then a record for the position?

6. From which club did Sheffield Wednesday sign Peter Atherton?

7. In which city was Trevor Francis born?

8. In which year was Everton's John Oster born?

9. For which club did Stan Cullis play his entire career?

10. Which league club play at the Alfred McAlpine Stadium?

11. From which club did Middlesbrough sign George Camsell in 1925?

12. From which club did Sunderland buy Lee Clark?

13. Which Arsenal player was out of the game for a year following injury in the 1952 F.A. Cup final?

14. From which Irish club did Danny Blanchflower join Barnsley in 1948?

15. Which football team play at Dean Court?

ANSWERS 1. Yugoslavia **2.** Jack Charlton **3.** Swindon Town **4.** 1991 **5.** Harry Hibbs **6.** Coventry City **7.** Plymouth **8.** 1978 **9.** Wolverhampton Wanderers **10.** Huddersfield Town **11.** Durham City **12.** Newcastle United **13.** Walley Barnes **14.** Glentoran **15.** AFC Bournemouth

THE ULTIMATE SPORTS FACT AND QUIZ BOOK

Quiz 17   BRITISH FOOTBALL

1. How many full caps did Billy Bonds win for England?

2. From which club did West Ham sign Eyal Berkovic?

3. In which year did Nigel Clough join Liverpool from Nottingham Forest?

4. How many league goals did midfielder Ian Bishop score for West Ham in his nine season career there?

5. With which league team did England player Bryan Douglas spend his entire career?

6. For which Scottish club did Craig Burley sign on leaving Chelsea?

7. With which club did Johnny Haynes turn pro in 1952?

8. Who was manager of Portsmouth from 1974-77?

9. Who managed Chelsea in their 1955 league championship year?

10. In which year did John Rudge take over as manager of Port Vale?

11. Which was Ray Clemence's first professional club?

12. From which club did Bolton Wanderers sign Gudni Bergsson?

13. Who captained England in his last international match, against Scotland, in 1933?

14. Which was Peter Beardsley's first league club?

15. Who was voted P.F.A. Young Footballer of the Year in 1987?

FOOTBALL AROUND THE WORLD

Quiz 01 FOOTBALL AROUND THE WORLD

1. Which Canadian team did Rudi Krol play for between spells at Ajax and Napoli?

2. Which team lost the 1960 & '68 European Championship finals?

3. Whose record of 33 international goals for Italy was beaten by Luigi Riva?

4. Which nation won the Copa America in 1979?

5. Which German club did ex-Austrian defender Ernst Ocwirk manage for a season?

6. From which team did David Platt join Juventus in 1992?

7. How many goals did Lato score in his Polish international career from 1971-84?

8. How many goals did Tostão score for Brazil in his 55 international appearances?

9. Which team won the Belgian League in 1996/7?

10. Who was African Footballer of the Year in 1976 & '90?

11. Which team won the 1996/7 French League?

12. How many goals did Stephan Stanis score for Racing Club Lens against Aubry-Asturias in a 1942 fixture?

13. How many goals did Fernando Morena score in his 49 match international career for Uruguay?

14. Which team finished bottom of Germany's top flight in 1996/7?

15. To which side did Molde sell Oyvind Leonhardsen?

ANSWERS 1. Vancouver Whitecaps 2. Yugoslavia 3. Giuseppe Meazza 4. Paraguay 5. Cologne 6. Bari 7. 45 8. 32 9. Lierse 10. Roger Milla 11. Monaco 12. 16 13. 20 14. St. Pauli 15. Rosenborg.

Quiz 02 FOOTBALL AROUND THE WORLD

1. Which Brazilian forward was known as 'The Black Diamond'?

2. In which three years did the USSR lose the European Championship final?

3. For which Belgian club did Jean-Pierre Papin play before joining Marseille in 1986?

4. How many times was Marco van Basten top scorer in the Dutch League?

5. Who in 1972 became West Germany's most capped goalkeeper?

6. Which Chelsea defender was born in Pointe-A-Pitre in 1971?

7. From which French club did Michel Platini join Juventus in 1982?

8. What was Brazilian footballer Artur Antunes Coimbra known as?

9. Who transferred to Napoli from Barcelona in 1984 for a record £6.9m?

10. From which team did Sheffield United buy Petr Katchuro?

11. In which year was Pelé born?

12. Which team finished bottom of Italy's Serie A in 1996/7?

13. Which club bought Karl-Heinz Rummenigge from Borussia Lippstadt in 1974?

14. From which team did Southampton buy Stig Johansen?

15. Which Italian club bought Uruguayan Juan Schiaffino in 1954 for a world record fee of £72,000?

Quiz 03 FOOTBALL AROUND THE WORLD

1. Which teams contested the 1992 European Championship final?

2. Which nation won the Copa America in 1975?

3. From which team did Barnsley buy Arjan de Zeeuw?

4. Chelsea 'keeper Dmitri Kharine has previously played for which three Moscow teams?

5. Which team won the 1997/8 Belgian League?

6. Which Czechoslovakian player was 1962 European Footballer of the Year?

7. Who was top scorer in the 1997/8 French League?

8. Which Argentinian team won the Copa Libertadores de America from 1968-70?

9. Which team won the 1997/8 Swedish League?

10. Who won the 1996/7 Spanish League?

11. From which club did Bayern Munich sign Lothar Matthäus?

12. Who was Belgian Footballer of the Year in 1962 & '65?

13. Which nation won the 1998 African Nations Cup?

14. What was Brazilian footballer Edvaldo Izidio Neto known as?

15. How many minutes of international football did Dino Zoff play between September 1972 & June 1974 without conceding a goal?

ANSWERS. 1. Denmark & Germany 2. Peru 3. Telstar 4. Torpedo Moscow, Dynamo Moscow & CSKA Moscow 5. F.C. Brugge 6. Josef Masopust 7. Stephane Guivarc'h 8. Estudiantes 9. Halmstad 10. Barcelona 11. Borussia Mönchengladbach 12. Paul van Himst 13. Egypt 14. Vava 15. 1143 minutes.

Quiz 04 FOOTBALL AROUND THE WORLD

1. In which year did Sandro Mazzola make his international debut for Italy?

2. From which Italian team did Juventus buy Sergio Porrini?

3. For which three Italian teams did German footballer Karl-Heinz Schnellinger play?

4. Which team finished bottom of the Russian 1st Division in 1996/7?

5. Which team won the 1997/8 German League?

6. In which country was Peter Ndlovu born?

7. Who was top scorer in Italy's Serie A in 1996/7?

8. For which club side was Allan Simonsen playing when he won 1977 European Footballer of the Year?

9. In which country are Shooting Stars and Rangers International leading club sides?

10. From which side did Aston Villa buy Savo Milosevic?

11. Which Argentinian was top scorer, for Juventus, in the Italian League in 1959?

12. In which position did Ajax finish in the 1996/7 Dutch League?

13. Which team won the 1994 African Nations Cup?

14. From which Italian club did Genoa buy Dan Petrescu?

15. For which German club team did Uwe Seeler play his entire career?

ANSWERS 1. 1963 2. Atalanta 3. Roma, Milan & Mantua 4. Lada 5. Kaiserslautern 6. Zimbabwe 7. Inzaghi 8. Borussia Mönchengladbach 9. Nigeria 10. Partizan Belgrade 11. Omar Sivori 12. Fourth 13. Nigeria 14. Foggia 15. SV Hamburg.

Quiz 05 FOOTBALL AROUND THE WORLD

1. Which Argentinian team won the Copa Libertadores de America from 1972-5?

2. What was Brazilian footballer Jose Eli de Miranda known as?

3. To which Italian club did Spaniard Luis Suarez move in 1961?

4. Who was top scorer in Italy's Serie A in 1997/8?

5. For which German team did Bertie Vogts play from 1966-79?

6. Which team won the 1966/7 Portuguese League?

7. Who was top scorer in the Spanish First Division in 1996/7?

8. From which side did Sampdoria buy Attilio Lombardo?

9. For which French club did Brazilian Jairzinho play?

10. Which team won the French Cup in 1996/7 but finished bottom of the top flight?

11. In which city was Frank Rijkaard born?

12. Which German scorer in the 1986 World Cup Final started his career with Kickers Offenbach?

13. Which team came bottom of Italy's Serie A in 1997/98?

14. Which Spanish goalkeeper conceded seven against England at Highbury in 1931?

15. From which club did Brann of Norway buy Tore Andre Flo?

ANSWERS **1.** Independiente **2.** Zito **3.** Internazionale **4.** Oliver Bierhoff **5.** Borussia Mönchengladbach **6.** Porto **7.** Ronaldo **8.** Cremonese **9.** Olympique Marseille **10.** Nice **11.** Amsterdam **12.** Rudi Völler **13.** Napoli **14.** Ricardo Zamora **15.** Tromso.

Quiz 06 FOOTBALL AROUND THE WORLD

1. Which former South American Player of the Year helped Valencia win the 1980 European Cup Winners' Cup?

2. In his 62 international matches how many goals did Gerd Müller score for Germany?

3. From which team did Juventus sign Fabrizio Ravenelli?

4. For which team did Russian Igor Netto play from 1948-66?

5. In which year was Nicolas Anelka born?

6. Who was top scorer in the French league in 1996/7?

7. At which team did Hungarian Sandor Kocsis win his first international cap?

8. Which Brazilian team won the Copa Libertadores de America in 1992-93?

9. From which club did Gianni Rivera move to Milan in 1960?

10. In his 26 league games for Molde in 1995 how many goals did Ole Gunnar Solskjaer score?

11. Which team won the 1990 African Nations Cup?

12. From which team did Parma buy Gianfranco Zola?

13. To which club did Lillestrom sell Jan-Aage Fjortoft?

14. Which German scored a hat-trick on his international debut versus Romania in 1940?

15. By how many points did Ajax win the 1997/8 Dutch championship?

ANSWERS 1. Mario Kempes 2. 68 3. Reggiana 4. Spartak Moscow 5. 1979 6. Stephane Guivarc'h 7. Ferencvaros 8. São Paulo 9. Alessandria 10. 20 11. Algeria 12. Napoli 13. Rapid Vienna 14. Fritz Walter 15. 17.

Quiz 07 FOOTBALL AROUND THE WORLD

1. Which Dutch player won European Cups with PSV Eindhoven in 1988 & Barcelona in '92?

2. Out of the six years from 1949-55, how many times did Gunnar Nordahl top the scoring chart of the Italian league?

3. In which city was Roberto Rivelino born?

4. Which team won the 1997/8 Portuguese league title?

5. Which team won the 1996/7 German league title?

6. To which Brazilian league club did Uruguayan Pedro Rocha move after the 1970 World Cup?

7. From which team did Rosenborg buy Trond Egil Soltvedt?

8. In which city was Blackburn keeper John Filan born?

9. From which club did Denilson transfer to Real Betis in 1997 for £22m?

10. With which Brazilian team did Mario Zagalo begin his professional career?

11. How many league goals did Gianluca Festa score for Internazionale from 1993-97?

12. To which team did Cosenza sell Marco Negri who later sold him on the Rangers?

13. For which Dutch club did Swedish defender Björn Nordqvist play?

14. For which Italian club did Paolo Rossi debut in 1977?

15. To which French club did Raymond Kopa move in 1951?

ANSWERS 1. Ronald Koeman 2. Five 3. São Paulo 4. Porto 5. Bayern Munich 6. São Paulo 7. Brann 8. Sydney 9. São Paulo 10. Flamengo 11. Three 12. Perugia 13. PSV Eindhoven 14. Juventus 15. Reims.

CRICKET

Quiz 01 CRICKET

1. Which country have been involved in two tied Tests?

2. How many sixes did Andrew Symonds hit for Gloucs in their August 1995 game against Glamorgan?

3. Which South African wicketkeeper made 26 dismissals in the 1961/2 series against New Zealand?

4. How many times did Patsy Hedren hit over 200 in his first-class career?

5. In which year did Zimbabwe play their first Test?

6. How many hat-tricks did Douglas Wright take in his first-class career?

7. Which wicketkeeper made 264 dismissals in the Sunday League from 1985-'97?

8. How many did Pakistan score in an innings against England at the Oval in 1987?

9. How many times have Gloucs come second in the County Championship since 1890?

10. Which three Australian fielders head the list of most Test catches?

11. Which two county cricket sides have a rose and crown on their badge?

12. How many centuries did Geoff Boycott hit in his first-class career?

13. Which county did Kim Barnett join for the 1999 season?

14. In his first class career from 1914-'36 how many times did Alfred 'Tich' Freeman take 10 or more wickets in a game?

15. Who headed Worcs bowling averages in the 1998 County Championship?

ANSWERS 1. Australia 2. 20 3. John Waite 4. 22 5. 1992 6. Seven 7. Stephen Rhodes. 8. 708 9. Six 10. Allan Border, Mark Taylor & Greg Chappell 11. Derbyshire & Hampshire 12. 151 13. Gloucestershire 14. 140 15. David Leatherdale.

Quiz 02
CRICKET

1. Which Englishman took 2,465 wickets in his first-class career from 1963-'87?

2. What flower is on the badge of Yorkshire?

3. How many centuries did Graham Gooch hit in his first-class career?

4. What was England's big score in a 1930 innings versus the West Indies in Kingston?

5. For which county did umpire Vanburn Holder play from 1968-'80?

6. Which team had a hat-trick of wins in the Gillette Cup from 1970-'72?

7. Who made 209 in his first-class debut in England in 1998?

8. Which two counties met in the 1998 Minor Counties championship final?

9. Which three teams in the County Championship have yet to win the Nat West Trophy or its predecessor?

10. Who made his debut for Zimbabwe versus Sri Lanka in the 1998 first Test?

11. How many times have Sussex finished second in the County Championship since 1890?

12. What was England's score when the first Test versus the West Indies in 1998 was abandoned?

13. Who won the three match Test series in 1998 between New Zealand & Sri Lanka?

14. Who won the three match Test series in 1998 between Pakistan & Australia?

15. Which team scored 413-4 versus Devon in the 1990 Nat West Trophy?

ANSWERS 1. Derek Underwood 2. White rose 3. 128 4. 849 5. Worcestershire 6. Lancashire 7. R.P. Arnold 8. Dorset & Staffordshire 9. Durham, Glamorgan & Leicestershire 10. M.W. Goodwin 11. Seven 12. 17-3 13. Sri Lanka 14. Australia 15. Somerset.

Quiz 03   CRICKET

1. In which year did Sri Lanka win their first Test?

2. Which West Indies wicketkeeper made 24 dismissals in the 1963 series versus England?

3. How many centuries did Dennis Amiss hit in his first-class career?

4. Whose England Test career lasted from 1899-1930?

5. Who took 10-10 for Yorkshire against Notts in July 1932?

6. In which year did Brian Lara score his record-breaking Test 375?

7. What has been Somerset's highest position in the County Championship?

8. Out of Bert Oldfield's 130 Test dismissals how many were stumpings?

9. Who headed Glamorgan's championship bowling averages in 1998 at 22.20?

10. How many times did Allan Border score centuries in Limited Over internationals?

11. Which Australian player headed Sussex's championship batting averages in 1998?

12. What is the highest match aggregate score in a Five Day Test?

13. For which county did umpire Mervyn Kitchen play from 1960-'79?

14. Which Englishman took 2304 wickets in his first-class career from 1949-'69?

15. Against whom did Alvin Kallicharan score 206 for Warwickshire in a 1984 Nat West Trophy game?

Quiz 04

CRICKET

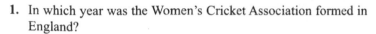

1. In which year was the Women's Cricket Association formed in England?

2. How many did Australia score in their innings and 579 run defeat by England at the Oval in 1938?

3. For which county did umpire Neil Mallender play from 1987-'94?

4. How many times did Gordon Greenidge score centuries in Limited Over internationals?

5. Who scored 239 for Lancs versus Hants in 1998?

6. How many wickets did Malcolm Marshall take in his first-class career?

7. In which year did New Zealand achieve a Test low score of 26 against England?

8. Who made his Test debut for the West Indies versus England in the fourth Test in 1998?

9. How many consecutive Tests did Allan Border play in from 1979-'94?

10. Who hit 210 for South Africa in the third Test versus England in 1998?

11. By how many runs did England win the fourth Test versus Australia in 1998?

12. Who is India's most capped Test player?

13. Who was part of both highest first and second wicket partnerships for Sussex, compiled in 1933 & 1921 respectively?

14. Who is New Zealand's top batsman in Limited Over internationals?

15. By what score did South Africa beat the West Indies in their 1998/99 Test series?

ANSWERS 1. 1926 2. 324 3. Somerset 4. 11 5. John Crawley 6. 1651 7. 1955 8. D. Ramnarine 9. 153 10. Gary Kirsten 11. 12 runs 12. Kapil Dev 13. E.H. Bowley 14. Martin Crowe 15. 5-0.

Quiz 05

CRICKET

1. Who scored 340 for Sri Lanka versus India in August 1997?

2. Of Jeffrey Dujon's 272 Test dismissals as the West Indies' wicketkeeper, how many were stumpings?

3. Which player scored 2,547 runs in the Gillette Cup/Nat West Trophy from 1973-'96?

4. Which Pakistan bowler took 1571 wickets in his first class career from 1957-'82?

5. Who scored 310 n.o. for England against New Zealand at Leeds in 1965?

6. For which county did umpire David Shepherd play from 1965-'79?

7. Who scored 203 for Kent versus Lancs in the 1998 season?

8. How many centuries did Leslie Ames make in his first-class career?

9. Who is Pakistan's most capped Test player?

10. Who was Warwickshire's overseas player in 1999?

11. How many Tests did Dennis Lillee take to accumulate 300 wickets?

12. Who was captain and overseas player for Worcs in 1999?

13. Which two West Indian players have made over 100 catches in Test cricket?

14. Who was made captain of Yorkshire in 1996?

15. For which two counties did umpire Chris Balderstone play?

ANSWERS 1. Sanath Jayasuriya 2. Five 3. Graham Gooch 4. Intikhab Alam 5. John Edrich 6. Gloucestershire 7. Carl Hooper 8. 102 9. Javed Miandad 10. Allan Donald 11. 56 12. Tom Moody 13. Garfield Sobers & Viv Richards 14. David Byas 15. Yorkshire & Leicestershire.

Quiz 06

CRICKET

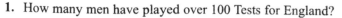

1. How many men have played over 100 Tests for England?

2. What was Mike Gatting's highest first-class score?

3. Who took 41 wickets for Australia in the Test series against England in 1978/79?

4. For which county did umpire Graham Burgess play from 1966-'79?

5. How many Tests did Ian Botham take to make 3,000 runs and take 300 wickets?

6. Who scored 1,950 runs in the Gillette Cup/ Nat West Trophy from 1963-'87?

7. Which Indian bowler took 1,560 wickets in his first-class career from 1961-'82?

8. Who is the West Indies' most capped Test player?

9. Against which three clubs did Graeme Hick score four consecutive hundreds in 1998?

10. Which England wicketkeeper made seven dismissals in an innings against India in 1980?

11. Who headed the batting averages in the 1998 Test series between India and Australia?

12. How many times did Garfield Sobers make over 300 runs and take 20 wickets in a Test series?

13. In which year was the International Women's Cricket Council founded?

14. Whose record did Mike Atherton pass in captaining England for the 42nd time?

15. For which county do Stuart Law and Danny Law play?

ANSWERS 1. Five 2. 258 3. Rodney Hogg 4. Somerset 5. 71 6. Dennis Amiss 7. Bishen Bedi 8. Viv Richards 9. Middlesex, Sussex (twice) & Surrey 10. Bob Taylor 11. Sachin Tendulkar 12. Three 13. 1958 14. Peter May 15. Essex.

Quiz 07   CRICKET

1. Who took 35 wickets for England in the 1896 three match Test series against South Africa?

2. How many centuries did Alvin Kallicharan make in his first-class career?

3. Which Australian fielder made 13 catches in a Test series twice?

4. Who took 81 wickets in the Gillette Cup/Nat West Trophy from 1963-'80?

5. Who has captained Pakistan in 48 Tests?

6. For which two counties did umpire David Constant play from 1961-'68?

7. In which year did Jack Russell make 11 catches against South Africa in a Test?

8. Who scored a hundred in each innings for South Africa versus Gloucs in 1998?

9. Which South African took 1417 wickets in his first-class career from 1965-'89?

10. Who headed the batting averages for South Africa versus England in the 1998 Test series?

11. In which year was the first Limited Overs international?

12. Of his 47 Tests as Indian captain, how many did Sunil Gavaskar win?

13. Who scored 827 for the West Indies in the 1955 Test series against Australia?

14. How many times did Fred Titmus take 100 first-class wickets in an English season?

15. Seven England players have taken over 200 wickets in Tests. Who are they?

ANSWERS 1. George Lohmann 2. 87 3. Bob Simpson 4. Geoff Arnold 5. Imran Khan 6. Kent & Leicestershire 7. 1995 8. Gary Kirsten 9. Mike Proctor 10. W.J. Cronje 11. 1971 12. Nine 13. Clyde Walcott 14. 16 15. Alec Bedser, Ian Botham, John Snow, Brian Statham, Fred Trueman, Derek Underwood and Bob Willis.

Quiz 08

CRICKET

1. How many dismissals did Alan Knott make in his career from 1965-'85?

2. Who was the oldest player to appear in a Test match?

3. Who took most wickets for Durham in the 1998 County Championship?

4. Who was captain of Essex in 1999?

5. Which batsman took 16 hours 39 minutes to compile his 337 for Pakistan versus the West Indies in 1958?

6. For which county did Mushtaq Ahmed play in 1998?

7. Who is South Africa's highest wicket taker in Test cricket?

8. Which two batsmen compiled the highest first wicket partnership for Middlesex in the 1998 County Championship?

9. Which Surrey bowler averaged 17.76, taking 63 championship wickets in 1998?

10. Who holds the record for sixes in a Test innings?

11. Who is the chief executive of Warwickshire?

12. Which fielder has taken most catches in Limited Overs internationals?

13. For which county did umpire John Holder play from 1968-'72?

14. Who scored 558 for the West Indies in the 1969 Test series versus New Zealand?

15. Who in 1999 became Northamptonshire's captain & overseas player?

ANSWERS 1. 1,344 2. Wilfred Rhodes 3. John Wood 4. Nasser Hussain 5. Hanif Muhammad 6. Somerset 7. Allan Donald 8. Mike Gatting & Justin Langer 9. Saqlain Mushtaq 10. Wasim Akram 11. Dennis Amiss 12. Mohammed Azharuddin 13. Hampshire 14. S.M. Nurse 15. Mathew Hayden.

THE ULTIMATE SPORTS FACT AND QUIZ BOOK

Quiz 09

CRICKET

1. How many dismissals did David Bairstow make in his career from 1970-90?

2. Of his 24 Tests as Australian captain, how many did Don Bradman win?

3. Which four teams other than the 18 county sides take part in the Benson & Hedges Cup?

4. Who scored 322 for Somerset versus Warwickshire in the 1985 County Championship?

5. By how many wickets did England beat the West Indies in the third Test in 1998?

6. How long did Walter Hammond's third hundred in his 336 n.o. for England versus New Zealand in 1933 take?

7. Who scored a century for England versus South Africa in the 1998 second Test?

8. In how many Tests did Australia's demon bowler Jeff Thomson play?

9. By how many did Railways beat Dera Ismail Khan at Lahore in December 1964?

10. Who was the Cricket Writers' Club Young Cricketer of the Year in 1998?

11. Who in 1928 took over 300 first-class wickets in an English season?

12. Who was Sussex's overseas player for the 1999 season?

13. Where was the second Test between Australia and England in 1998/9 played?

14. For which club did Philip DeFreitas play from 1985-'88?

15. What is David Boon's middle name?

ANSWERS 1. 1,099 **2.** 15 **3.** Ireland, Scotland, Minor Counties & Combined Universities **4.** Viv Richards **5.** Three **6.** 47 minutes **7.** Nasser Hussain **8.** 51 **9.** An innings and 851 runs **10.** Andrew Flintoff **11.** Alfred 'Tich' Freeman **12.** Michael Di Venuto **13.** Perth **14.** Leicestershire **15.** Clarence.

Quiz 10

CRICKET

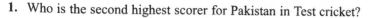

1. Who is the second highest scorer for Pakistan in Test cricket?

2. How many dismissals did Farokh Engineer make in his first-class career?

3. Who is the West Indies' highest scorer in Limited Overs internationals?

4. Who took 83 wickets for Warwickshire in the 1998 County Championship?

5. Which West Indies batsman made 37,354 runs in his first-class career?

6. Whose wicket did Richard Illingworth take with his first ball in Test cricket?

7. Which batsman scored two double centuries for Kent versus Essex in 1938?

8. Who scored 123 in a tenth wicket partnership for Kent versus Hampshire in 1998?

9. In which season did Bill Edrich score 3,539 first-class runs?

10. Who was Yorkshire's overseas player in 1999?

11. Seven Australians have scored over 6,000 runs in Test cricket. Who are they?

12. Who headed the batting averages in the 1998 Test series between South Africa and Pakistan?

13. Which all-rounder hit 80 sixes in the 1985 first-class season?

14. Which three of the 18 county sides have yet to win the Benson & Hedges Cup?

15. By how many runs did England beat South Africa in the 1998 Fifth Test?

ANSWERS 1. Saleem Malik 2. 824 3. Desmond Haynes 4. Edward Giddins 5. Gordon Greenidge 6. P.V. Simmons 7. Arthur Fagg 8. D.W. Headley & M.M. Patel 9. 1947 10. Gregory Blewett 11. David Boon, Allan Border, Don Bradman, Greg Chappell, Neil Harvey, Mark Taylor & Steve Waugh 12. Azhar Mahmood 13. Ian Botham 14. Durham, Sussex & Glamorgan 15. 23 runs.

Quiz 11 CRICKET

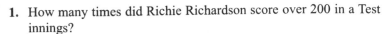

1. How many times did Richie Richardson score over 200 in a Test innings?

2. Who was the Cricket Writers' Club Young Cricketer of the Year in 1978?

3. Who is India's highest scorer in Limited Overs internationals?

4. How many times did Andy Caddick take 10 wickets or more in a match in the 1998 County Championship?

5. Which New Zealand batsman made 34,346 runs in his first-class career?

6. For which club does Ronnie Irani play?

7. How many times did Alfred 'Tich' Freeman take all ten wickets in an innings?

8. Which wicketkeeper heads the list for most dismissals in an English season?

9. Who is New Zealand's second highest scorer in Test cricket?

10. Who headed the batting averages in the 1998 Test series between New Zealand and Zimbabwe?

11. Who took 10-28 for Rawalpindi B versus Peshaware in December 1995?

12. Who won the 1998 Test series between India and Australia?

13. How many catches did Brian Close take in his first-class career from 1949-'86?

14. What is Glamorgan player Matthew Maynard's middle name?

15. In which year was 'Jack' Russell born?

ANSWERS 1. None 2. David Gower 3. Mohammad Azharuddin 4. Three 5. Glenn Turner 6. Essex 7. Three 8. Leslie Ames 9. John Wright 10. C.D. McMillan 11. Naeem Akhtar 12. India 13. 813 14. Peter 15. 1963.

Quiz 12

CRICKET

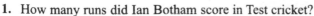

1. How many runs did Ian Botham score in Test cricket?
2. Who was the Cricket Writers' Club Young Cricketer of the Year in 1974?
3. How many times did Viv Richards score centuries in Limited Overs internationals?
4. How many times did Saqlain Mushtaq take 11 wickets in a match in the 1998 County Championship?
5. What low score did Nottinghamshire achieve in an innings against Yorkshire in June 1901?
6. In which year did Derbyshire register their only County Championship title win?
7. Against whom did Brian Lara score 501 n.o. for Warwickshire in June 1994?
8. Who headed the championship batting averages for Middlesex in 1998?
9. How many catches did Mickey Stewart make in his first-class career from 1954-'72?
10. For which county does Andy Caddick play?
11. Which team scored 388-7 versus Scotland in the 1992 Benson & Hedges Cup?
12. Who headed Warwickshire's championship batting averages in 1998?
13. Who took most wickets for Derbyshire in the 1998 County Championship?
14. Which teams finished bottom of the Minor Counties (Eastern Division) & (Western Division) in 1998?
15. By how many wickets did West Indies beat England in the second Test in 1998?

ANSWERS 1. 5,200 2. Phil Edmonds 3. Eleven 4. Three 5. 13 6. 1936 7. Durham 8. Justin Langer 9. 634 10. Somerset 11. Essex 12. Nick Knight 13. Kevin Dean 14. Cumberland & Oxfordshire 15. Three.

Quiz 13   CRICKET

1. How many times have Hampshire won the County Championship?

2. Against whom did Graeme Hick hit 405 n.o. in May 1988?

3. How many minutes did Denis Compton take to hit 300 runs for the MCC versus N.E. Transvaal in December 1948?

4. Who scored a century for England in the first Test versus South Africa in 1998?

5. Who scored 226 for Warwickshire versus Middlesex in 1998?

6. Which fielder holds the record for most catches in an English season?

7. Where was the first Test played in the 1998/9 Ashes series?

8. Who took 7-12 for Middlesex versus Minor Counties (East) in the 1978 Benson & Hedges Cup?

9. Who was the Cricket Writers' Club Young Cricketer of the Year in 1990?

10. Who holds the record of 149 for most wickets taken in the Benson & Hedges Cup?

11. On which island was Hampshire player Lee Savident born?

12. In which city was Kent bowler Minal Patel born?

13. For which county did Muttiah Muralitharan play in 1999?

14. In which year did Garfield Sobers famously hit six sixes off Malcolm Nash?

15. What animal is on the badge of Leicestershire?

Quiz 14　　CRICKET

1. Which year saw Glamorgan's first County Championship title win?

2. Which wicketkeeper has made most dismissals in the Benson & Hedges Cup?

3. Who headed Nottinghamshire's bowling averages in the 1998 County Championship?

4. Who scored 200 n.o. for Yorkshire versus Warwickshire in 1998?

5. Who scored a century for South Africa in the second Test versus England in 1998?

6. Who was the Cricket Writers' Club Young Cricketer of the Year in 1952?

7. Which two county cricket badges feature three axes?

8. Who finished bottom in the 1998 County Championship?

9. How many times did Javed Miandad score 200 or more in his Test career?

10. Who took 16-136 for India against the West Indies on his Test debut in 1988?

11. In which year did David Boon make his Durham debut?

12. At what average did Sydney Barnes take his 189 England Test wickets?

13. Which two Lancashire bowlers took 48 wickets each in the 1998 County Championship?

14. Which two Pakistan players are the highest wicket takers in Limited Over internationals?

15. Who headed the batting averages for Northamptonshire in the 1998 County Championship?

THE ULTIMATE SPORTS FACT AND QUIZ BOOK

Quiz 15   CRICKET

1. Who is the second highest scorer for India in Test cricket?

2. In which year did Nottinghamshire last win the County Championship?

3. How many times did Imran Khan take ten wickets or more in a Test?

4. Since the County Championship started in 1890, how many of the 18 teams have yet to win it?

5. How many centuries did Garfield Sobers score in his Test career?

6. Which team have tied the County Championship on two occasions?

7. Of his 83 dismissals in the Benson & Hedges Cup, how many by Geoff Humpage were stumpings?

8. For which county does Dr. Barton de Courcy Thomson play?

9. How many times did Don Bradman score over 500 runs in a Test series?

10. Who was Leicestershire's captain in 1999?

11. Who was Nottinghamshire's overseas player for the 1999 season?

12. Which Test ground has seen a nine-wicket innings bowling performance on three occasions?

13. Who scored 34 off an over by A.J. Tudor in 1998?

14. Who are the two highest wicket takers in Limited Over internationals for the West Indies?

15. In which year was the John Player League introduced?

Quiz 16   CRICKET

1. In which year did Yorkshire last win the County Championship?

2. How many times did Don Bradman score 200 or over in his Test career?

3. How many batsmen have scored over 8,000 runs in Test cricket?

4. Which Australian took 16-137 at Lord's on his Test debut in 1972?

5. How many times did Dennis Lillee take 10 wickets or more in Test matches?

6. Who was made captain of Middlesex in 1997?

7. Which wicketkeeper has made most dismissals in Limited Over internationals?

8. Who took 9-65 for Sri Lanka versus England at the Oval in 1998?

9. Which team have won the Gillette Cup/Nat West Trophy the most times?

10. How many players took hat-tricks in the 1998 County Championship?

11. Which three county sides of the 18 have yet to win the Sunday league?

12. Which two England fielders made 120 catches in Test cricket?

13. How many centuries did Allan Border score in his Test career?

14. Who is South Africa's most successful wicketkeeper in terms of dismissals?

15. How many times did Joel Garner take 10 wickets or more in a Test match?

ANSWERS 1. 1968 2. 12 3. 8 4. Bob Massie 5. Seven 6. Mark Ramprakash 7. Ian Healy 8. Muttiah Muralitharan 9. Lancashire 10. Four 11. Gloucestershire, Northamptonshire and Durham 12. Ian Botham & Colin Cowdrey 13. 27 14. Dave Richardson 15. None.

Quiz 17   CRICKET

1. How many centuries did Len Hutton make in his first-class career?

2. Who were the first winners of the Gillette Cup in 1963?

3. Who were the first winners of the NatWest Trophy in 1981?

4. For which county cricket side does Dominic Cork play?

5. Who had figures of 0-0 in eight overs for Somerset against Essex in the John Player League in 1969?

6. Who scored most runs for Gloucestershire in the 1998 County Championship?

7. Who took 62 wickets for Hampshire in the 1998 County Championship?

8. For which county does Dean Headley play?

9. Who scored 227 for Glamorgan versus Northamptonshire in 1998?

10. Who headed the batting averages in the 1998 Test series between the West Indies and England?

11. Who made his Test debut for England in the fourth Test versus South Africa in 1998?

12. How many overs did Muttiah Muralitharan bowl for Sri Lanka versus England at the Oval in 1998?

13. Who is England's second highest wicket taker in Test cricket?

14. How many England wicketkeepers have made over 150 dismissals in Test cricket?

15. How many centuries did Sunil Gavaskar score in his Test career?

ANSWERS 1. 129 2. Sussex 3. Derbyshire 4. Derbyshire 5. Brian Langford 6. Timothy Hancock 7. Nixon McLean 8. Kent 9. Stephen James 10. Mark Ramprakash 11. Andrew Flintoff 12. 113.5 13. Bob Willis 14. Four 15. 34.

WHO SAID THAT?

Quiz 01

WHO SAID THAT?

1. "In general, Italians are a pain in the neck to British people because we dress well, know how to eat well and drink with taste." Which Italian footballer?

2. "Geoff is a cricketing legend and his views on the sport are greatly valued". Which media man on which cricketer?

3. "I'm cold and ruthless - as far as I'm concerned it's kill or be killed". Which imposing British sportsman?

4. "If I can do half as well as Don Revie then I'll be delighted." Which Leeds United manager after equalling a seventh successive win record?

5. "If I'm going to lose, I'm going to do it my way." Which tennis player at the 1999 Italian Open?

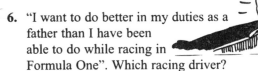

6. "I want to do better in my duties as a father than I have been able to do while racing in Formula One". Which racing driver?

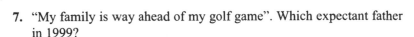

7. "My family is way ahead of my golf game". Which expectant father in 1999?

8. "I was shocked with England in the sense that once they went 1-0 behind they didn't want to fight anymore." Which imported player talking about France's February 1999 defeat of England?

9. "He's a bit of a singer you know, and plays the guitar. And he does weights." The Australian coach speaking about which multi-talent?

10. "Chris was the same colour the day he left as the day I made him a manager". Which Premier League chairman?

Quiz 02

WHO SAID THAT?

1. "Wes is Mr. Cool". Which Manchester United old boy on which new intake?

2. "It's like waiting for the hangman". Which boxer on the waiting before a fight?

3. "Welcome to world cricket". Which Australian to new boy Alex Tudor in his debut Test at Perth in 1998?

4. "I have not taken drugs, I do not take drugs and I will not take drugs." Which cyclist in 1999?

5. "...I told them to keep their heads up and that they could put themselves in the shop window." Which rugby coach in 1999?

6. "Not one of you forget for a second that victory is imperative and we fight like cornered tigers till the deed is done." Which inspiring cricket captain?

7. "I'm still fighting a lot of demons." Which troubled golfer in 1999?

8. "Kick and run is Coventry's way." Which unhappy Romanian?

9. "We played dumb basketball." Which succinct coach?

10. "I was absolutely rubbish." Which snooker player at the 1998 Rothmans Malta Grand Prix?

ANSWERS 1. Nobby Stiles on Wes Brown 2. Billy Schwer 3. Steve Waugh 4. Jan Ullrich 5. Gary Mercer at Halifax Blue Sox 6. Imran Khan at the 1992 World Cup Final 7. John Daly 8. Viorel Moldovan 9. Billy Mims of Greater London Leopards 10. John Higgins.

(?) Quiz 03   WHO SAID THAT? **(?)**

1. "I am sorry if you misinterpreted my actions during the game, which were not meant to cause any offence to yourself or anyone else." Which repentant soul?

2. "If you do anything you want to be the best - the only way of doing that is by competing and winning at the highest level. That's the buzz." Which rugby player in need of a buzz?

3. "If I was the manager of Real Madrid - or Barcelona or any leading club - I would want Steve McManaman in my side." Which fan of the ex-Liverpool player?

4. "We've been at the bottom. It's far better to be at the top." Which Springbok?

5. "All I ever see when I pick up a paper is Leeds but they still haven't won anything." Which rugby league coach in March, 1999?

6. "Every time Birmingham went forward they looked like scoring." Which boss after a 7-1 home defeat by the rampant Blues?

7. "He's a nice, quiet intelligent lad, experienced for all that he's young." Which Italian on which Brazilian?

8. "Neil Redfearn cheated the referee." Which Premier League boss in accusative mode?

9. "Tennis is my life. I will play in 1999." Which women's tennis star?

10. "I just wanted to give you a hug." Which friendly golfer to Greg Norman after his return to competition after a lay-off?

ANSWERS 1. Robbie Fowler after his bottoming out against Graeme Le Saux 2. Lawrence Dallaglio 3. Gérard Houllier, Liverpool boss 4. Gary Teichmann 5. John Monie, Wigan coach 6. Malcolm Shotton of Oxford 7. Roberto Baggio on Ronaldo 8. Arsene Wenger 9. Steffi Graf 10. Nick Faldo.

Quiz 04

WHO SAID THAT?

1. "I want to be 6ft 1in." Which swimmer in 1998?

2. "In most American sports you use your hands." Which philosophical goalkeeper?

3. "Scottish rugby is on the verge of tragedy." A joint statement by which witches?

4. "You can score 10 goals a season and they might all be the 'one' when you get beaten 4-1". Which positive Chelsea player?

5. "Lara and Hooper will not be going to South Africa." Which unreliable Cassandra on the West Indies cricket board in November 1998?

6. "We've not lost for 18 matches and we don't intend to start now." Which rugby union coach?

7. "Yugoslavs are not assassins and we haven't eaten anybody." Which footballer?

8. "I have cried. I cried at that film Shenandoah when James Stewart came back from the Civil War." Which lachrymose Premier League boss?

9. "Frankly I never thought I'd see this day." Who, on seeing the MCC Women's first game in May 1999?

10. "The weather's something else, it can only improve." Which U.S. jockey on his first visit to Goodwood in June 1999?

 **Quiz 05** **WHO SAID THAT?**

1. "Manchester deserved the victory just as much as we did". Which coach?

2. "It will be very tough for the next four or five days to get over this." Which underwhelmed tennis player?

3. "I don't know how he'll react, but he'll either win by 10 or miss the cut." Which golfer on new dad Ernie Els before the 1999 Volvo P.G.A. Championship.?

4. "In boxing your health is your wealth." Which trainer's a poet and don't know it?

5. "Our form is encouraging." Which soon-to-be disappointed coach?

6. "He was always too busy, didn't come to any of the tournaments." Which golfer on which guru?

7. "I've never seen an English match live at the stadium but I watch the Premier League on T.V. in Germany and I like it very much." Which top flight new-boy?

8. "We are looking at August now." Who, on what?

9. "I don't even know who I'll be playing in the next round." Which Wimbledon bright spark in 1999?

10. "I regret creatine is not forbidden." Which un-Piaf-like politician?

Quiz 06

WHO SAID THAT?

1. "It took me a long time to forget last year's final but now it's a new Wimbledon I feel I have a chance." Who in 1999?

2. "I was born with a gift that the Lord gave me, but you have to work at your talent." Which record-breaking athlete?

3. "This is my favourite course from a design standpoint." Which golfer on Pinehurst No. 2?

4. "No one is a born leader. I have made millions of mistakes." Which Test cricket captain?

5. "I am under no financial illusions about the financial position of this club." Which First Division boss refusing to be mesmerized?

6. "He is married to Fulham and will not be able to divorce us." Which barrack-room grocer?

7. "When Huddersfield play Bradford there's real animosity between the supporters." Which Huddersfield member of staff in February 1999?

8. "I am a citizen of the world. I have no problem living anywhere in the world." Which boxer in 1999?

9. "What use is money if you are not happy as a private person." Which malcontent?

10. "There's a lot of mutual respect between me and Michael". Which racing driver about Herr Schumacher?

ANSWERS 1. Goran Ivanisevic 2. Maurice Greene 3. Jack Nicklaus 4. Wasim Akram 5. Adrian Heath at Sheffield United 6. Mohammed Al Fayed 7. Terry Yorath, appointed to Bradford's coaching staff in 1999 8. Trevor Berbick, facing deportation from Canada 9. Michael Laudrup 10. Mika Hakkinen.

Quiz 07

WHO SAID THAT?

1. "I'm disappointed with the amount of rough. I think it's a bit too short, a little bit too easy." Which golfer, before missing the cut after 36 holes at the 1999 U.S. Open?

2. "I would love it if we could beat them, love it." Which overheated Premier League manager?

3. "They were really having a go at each other...it only ended when they were parted by the police". Which loving couple at St. James' Park in 1999?

4. "He was given the verdict, which I thought was an injustice." Which boxer on losing his fight against Zaragoza in 1997?

5. "I got a rush out of gambling but I don't have the money to gamble anymore." Which former gambler?

6. "Many people frown on the InterToto Cup, but not in Aberystwyth." Near universal thumbs up for football's least wanted, by whom?

7. "I feel like a spring chicken." Which tennis player in the French Open in 1999?

8. "It is possible to lead for 90 minutes and still lose the match." Which chief executive on what?

9. "Can you fall in love with a woman just reading about her? No, it's not possible. It's the same without seeing the bid cities." Which I.O.C. member?

10. "Her volley isn't so great." Which gloating tennis player in 1999?

Quiz 08

WHO SAID THAT?

1. "It's very important for a batsman to be selfish." Which Australian?

2. "It will go to the wire, between Chelsea, Arsenal, United and Villa - although not necessarily in that order." Which punter's friend in December 1998?

3. "When Benny's in that mood there's nobody better." Which Premier League boss on whom?

4. "We need a multi-millionaire and if there is one out there, please help Pompey." Which t.v. personality on Portsmouth's plight?

5. "They must remember that playing for the West Indies is a privilege, not a right." Which leading figure in West Indies cricket?

6. "I could not believe Dennis did it." Which dumbfounded Romanian?

7. "That's it exactly. I've been muzzled". I.O.C. member Marc Hodler on what?

8. "Not too many people sleep absolutely soundly before a Test, I can assure you." Which Test cricket captain in 1998?

9. "Anyone who suggested that he wasn't international class should be embarassed." Which enthusiast on Dion Dublin?

10. "I was on the verge of packing up and going to New Zealand". Which desperate man?

ANSWERS 1. Coach Geoff Marsh 2. Derby boss Jim Smith 3. Danny Wilson on Benito Carbone 4. Fred Dinenage 5. Sir Garfield Sobers 6. Dan Petrescu on Dennis Wise's handball against Oxford United 7. The I.O.C. bribery scandal 8. Mike Atherton 9. Glenn Hoddle 10. Jockey Mick Fitzgerald after winning the Cheltenham Gold Cup in 1999.

Quiz 09 WHO SAID THAT?

1. "I want to play for a club with ambition and ability." Which departee from Sheffield Wednesday?

2. "Alex's welfare comes first. He has a few personal problems and has gone away to sort them out." Which Alex?

3. "I wouldn't go back to Newcastle United. Definitely not, one thousand percent." Which mathematician?

4. "No time was I consulted about his transfer." Which hands-off Premier League boss?

5. "Southend's best ever buy". Who, according to the law?

6. "It's taken a long time to get over the disappointment. I was so upset that for three nights after the match I could not sleep at all." Which French insomniac?

7. "The only time we are happy is when we go to the big shopping centre where we spend our free time." Which Italian lotus eater?

8. "If he were French and I was still captain of the French team he would play forever." Which tennis player on whom?

9. "It's cured my number one fault for ever; now I can get a lot better turn with the legs." Who, on what?

10. "Michael's a natural footballer from Whitley Bay, which is not quite Brazil but there's a beach there so it's no surprise he's got magic feet." Which student of geography on footballer Michael Bridges?

ANSWERS **1.** Dan Petrescu **2.** Alex Rae, Sunderland midfielder **3.** Kevin Keegan **4.** Walter Smith following Duncan Ferguson's departure to Newcastle **5.** Stan Collymore, subject of a legal claim by ex-boss Colin Murphy resulting in a £78,000 award **6.** Rugby star Thomas Castaignède **7.** Benito Carbone **8.** Yannick Noah on John McEnroe **9.** Nick Faldo on advice on his club grip **10.** Niall Quinn.

BOXING

Quiz 01

BOXING

1. Over how many rounds did Jim Belcher fight Jack Bartholomew in August 1799?

2. In which European country was world bantamweight champ Kid Williams born?

3. How many bouts did featherweight Abe Attell lose in his 171 fight career?

4. From whom did Muhammad Ali take the world heavyweight title in 1964?

5. Which boxer did John L. Sullivan call 'a fighting machine on stilts'?

6. Whose first pro fight was against Joe Echevarria in October 1940?

7. How did WBC featherweight champion Salvador Sanchez die in 1982?

8. Which middleweight boxer was known as the 'Phantom of St. Paul'?

9. At what two weights was Michael Spinks a world champion?

10. Was light-heavyweight champion Maxie Rosenbloom right or left-handed?

11. What was the real name of boxer Jersey Joe Walcott?

12. Who did Sandy Saddler beat in 1949 to take the vacant junior lightweight crown?

13. Whose first pro fight in September 1953 was against Don Smith?

14. Which middleweight boxer recited a passage from Psalm 144 before each bout?

15. In which year were 'Broughton's Rules' devised, which included the banning of all but fighters and seconds from the ring?

ANSWERS 1. 51 2. Denmark 3. Nine 4. Sonny Liston 5. Bob Fitzsimmons 6. Sugar Ray Robinson 7. In a car accident 8. Mike Gibbons 9. Light-heavyweight and Heavyweight 10. Right-handed 11. Arnold Raymond Cream 12. Orlando Zulueta 13. Sonny Liston 14. Tiger Flowers 15. 1743.

Quiz 02

BOXING

1. What was the nickname of 19c boxer James Burke?

2. Who was Ezzard Charles's last professional opponent in September 1959?

3. In which city was heavyweight Max Baer born?

4. What was the nickname of boxer Joe Brown?

5. At what three weights was Barney Ross a world champion?

6. In which year did former WBC light-heavyweight champion Saad Muhammad retire?

7. In which year did Jack Britton defeat Ted 'Kid' Lewis to first take the world welterweight title?

8. Who promoted the 1974 'Rumble in the Jungle'?

9. Who did Joe Gans knock out in the first on May 12, 1902 to win the world lightweight title?

10. Which boxer was born Judah Bergman in London in 1909?

11. In which city was flyweight Frankie Genaro born?

12. Which boxer's first pro fight was against Tunney Hunsaker in October 1960?

13. Who did Nino Benvenuti beat to win the world junior middleweight title in 1965?

14. Who did Wilfred Benitez beat in 1981 to win the WBC junior middleweight title?

15. Who did Jack Sharkey beat over 15 rounds in 1932 to take the world heavyweight crown?

ANSWERS 1. The Deaf 'Un 2. Alvin Green 3. Omaha 4. Old Bones 5. Lightweight, Junior Welterweight & Welterweight 6. 1992 7. 1916 8. Don King 9. Frank Erne 10. Jackie 'Kid' Berg 11. New York 12. Cassius Clay 13. Sandro Mazzinghi 14. Maurice Hope 15. Max Schmeling.

Quiz 03

BOXING

1. In which year was world heavyweight boxing champion Max Schmeling born?

2. Against whom in 1974 did Muhammad Ali regain the world heavyweight crown?

3. On which island was world welterweight champion Luis Rodriguez born?

4. Over how many rounds did Tom Cribb fight George Maddox in 1805?

5. Which boxer, known as 'Professor', did John L. Sullivan fight two four-round exhibition matches with in 1880 & '81?

6. To whom did Giovanni Benvenuti lose his world middleweight title in 1970?

7. At what weight was Panama Al Brown world champion from 1929-35?

8. How did Algeria-born boxer Marcel Cerdan die in 1949?

9. In which English city did Freddie Miller win the vacant world featherweight title in 1934?

10. Which light heavyweight world champion was known as 'The Pittsburgh Kid'?

11. Who did Bob Foster defeat in 1968 to become world light heavyweight champion?

12. Of his 285 bouts how many ended in a knock-out win for Young Stribling?

13. In which round did Floyd Patterson knock out Brian London in 1959 to retain his world heavyweight title?

14. From which island group did world flyweight champion Pancho Villa hail?

15. In which city was Tommy Farr's 1937 world heavyweight title fight with Joe Louis?

ANSWERS 1. 1905 2. George Foreman 3. Cuba 4. 76 5. Mike Donovan 6. Carlos Monzon 7. Bantamweight 8. In a plane crash 9. Liverpool 10. Billy Conn 11. Dick Tiger 12. 125 13. Eleventh 14. Philippines 15. New York.

THE ULTIMATE SPORTS FACT AND QUIZ BOOK

Quiz 04

BOXING

1. Who was world flyweight champion from 1954-60?

2. Which fighter fought a four-match series with Jack McGinty in Boston in 1887/88?

3. At what two weights was Sugar Ray Robinson world champion?

4. In which year was the WBC formed?

5. Which Cleveland boxer was world lightweight champion from 1941-42?

6. Which boxer won his first 32 pro fights before losing to Tony Canzoneri for the vacant world lightweight title?

7. To whom in 1978 did Muhammad Ali lose the world heavyweight title?

8. How many of his 242 professional bouts did featherweight Willie Pep win?

9. How much was the purse, in dollars, of Tommy Burns's 1906 world heavyweight title fight with Marvin Hart?

10. In which round was Michael Spinks knocked out by Mike Tyson in their 1988 heavyweight fight?

11. Against whom in 1934 did world welterweight champion Jimmy McLarnin lose then regain the title?

12. Who was world light heavyweight champion from 1965-66?

13. Of his 192 total bouts from 1924-45, how many did Jackie 'Kid' Berg win?

14. Who did Battling Nelson knock out in 1908 to win the world lightweight title?

15. Who was the first Colombian, in 1972, to win a world championship?

THE ULTIMATE SPORTS FACT AND QUIZ BOOK

Quiz 05

BOXING

1. Which boxer died in 1948, days after a defeat by Ezzard Charles?

2. In which year was the IBF formed?

3. Which Philippines boxer was world junior lightweight champion from 1960-67?

4. Aaron Pryor's only defeat in 40 bouts, in 1987, was against whom?

5. In his 83 bouts Gene Tunney only lost once, in 1922. To whom?

6. At which two weights was Nigerian boxer Dick Tiger world champion?

7. Who was world lightweight champion from 1956-62?

8. How did welterweight world champion Joe Walcott die in 1935?

9. Who was the only boxer to knock out heavyweight Tommy Gibbons, in 1925?

10. Which Welsh boxer was world lightweight champion from 1914-17?

11. In what round did Sonny Liston knock out Floyd Patterson in 1962 to win the world heavyweight crown?

12. Joe Louis lost only three times in his 71 bout career. To which three fighters?

13. Who was world light-heavyweight champion from 1950-52?

14. What was the real name of 19c fighter 'Dutch Sam'?

15. Which former world middleweight champion was convicted in 1988 of murdering his estranged lover?

Quiz 06

BOXING

1. To whom did Ken Norton lose in his last pro fight in 1981?

2. In which year was lightweight boxer Tony Canzoneri's last fight - his only knock out defeat?

3. In which U.S. city did Jersey Joe Walcott beat Ezzard Charles in 1951 to win the world heavyweight title?

4. At what two weights was New Jersey-born Mickey Walker world champion?

5. How many times did Carlos Ortiz lose in his 70 fight pro career?

6. Who did Rocky Marciano beat in September 1955 to retain his world heavyweight crown?

7. At what weight was Albert 'Chalky' Wright world champion from 1941-42?

8. In which year did former world middleweight champion Tony Zale die?

9. Which boxer, born in 1695, is regarded as 'the Father of Boxing'?

10. Who beat Henry Armstrong in October 1940 to take the world welterweight title?

11. In which country was featherweight boxer Young Griffo born?

12. Whose first professional fight in March 1947 was against Lee Epperson?

13. How did heavyweight Jack Johnson die in 1946?

14. Against whom in 1971 did Jose Napoles regain his world welterweight title?

15. Which lightweight champion was nicknamed 'The Bobcat'?

ANSWERS 1. Gerry Cooney 2. 1939 3. Pittsburgh 4. Welterweight and Middleweight 5. Seven 6. Archie Moore 7. Featherweight 8. 1997 9. James Figg 10. Fritzie Zivic 11. Australia 12. Rocky Marciano 13. A car accident 14. Billy Backus 15. Bob Montgomery.

Quiz 07
BOXING

1. In which round did Tom King defeat Bill Clamp in his first pro engagement?

2. To whom did Manuel Ortiz lose his world bantamweight crown in 1947?

3. How old was Pete Herman when he won the world bantamweight title in 1917?

4. In what round did Sonny Liston knock out Floyd Patterson in 1963 to retain his world heavyweight title?

5. In which round did James J. Jeffries knock out Bob Fitzsimmons in 1899 to take the world heavyweight crown?

6. How many times did Rocky Marciano fight as a professional?

7. In which city was world bantamweight champion Ruben Olivares born?

8. Which middleweight boxer was known as 'The Pittsburgh Windmill'?

9. To whom did Floyd Patterson lose his world heavyweight crown in June 1959?

10. Who did Isiah 'Ike' Williams beat in 1947 to win the vacant world lightweight title?

11. In which country was Carlos Zarate, former WBC bantamweight champion, born?

12. Whose first pro fight in July, 1934, was against Jack Kracker?

13. Which Welsh boxer was world flyweight champion from 1916-23?

14. Which welterweight boxer was known as 'Homicide Hank'?

15. To whom did Wilfred Benitez lose the world welterweight title in 1979?

ANSWERS 1. First 2. Harold Dade 3. 20 4. One 5. Eleven 6. 49 7. Mexico City 8. Harry Greb 9. Ingemar Johansson 10. Bob Montgomery 11. Mexico 12. Joe Louis 13. Jimmy Wilde 14. Henry Armstrong 15. Sugar Ray Leonard.

Quiz 08

BOXING

1. What did boxer Tom Sayers call opponent Nat Langham's left hand?

2. Whose last pro fight in June 1970 was against Chuck Wepner?

3. In which year was the NBA formed in the U.S.?

4. Who did Rocky Graziano box in March 1942 in his first pro fight?

5. In which country was champion boxer Wilfredo Gomez born in 1956?

6. As what did Georges Carpentier serve in World War I?

7. In which year was middleweight champion Joey Giardello born?

8. Which boxer was known as 'The Boston Tar Baby'?

9. In which year did Sugar Ray Robinson lose and regain his middleweight world title to Randolph Turpin?

10. Which American boxer was world bantamweight champion in 1899 and world featherweight champion in 1900?

11. Which future heavyweight champion defeated Jack Delaney in the first round of a fight on April 30, 1928?

12. In which country was boxing promoter George Parnassus born?

13. Who did Jim Driscoll knock out in 1912 to win the vacant British and European world featherweight titles?

14. What weight was Jake LaMotta when knocked out by Bob Murphy in June 1951?

15. Which female boxer was known as the "Fleetwood Assassin"?

Quiz 09

BOXING

1. Against whom was Ezzard Charles's first world heavyweight title defence in 1950?

2. Which boxer toured in the play *Honest Hearts and Willing Hands* from 1889-92?

3. In which year was trainer Angelo Dundee born?

4. In which year did the European Boxing Union replace the International Boxing Union?

5. What did John Graham Chambers author in 1867?

6. What name did Cuban boxer Eligio Sardinias-Montalbo fight under?

7. Which boxer was known as 'The Croat Comet'?

8. Who did Alexis Arguello knock out in 1974 to take the WBA featherweight title?

9. In his 103 bout career how many fights did heavyweight Harry Wills lose?

10. Who beat Harold Hardwick in 1916 to capture the Australian heavyweight title?

11. What was the real name of world champion Kid Williams?

12. Which boxer born in 1862 was nicknamed 'The Nonpareil'?

13. In which year did Muhammad Ali fight Joe Frazier in the Philippines?

14. Of his 212 bouts in the ring how many times was lightweight champion Benny Leonard knocked out?

15. Whose first pro fight in May 1973 was against Terry Ryan?

ANSWERS 1. Nick Barone 2. John L. Sullivan 3. 1923 4. 1946 5. The Marquess of Queensbury Rules 6. Kid Chocolate 7. Fritzie Zivic 8. Ruben Olivares 9. Eight 10. Les Darcy 11. John Gutenko 12. Jack Dempsey 13. 1975 14. Four 15. Marvin Hagler.

Quiz 10

BOXING

1. Who beat Sugar Ray Robinson in September 1957 to take the world middleweight title?

2. In which year did light-heavyweight boxer Joe Choynski die?

3. Over how many rounds was the 1892 world heavyweight title fight between James J. Corbett and John L. Sullivan?

4. Who did Joe Frazier beat in 1970 to win the vacant world heavyweight crown?

5. Which former world light-heavyweight champ lost to Primo Carnera in a 1934 heavyweight title fight?

6. On which island was world welterweight champion Kid Gavilan born?

7. How many times did Emile Griffith hold the world welterweight championship?

8. Who was world featherweight boxing champion from 1912-23?

9. At what two weights was Masahiko 'Fighting' Harada world champion?

10. To whom did Sugar Ray Robinson lose the world middleweight crown in January 1957?

11. Which world middleweight champion was inventor of the 'Corkscrew' punch?

12. In which year did middleweight boxer Rocky Graziano die?

13. Who did Joey Giardello beat in December 1964 to retain the world middleweight title?

14. To whom did Jack Dillon lose the world light-heavyweight title in 1916?

15. In which year did the NBA of the U.S. change its name to the WBA?

ANSWERS 1. Carmen Basilio 2. 1943 3. 21 4. Jimmy Ellis 5. Tommy Loughran 6. Cuba 7. Three 8. Johnny Kilbane 9. Flyweight & Bantamweight 10. Gene Fullmer 11. Charles 'Kid' McCoy 12. 1990 13. Ruben Carter 14. Battling Levinsky 15. 1962.

Quiz 11   BOXING

1. In which year was the Walker Law, under which boxing became legal in the state of New York?

2. Who won the vacant world light-heavyweight crown in May 1962?

3. In which year did Jack Dempsey beat Jess Willard to take the world heavyweight title?

4. Who lost to Kid Gavilan in an August 1951 world welterweight title fight?

5. What was featherweight boxer Giuseppe Carrora better known as?

6. What was the real name of lightweight champion Beau Jack?

7. How did middleweight boxer Stanley Ketchel a.k.a. 'The Michigan Assassin' die in 1910?

8. Which middleweight boxing champion's first defence of his crown was in 1981 against Fulgencio Obelmeijas?

9. Who was world light-heavyweight champion from 1935-39?

10. In which Japanese city did Eder Jofre lose his world bantamweight title to 'Fighting' Harada in 1965?

11. Which Scottish boxer was world flyweight champion from 1937-38?

12. How many times did Jake LaMotta lose in his 106 bout career?

13. Who did Sammy Mandell defeat in 1926 to take the world lightweight title?

14. Which boxer was 1976 Olympic light-welterweight gold winner?

15. How many times was Cardiff welterweight Arnold 'Kid' Sheppard defeated in his career?

ANSWERS 1. 1920 2. Harold Johnson 3. 1919 4. Billy Graham 5. Johnny Dundee 6. Sidney Walker 7. He was shot and killed 8. Marvin Hagler 9. John Henry Lewis 10. Nagoya 11. Benny Lynch 12. 19 13. Rocky Kansas 14. Sugar Ray Leonard 15. 154 times.

OLYMPIC GAMES

Quiz 01 OLYMPIC GAMES

1. What was the job of Spyridon Louis, winner of the 1896 men's Olympic marathon?

2. What was the venue for the football tournament at the 1984 Los Angeles Games?

3. Which Pole took the 1964 & '68 light-welterweight boxing title?

4. How many golds did the U.S.A. take at the 1948 summer Games?

5. In which year was the 4,000m individual pursuit in cycling first held?

6. On which horse did Mark Todd win individual Olympic gold in 1984 & '88?

7. Who were the three scoring members of Great Britain's 1972 gold-winning Three-Day Event team?

8. In which year was team dressage introduced into the Olympics?

9. Which male Japanese gymnast won the 1972 & '76 parallel bars event?

10. Which German was 1980 featherweight boxing champion?

11. Who took bronze in the 1972 & '76 men's high jump?

12. In which year was electronic scoring introduced for the épée in fencing?

13. Out of a possible 2,880 points how many did Darrell Pace score to take gold in the 1976 archery competition?

14. Since 1908, soccer has only failed to feature once at the Games. Which one?

15. Which American won the standing high jump, standing long jump and standing triple jump in 1900 & '04?

THE ULTIMATE SPORTS FACT AND QUIZ BOOK

Quiz 02 OLYMPIC GAMES

1. In which year did Baron de Coubertin first give a lecture at the Sorbonne publicly advancing the idea of a revival of the Games?

2. Which university hosted the tennis tournament at the 1984 Los Angeles Games?

3. Who did gold-winning boxer Laszlo Papp beat in the 1948 middleweight final?

4. Which figure skater partnered Lyudmila Belousova to gold in 1964 & '68?

5. Which Italian won individual gold at the foil event in fencing in 1912 & '20?

6. Has roller hockey been included in the Olympics as a medal event?

7. Who took bronze in the 1948 men's pole vault and gold in the event in 1952 & '56?

8. Perti Karppinen was men's single sculls rowing champion from 1976-84. Which country did he represent?

9. Which German was runner-up to Bruce Jenner in the 1976 decathlon?

10. Which American was 1984 lightweight boxing champion?

11. Which American won the 1952 men's long jump?

12. When was rugby union last included in an Olympic Games?

13. When did men's basketball first appear in the games as a medal event?

14. When was laser sailing first included in the Olympics?

15. Which American won the 60m, 110m hurdles, 200m hurdles & long jump in 1900?

Quiz 03   OLYMPIC GAMES

1. What was the first event on the second day of the 1984 heptathlon event?

2. Which country did all three medal winners at the 1904 individual épée event represent?

3. How many clay birds are released per shooter in Olympic trap shooting?

4. Which male Japanese gymnast won the 1956 & '60 Horizontal Bar event?

5. For what discontinued gymnastic event did George Roth win gold in 1932?

6. Which Italian marathon runner was disqualified in 1908 after being helped by officials?

7. In which year did women's judo become a medal sport?

8. Which Cuban boxer was 1972 & '76 heavyweight champion?

9. How many men competed in 1996 for the Olympic Modern Pentathlon title?

10. Of the eight field hockey golds between 1928-64, how many did India win?

11. How many competitors took part in Atlanta, 1996?

12. Who took soccer gold at the 1956 Games?

13. How many nations took part in the 1998 Winter Olympics?

14. Who was the first British woman to win a medal in the 100m event?

15. In which year were the Winter Olympics held at Cortina d'Ampezzo?

Quiz 04   OLYMPIC GAMES

1. To which city were the summer Olympic Games in 1916 awarded?

2. How many medals did Boris Shakhlin win for gymnastics from 1956-64?

3. Who were the three members of Britain's gold-winning Modern Pentathlon team in 1976?

4. Four countries have won a single medal - gold - in the 100 year history of the summer Olympics. Who are they?

5. When was the men's 100m butterfly swimming event first held?

6. When was the women's 100m butterfly swimming event first held?

7. Kennedy McKinney became a world junior featherweight boxing champion in 1992. At what weight did he win Olympic gold in 1988?

8. Which Briton took women's 200m bronze in 1948?

9. How many golds did Vera Caslavska win for gymnastics from 1964-8?

10. What was the last event on day one of the 1984 Decathlon?

11. Which is the only team to have won medals at the Winter but not Summer Olympics?

12. Which country won two medals - both gold - at the 1968 summer Olympics?

13. At which Olympics did swimmer Johnny Weissmuller win three sprint golds?

14. Has shinty ever been included as an Olympic sport?

15. Of the 83 nations which appeared at the 1960 Games, how many won at least one gold?

ANSWERS 1. Berlin 2. 13 3. Jeremy Fox, Robert Nightingale & Adrian Parker 4. Burundi, Hong Kong, Zimbabwe & Ecuador 5. 1968 6. 1956 7. Bantamweight 8. Audrey Williamson 9. Seven 10. 400m 11. Liechtenstein 12. Turkey 13. 1924 14. No 15. 23.

Quiz 05   OLYMPIC GAMES

1. Which Briton won 1984 & '88 small-bore rifle - three positions gold?

2. At what weight was Sören Petersen a boxing silver medalist in 1920 & '24?

3. What simulated animal is used as a target in Olympic running target shooting?

4. Which country won most golds at the 1956 summer Olympics?

5. What are the two skiing disciplines in Alpine combination?

6. Which country won one medal - gold - at the 1972 summer Olympics?

7. Who was 1996 Olympic women's singles tennis champion?

8. Which horse did Takeichi Nishi ride to win individual show jumping gold in 1932?

9. Why was the runner Lorz expelled from the 1904 men's marathon?

10. Which country took 16 golds at the 1948 summer Olympics?

11. When did the Olympics first take place in the southern hemisphere?

12. Which German took the men's 10km & 20km biathlon title at the 1988 Olympics?

13. In which year was the men's Modern Pentathlon introduced to the summer Games?

14. Gillis Grafström was men's figure skating champion from 1920-28. Which country did he represent?

15. When were the first Winter Olympics held?

ANSWERS **1.** Malcolm Cooper **2.** Heavyweight **3.** A boar **4.** U.S.S.R. **5.** Downhill and slalom **6.** Denmark **7.** Lindsay Davenport **8.** Uranus **9.** He got a lift in a car during the race **10.** Sweden **11.** 1956 **12.** Frank-Peter Rötsch **13.** 1912 **14.** Sweden **15.** 1924.

Quiz 06

OLYMPIC GAMES

1. How many countries participated in the 1912 Games in Stockholm?

2. From 1896-1996, Canada & the Netherlands both won an equal number of golds at the Summer Olympics. How many?

3. Which men's team were silver winners in the 1948 basketball event?

4. In which year did Great Britain win ice hockey gold?

5. Who did Chris Finnegan beat to take the 1968 middleweight boxing title?

6. Which country won one medal - gold - at the 1952 Olympics?

7. In which year was the 1,000m time-trial cycling race first held?

8. In which year was canoeing introduced into the Olympics?

9. What are the three positions in small-bore rifle shooting?

10. When was tug-of-war last included in the Olympics?

11. Who took soccer gold in the 1972 Games?

12. Which European country were 1992 women's hockey winners?

13. Which East German won the 1976 women's long jump?

14. Who were men's volleyball champions in 1972?

15. Which U.S. athlete won the 400m & 800m at the 1906 Games?

ANSWERS 1. 28 2. 49 3. France 4. 1936 5. Aleksey Kisselyov 6. Luxembourg 7. 1928 8. 1936 9. Prone, kneeling & standing 10. 1920 11. Poland 12. Spain 13. Angela Voigt 14. Japan 15. Paul H. Pilgrim.

Quiz 07   OLYMPIC GAMES

1. How many countries entered the 1924 Games at Paris?

2. Which country was originally awarded the 1908 Games?

3. How many golds did the U.S. win at the 1952 Summer Olympics?

4. When did Great Britain last win Olympic water polo gold?

5. When were losing boxing semi-finalists first both awarded bronze medals?

6. How many gold medals did Carl Lewis win at the 1984 Games?

7. Who was women's 1,500m runner-up in 1972 & '76?

8. How many medals did Ville Ritola win at the 1924 Games?

9. How many golds did the U.S.S.R. win at the 1980 Summer Olympics?

10. Who in 1948 became the youngest men's gold winner?

11. Which country won one medal - gold - at the 1976 Summer Olympics?

12. Erik Lemming won seven medals from 1906-12. For which country?

13. Which Briton was men's 100m bronze winner in 1960?

14. Which country were soccer runners-up in 1948, '52 & '56?

15. Ariel Hernandez was 1992 & '96 middleweight boxing champion. Which country did he represent?

ANSWERS 1. 44 2. Italy 3. 40 4. 1920 5. 1952 6. Four 7. Gunhild Hoffmeister 8. Six 9. 80 10. Bob Mathias 11. Trinidad & Tobago 12. Sweden 13. Peter Radford 14. Yugoslavia 15. Cuba.

Quiz 08

OLYMPIC GAMES

1. Which Russian was 1960 & '64 women's asymmetrical bars champion?

2. At which Games did Germany appear after the First World War?

3. How many golds has the U.K. won in the Winter Olympics since their inception?

4. Which Jamaican took men's 100m silver in 1968 & bronze in 1972?

5. When was the last time polo was included at the Olympics?

6. Which city was the intended venue for the 1940 Winter Olympics?

7. Has real tennis ever been included in the Olympics?

8. Frankie Genaro was 1920 Olympic flyweight boxing champion. In which year did he become world champion at this weight?

9. Who holds the Olympic record for men's 200m breaststroke swimming?

10. On which horse did Nicole Uphoff win 1988 & '92 individual dressage gold?

11. What were swallow, tempest and dragon?

12. For what discontinued gymnastics event did Rowland Wolfe win gold in 1932?

13. Who was 1988 men's slalom and giant slalom skiing champion?

14. Who were women's volleyball champions in 1984?

15. Which individual gold in fencing did Alessandro Puccini win in 1996 - sabre, foil or épée?

ANSWERS 1. Polina Astakhova 2. 1928 3. Seven 4. Lennox Miller 5. 1936 6. Sapporo 7. Yes, in 1908 8. 1928 9. Mike Barrowman 10. Rembrandt 11. Now discontinued sailing events 12. Tumbling 13. Alberto Tomba 14. China 15. Foil.

Quiz 09   OLYMPIC GAMES

1. Why might Ralph Metcalfe have felt aggrieved at losing the 1932 200m by 0.3 second?

2. What was the venue for the 1988 Summer Olympics?

3. Which country won two medals - both gold - at the 1980 Olympics?

4. Which country were runners-up in the 1984 & '88 soccer tournament?

5. Myriam Bédard won women's 7.5km & 15km biathlon at the 1994 Olympics. Which country does she represent?

6. Who holds the Olympic record for men's 200m butterfly swimming?

7. Which American won 1996 light-middleweight boxing gold?

8. How many times have the Summer Olympics been held in Germany?

9. At what weight did Floyd Patterson win Olympic boxing gold in 1952?

10. In which year was boardsailing included in the Olympics?

11. Who won the 1960 individual show jumping gold on Posillipo?

12. Who won the inaugural women's triple jump in 1996?

13. Which Briton won the 10 miles walk in 1908 - its only appearance as an event?

14. Who won the women's pentathlon in 1964?

15. In which year was rackets included in the Olympics?

ANSWERS 1. His lane was later discovered to be 1m too long 2. Seoul 3. Switzerland 4. Brazil 5. Canada 6. Melvin Stewart 7. David Reid 8. Twice 9. Middleweight 10. 1984 11. Raimondo d'Inzeo 12. Inessa Kravets 13. George Larner 14. Irina Press 15. 1908.

Quiz 10

OLYMPIC GAMES

1. Which country won team Three-Day Eventing in 1992 & '96?

2. Where were the 1932 Summer Olympics held?

3. Which African country were 1980 women's hockey winners?

4. Which country won the men's team sabre gold at the Olympics from 1928-60?

5. In which year did the U.S.S.R., Russia or C.I.S. last fail to win figure skating pairs gold?

6. Which Jamaican took men's 400m silver in 1948 & '52?

7. Which male skier last won slalom, giant slalom & downhill events in the same year?

8. Where were the second Winter Olympics held?

9. What two snowboarding events were held in the 1998 Olympics?

10. Who was 1992 women's singles badminton champion?

11. Who holds the Olympic record for men's 100m freestyle swimming?

12. Which Russian won 1996 welterweight boxing gold?

13. Who was 1972 men's 1500m champion?

14. Which Briton was flyweight boxing silver winner in 1924?

15. Who was 1992 men's 5,000m champion?

ANSWERS 1. Australia 2. Los Angeles 3. Zimbabwe 4. Hungary 5. 1960 6. Herbert H. McKenley 7. Jean-Claude Killy 8. St. Moritz 9. Giant slalom & halfpipe 10. Susi Susanti 11. Matt Biondi 12. Oleg Saitov 13. Pekka Vasala 14. James McKenzie 15. Dieter Baumann.

Quiz 11

OLYMPIC GAMES

1. To which city were the 1940 summer Games originally awarded?

2. Which country won third-most golds at the 1956 Melbourne Olympics?

3. Who was 1992 men's 10,000m champion?

4. Which two countries have each won the women's basketball title three times?

5. How many times have the Summer Olympics been held in Africa?

6. In which year did men's biathlon enter the Olympic programme?

7. Which country did cyclist Erika Salumäe represent in winning the 1988 1,000m sprint?

8. Which Cuban won 1992 & '96 light-welterweight boxing gold?

9. Which country has won most medals at the Winter Olympics?

10. Which country did cyclist Erika Salumäe represent in winning the 1992 1,000m sprint?

11. New Zealand and Turkey have won an equal number of summer Olympic golds. How many?

12. Which country were disqualified from taking the 1920 soccer runners-up medal after walking off the pitch in a protest against bad refereeing?

13. Who was 1992 men's 1,500m champion?

14. How many nations took part in Atlanta in 1996?

15. Who holds the record for men's 1,500 freestyle swimming?

ANSWERS 1. Tokyo 2. Australia 3. Khalid Skah 4. U.S.A. & U.S.S.R. 5. Never 6. 1960 7. U.S.S.R. 8. Hector Vinent 9. Norway 10. Estonia 11. 30 12. Czechoslovakia 13. Fermin Cacho 14. 197 15. Kieren Perkins.

Quiz 12

OLYMPIC GAMES

1. Which country won third-most golds at the 1960 Rome Olympics?

2. After 1912, when was the next year in which the Russians appeared at the Games?

3. Petrus Kastenman won 1956 individual Three-Day Eventing gold on Iluster. Which country did he represent?

4. Which American was runner-up to Alberto Juantorena in the 1976 400m?

5. Which South American country won 1924 & '28 soccer gold?

6. How many countries competed at the 1936 Winter Olympics?

7. Who were women's volleyball champions in 1964?

8. Who were women's doubles badminton champions in 1996?

9. Which American was 1964 men's 10,000m champion?

10. Which Spaniard won the 1992 1,000m time trial in cycling?

11. How many golds has China won at the Winter Olympics?

12. Who in 1952 became the youngest women's gold winner?

13. Lia Manoliu contested six Games from from 1952-72. In which event?

14. Who holds the Olympic record for men's 100m backstroke swimming?

15. Which Yugoslav was 1972 light-heavyweight Olympic boxing champion?

ANSWERS 1. Italy 2. 1952 3. Sweden 4. Fred Newhouse 5. Uruguay 6. 28 7. Japan 8. Ge Fei & Gu Jun 9. William Mills 10. José Manuel Moreno 11. None 12. Barbara Pearl Jones 13. Discus 14. Mark Tewksbury 15. Mate Parlov.

Quiz 13 — OLYMPIC GAMES

1. Which Briton was 1924 & '28 men's 800m champion?

2. In which year was ice hockey contested at the Summer Olympics?

3. What height in metres did Dick Fosbury jump in 1968 to take the high jump title?

4. How many golds did Bjørn Dæhlie win for Nordic skiing from 1992-8?

5. Which American city withdrew its application to host the 1976 Winter Olympics?

6. How old was Oscar Swahn when he won a silver medal in 1920 for shooting?

7. Which pair won men's two-seater luge tobogganing at the 1976 & '80 Olympics?

8. From 1896-1996 which team has won most Olympic golds?

9. Who was 1968 & '72 men's sprint cycle champion?

10. Which American holds the Olympic women's 800m freestyle swimming record?

11. Zoltan Magyar was men's pommel horse champion in 1976 & '80. Which country did he represent?

12. Which Italian won the 1964 light-heavyweight boxing gold?

13. Which U.S. swimmer won six silver medals from 1972-76?

14. When did table tennis become an Olympic sport?

15. Between Paavo Nurmi's 1920 & 1928 triumphs in the 10,000m, which Finn took the 1924 title?

ANSWERS 1. Douglas Lowe 2. 1920 3. 2.24m 4. Eight 5. Denver 6. 72 7. Hans Rinn & Norbert Hahn 8. U.S.A. 9. Daniel Morelon 10. Janet Evans 11. Hungary 12. Cosimo Pinto 13. Shirley Babashoff 14. 1988 15. Ville Ritola.

Quiz 14

OLYMPIC GAMES

1. Which country won third-most golds at the 1964 Tokyo Olympics?

2. Has Taekwondo been an Olympic sport?

3. Which American was 1992 men's horizontal bar champion in gymnastics?

4. Who was 1992 men's singles tennis champion?

5. Women's ice hockey was introduced in 1998. Which team won?

6. Who were men's volleyball champions in 1964?

7. Kerstin Palm participated at seven games from 1964-88 at fencing. For which country?

8. David Hemery won the men's 400m hurdles in 1968. Which medal did he take in the same event in 1972?

9. Which Briton won the 1956 lightweight boxing title?

10. What was the name of the bear which served as a mascot for the 1980 Moscow Olympics?

11. Which Jamaican was runner-up to Malvin Whitfield at 800m in the 1948 & '52 Games?

12. When did beach volleyball become included in the Olympics?

13. Santiago Lovell was 1932 heavyweight boxing champion. Which country did he represent?

14. Which European country were men's water polo champions in 1996?

15. Which country won the 1996 baseball gold medal?

ANSWERS 1. Japan 2. No, but it is to be included in the 2000 Games 3. Trent Dimas 4. Marc Rosset 5. U.S.A. 6. U.S.S.R. 7. Sweden 8. Bronze 9. Richard McTaggart 10. Misha 11. Arthur S. Wint 12. 1996 13. Argentina 14. Spain 15. Cuba.

Quiz 15   OLYMPIC GAMES

1. Which Britons finished 2nd & 3rd in the 1956 men's 5,000m?

2. When did badminton become a medal sport at the Olympics?

3. At which Californian resort were the 1960 Winter Olympics held?

4. When did Yugoslavia win their only Olympic men's basketball gold?

5. Why was the 1908 men's sprint cycle race declared void?

6. Which team has won more golds at the Summer Olympics - France or the U.K.?

7. Which male Chinese gymnast was 1984 & '88 horse vault champion?

8. Edward Eagan won gold at the 1920 Summer Olympics and 1932 Winter Olympics. At what events?

9. Krisztina Egerszegi holds the Olympic swimming record for 100m & 200m backstroke. Which country does she represent?

10. In what time did Hasely Crawford win the 1976 100m gold?

11. Who won individual show jumping gold in 1976 on Warwick Rex?

12. Who holds the Olympic record for men's 200m?

13. Which Cuban was 1992 & '96 Olympic heavyweight boxing champion?

14. Which country did the men's 800m gold winners represent from 1920-32?

15. Who was men's single-seater luge tobogganing champion from 1992-98?

ANSWERS 1. Gordon Pirie & Derek Ibbotson 2. 1992 3. Squaw Valley 4. 1980 5. The riders exceeded the time limit 6. U.K. 7. Lou Yun 8. Boxing & bobsleigh 9. Hungary 10. 10.06 11. Alwin Schockemöhle 12. Marvin Johnson 13. Felix Savon 14. U.K. 15. Georg Hackl.

Quiz 16

OLYMPIC GAMES

1. Which German won the flyweight boxing gold in 1936?

2. In which year was women's basketball first played at the Olympics?

3. Dick Quax was runner-up to Lasse Viren in the 1976 5,000m. What nationality was he?

4. Which country scored the biggest win, 17-1, in a soccer tournament?

5. Which Ethiopian finished third in the 1972 men's 10,000m?

6. Which Russian man won 1972 & '76 floor exercise gold in gymnastics?

7. Willie Davenport won the 1968 men's 110m hurdles. Which medal did he win at the same event in 1976?

8. Is the handball tournament played indoors or outdoors?

9. How much in dollars did the 1972 Winter Olympics cost to stage?

10. Sjoukje Dijkstra was 1964 women's figure skating champion. Which country did she represent?

11. Which country won two medals - both gold - at the 1956 Summer Olympics?

12. What nationality was Sébastian Flute, 1992 Olympic individual archery champion?

13. Gustav Weder & Donald Acklin won two-man bob at the 1992 & '94 Olympics. What country did they represent?

14. When were the summer Games first held in Canada?

15. Which men's team beat the U.S.A. 24-1 at hockey in 1932?

ANSWERS 1. Willi Kaiser 2. 1976 3. New Zealander 4. Denmark 5. Miruts Yifter 6. Nikolay Andrianov 7. Bronze 8. Indoors 9. $61 million 10. Holland 11. New Zealand 12. French 13. Switzerland 14. 1976 15. India.

Quiz 17   OLYMPIC GAMES

11. What is the Latin motto of the Olympics?

2. Where were the 1998 Winter Olympics held?

3. Who was 1992 Olympic super-heavyweight boxing champion?

4. When was the women's soccer tournament first held?

5. Which Asian team were women's archery champions from 1988-96?

6. When were mountain bike cross-country races held for the first time at the Olympics?

7. Where were the 1952 Winter Olympics held?

8. Which American won 1976 individual Three-Day Eventing gold on Bally-Cor?

9. Which Briton finished second to Abebe Bikila in the 1964 marathon?

10. At which two Olympics was there a Skeleton bob competition?

11. Which American won the men's 1,500m in 1904 & 1906?

12. In which year did baseball become a medal sport at the Olympics?

13. Which Cuban boxer won the 1976 featherweight title?

14. What number was Horace Ashenfelter wearing when he won the 1952 3,000m steeplechase?

15. How many countries took part in the 1968 Summer Olympics?

ANSWERS 1. Citius, Altius, Fortius 2. Nagano 3. Roberto Balado 4. 1996 5. South Korea 6. 1996 7. Oslo 8. Edmund Coffin 9. Basil Heatley 10. 1928 & 1948 11. James D. Lightbody 12. 1992 13. Angel Herrera 14. 998 15. 112.

RUGBY

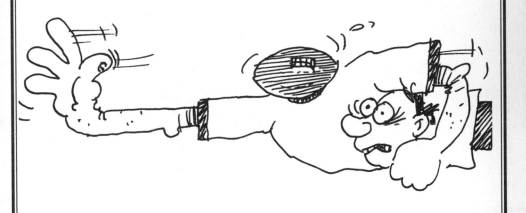

Quiz 01   **RUGBY UNION**

1. Who scored the try against England that gave Scotland the 1990 Grand Slam?

2. Which university has won the most varsity matches - Cambridge or Oxford?

3. Who scored 126 points for New Zealand in the 1987 World Cup?

4. Which two teams shared the 1967 English County Championship?

5. In which year did France make the international championship the 'Five Nations'?

6. What did the Pilkington Cup become in 1997/98?

7. In which year did Ireland win their only Five Nations Grand Slam?

8. Two teams, in 1990 & '98, scored 48 points in the RFU knock-out competition final. Who were they?

9. Which two countries contest the Bledisloe Cup?

10. Who won the 1996/7 Welsh League?

11. How many caps did Philippe Sella win for France from 1982-95?

12. How many games did Fylde win in Premiership Two in 1997/8?

13. Who is the leading try scorer for South Africa in internationals?

14. Which two clubs merged to form Leeds in 1992?

15. From which club did Dean Lax join Rotherham?

THE ULTIMATE SPORTS FACT AND QUIZ BOOK

Quiz 02

RUGBY UNION

1. Which city was chosen as the venue for the 1999 World Cup final?

2. With which club did Wakefield's Matthew Greenwood start his career?

3. In which year was there a five-way tie in the Five Nations?

4. Cardiff and Bridgend drew the 1982 Schweppes Cup 12-12. Who won it on most tries?

5. Who holds the record for the number of English caps?

6. Which club had two points deducted in Jewson Two (South) in 1997/8 for fielding an ineligible player?

7. Who captained Saracens in their 1997/8 Tetley's Bitter Cup win?

8. Who is the leading points scorer in Welsh international rugby?

9. Which two teams shared the 1982 John Player Special Cup?

10. Of his 55 games as England captain, in how many was Will Carling on the winning side?

11. How many tries did Ian Smith score for Scotland from 1924-33?

12. Which Welshman scored 188 points on a Lions tour of Australia & New Zealand?

13. Who won the Hong Kong Sevens championship in 1998?

14. Which team scored 1001 points in Jewson One, 1997/8?

15. Who scored 24 dropped goals for Argentina in his 1972-90 career?

ANSWERS 1. Cardiff 2. Roundhay 3. 1973 4. Cardiff 5. Rory Underwood 6. Metropolitan Police 7. Tony Diprose 8. Neil Jenkins 9. Gloucester & Moseley 10. 44 11. 24 12. Barry John 13. Fiji 14. Worcester 15. Hugo Porta.

Quiz 03

RUGBY UNION

1. Which country was chosen to host Pool A games in the 1999 World Cup?

2. Who holds the record for the number of New Zealand caps?

3. Which two teams shared the 1907 English County Championship?

4. Who is the leading points scorer in South African international rugby?

5. Who defeated Norway in the first 1999 World Cup qualifying game on 26 September, 1996?

6. Who did Melrose beat in the 1997 Tennants Cup final?

7. By what score did Australia beat England in the 1991 World Cup final?

8. Which team have won the French championship most times?

9. Which country suffered a whitewash in the Five Nations from 1952-54, losing all their games in that period?

10. How many teams competed in the 1900 Olympic rugby event?

11. How many points did England score in the 1998 Five Nations championship?

12. Which England and Gloucester prop was born in Barnstaple, Devon, in 1976?

13. Who is the leading French try scorer in international rugby?

14. How many Premiership One games did Newcastle lose in 1997/8?

15. In which tournament do the winners receive the Russell-Cargill Memorial Cup?

ANSWERS 1. Scotland 2. Sean Fitzpatrick 3. Devon & Durham 4. Naas Botha 5. Latvia 6. Boroughmuir 7. 12-6 8. Toulouse 9. Scotland 10. Three 11. 146 12. Philip Vickery 13. Serge Blanco 14. Three 15. Middlesex Sevens.

Quiz 04

RUGBY UNION

1. Which player scored most points for France in the 1998 Five Nations Championship?

2. Against which team did Craig Quinnell make his international debut for Wales in 1995?

3. How many caps did David Campese win for Australia from 1982-96?

4. Who won the Scottish Club Championship in 1980 & '83?

5. Who captained the British Lions on their 1977 tour of New Zealand & Fiji?

6. In which year were Harlequins formed?

7. What was West Hartlepool's best Division One finish, in 1994/5?

8. By what score did the British Lions beat Australia at Brisbane in June 1966?

9. Which team's home ground is Franklin's Gardens?

10. Which Leicester player captained the England U-21 team in Australia in 1997?

11. Which team won the 1993 All-Ireland League?

12. From which Scottish club did Craig Joiner join Leicester?

13. How many games did Bristol win in Premiership One in 1997/8?

14. Which team suffered a whitewash in the Five Nations from 1924-26, not winning a game?

15. Which four teams were drawn in Pool C of the 1999 World Cup?

ANSWERS 1. Christophe Lamaison 2. Fiji 3. 101 4. Gala 5. Phil Bennett 6. 1866 7. Ninth 8. 31-0 9. Northampton 10. Paul Gustard 11. Young Munster 12. Melrose 13. Two 14. France 15. France, Canada, Fiji & Namibia.

Quiz 05

RUGBY UNION

1. Who holds the record for the number of Welsh caps?

2. Where was the third rugby union World Cup held?

3. Which Welsh team lost in the final of the 1995/6 Heineken European Cup?

4. How many points did France score in the 1998 Five Nations Championship?

5. How many games did Saracens lose in Premiership One in 1997/98

6. Of the British Lions 43 Tests against South Africa, how many have they won?

7. What was Coventry's best finish in Division One in 1987/88?

8. In which year were London Welsh formed?

9. By what score did New Zealand beat Japan in the 1995 World Cup?

10. In which country was Mike Catt born?

11. In which year did the British Lions go on their first tour?

12. From which club did Aadel Kardooni join Bedford in 1997?

13. Which club's home ground is Kingsholm?

14. In which year did Wales last achieve a Grand Slam in the Five Nations?

15. In which country was Gloucester player Stephen Ojomoh born?

ANSWERS **1.** Ieuan Evans **2.** South Africa **3.** Cardiff **4.** 144 **5.** Three **6.** 16 **7.** Eleventh **8.** 1878 **9.** 145-17 **10.** South Africa **11.** 1888 **12.** Leicester **13.** Gloucester **14.** 1978 **15.** Nigeria.

Quiz 06

RUGBY UNION

1. Which two players scored seven tries each in the 1995 World Cup finals?

2. In which year were London Irish formed?

3. How many points did Didier Camberabero score for France versus Zimbabwe in the 1987 World Cup?

4. Which team were top scorers in Jewson Two (North) in 1997/8?

5. Which player scored most points for Scotland in the 1998 Five Nations Championship?

6. In which year did USA Perpignon last win the French championship?

7. Who captained the British Lions on their 1980 tour of South Africa?

8. How many points did Michael Kiernan score for Ireland from 1982-91?

9. In which year did Philip de Glanville first captain Bath?

10. From which club did London Scottish sign Guy Easterby in 1998?

11. Who scored 24 points for France against Ireland in the 1992 Five Nations?

12. In which city was Rory Underwood born?

13. In which year did France first achieve the Grand Slam in the Five Nations?

14. Who is the leading try scorer for New Zealand in international rugby?

15. Which four teams were drawn in Pool E of the 1999 World Cup?

ANSWERS 1. Marc Ellis & Jonah Lomu 2. 1898 3. 30 4. Manchester 5. Craig Chalmers 6. 1955 7. Bill Beaumont 8. 308 9. 1995 10. Rotherham 11. Sébastien Viers 12. Middlesbrough 13. 1968 14. John Kirwan 15. Australia, Ireland, Romania and U.S.A.

Quiz 01

RUGBY LEAGUE

1. Which two teams merged in 1997 to become Barrow Border Raiders?

2. Who were Division Three champions in 1991/2?

3. Who was coach of Leeds from 1983-85?

4. What is the name of Batley Bulldogs' ground?

5. From which French club did Whitehaven Warriors sign David Fatialofa in 1996?

6. What is the name of Warrington's rugby league team?

7. Which player holds the record for Bradford for points scored in a season?

8. Who scored 450 points for Hull Kingston Rovers in the 1989/90 season?

9. Who took over as coach of York in December 1996?

10. For which two clubs did Davide Longo play in 1998?

11. Who scored five tries for St. Helens against London Broncos in September 1998?

12. Against which team did Andrew Farrell of Wigan Warriors score 24 points in the 1998 Challenge Cup?

13. In which season did Leigh last win the Challenge Cup?

14. Who was the leading try scorer in seasons 1984/5 & 1986/7?

15. Who beat Egremont Rangers 84-6 in a 1998 Challenge Cup game?

ANSWERS **1. Barrow Braves & Carlisle Borders 2.** Huddersfield **3.** Maurice Bamford **4.** Mount Pleasant **5.** Palau **6.** Warrington Wolves **7.** Eddie Tees **8.** Mike Fletcher **9.** Dean Robinson **10.** Swinton Lions & Keighley Cougars **11.** Anthony Sullivan **12.** Dewsbury Rams **13.** 1970/71 **14.** Ellery Hanley **15.** Sheffield Eagles.

Quiz 02

RUGBY LEAGUE

1. At which ground do Bramley play?

2. For which club did St. John Ellis play in 1998?

3. Who holds the record for most goals in a season, compiled in 1972/73?

4. Who was Castleford coach from 1974-87?

5. Who was the season's leading try scorer from 1987/8 - 1990/91?

6. Who is the flamboyant chairman of London Broncos?

7. Which Batley Bulldogs player scored in every one of his club's 23 matches in 1998?

8. What is the name of Widnes's rugby league team?

9. At which ground do Hull Sharks play?

10. In Australia, what is the name of Parramatta's rugby league team?

11. In which season did Oldham last win the Challenge Cup?

12. Who is credited with the longest successful drop goal?

13. For which club did John Donno play in 1997?

14. In which year was an eight-club league launched in Russia?

15. Which Super League club averaged the lowest league attendance in 1998?

ANSWERS 1. Headingley 2. Hunslet Hawks 3. David Watkins 4. Malcolm Reilly 5. Martin Offiah 6. Richard Branson 7. Richard Price 8. Widnes Vikings 9. The Boulevard 10. Parramatta Eels 11. 1926/27 12. Joe Lydon 13. Lancashire Lynx 14. 1991 15. London Broncos.

Quiz 03

RUGBY LEAGUE

1. At which ground do Doncaster Dragons play?

2. In which season did Widnes last win the Challenge Cup?

3. Which First Division club averaged the highest league attendance in 1998?

4. In which season did Dale Laughton make his debut for Sheffield Eagles?

5. At which ground do Swinton Lions play?

6. What was Lionheart Stadium, the ground of Featherstone Rovers, previously called?

7. Who holds the record at Wigan for points scored in a season?

8. In which year was Maurice Lindsay appointed R.L. Chief Executive?

9. Since 1974, who has been Halifax's longest reigning coach?

10. At what ground do Rochdale Hornets play?

11. In Australia what is the name of Western Suburbs's R.L. team?

12. Who took over as coach for Wakefield Trinity in June 1997?

13. At which ground do Workington Town play?

14. Who did Hull Sharks whitewash 32-0 in an August 1998 fixture?

15. Who took over as coach of St. Helens in October 1998?

ANSWERS 1. Belle Vue 2. 1983/4 3. Hull Kingston Rovers 4. 1991/2 5. Gigg Lane, Bury 6. Post Office Road 7. Frano Botica 8. 1992 9. Chris Anderson 10. Spotland 11. Western Suburbs Magpies 12. Andy Kelly 13. Derwent Park 14. Salford Reds 15. Ellery Hanley.

ATHLETICS

Quiz 01
ATHLETICS

1. How old was Stefano Tilli when he finished fourth in the 1998 European Championships in the 100m?

2. Which American won the men's high jump at the 1998 IAAF World Cup?

3. How many nations took part in the 1983 IAAF World Championships?

4. Erkki Nool won the decathlon at the 1998 European Championships. Which country does he represent?

5. Who holds the women's 400m & 800m records at the IAAF World Championships?

6. In which country were the 1998 Asian Championships held?

7. Which London-born marathon runner died in January 1999?

8. Who won women's 100m and 200m at the 1998 IAAF World Cup?

9. In which country were the 1998 European Cross-country Championships held?

10. Which Zambian won the men's 400m hurdles in the 1998 IAAF World Cup?

11. Who was Scotland's 1998 men's cross-country champion?

12. Which country won the women's 4x100m at the 1998 Asian Championships?

13. At which field event does Harri Hakkarainen compete?

14. When did Rosa Mota set a marathon record of 2:25:17 in the IAAF World Championships?

15. At what event does Guatemalan Julio Martinez specialise?

THE ULTIMATE SPORTS FACT AND QUIZ BOOK

Quiz 02   ATHLETICS

1. Which woman set a European Championship record in winning the 100m in 1998?

2. Who was England's 1998 men's cross-country champion?

3. In winning the 100m at the 1998 European Championships Darren Campbell set a record for the tournament. What time did he run?

4. Which Irish athlete won the 1997 Berlin women's marathon?

5. Who did Sugath Tillakaratne represent in winning the men's 400m at the 1998 Asian Championships?

6. Which Italian man won the 1996 New York marathon?

7. In which country were the IAAF World Road Relay Championships held in 1998?

8. In what year was Jamie Baulch born?

9. Which Algerian runner broke the men's 1500m world record in September 1992?

10. What country does women's 400m runner Olabisi Afolabi represent?

11. Which Panamanian, bronze winner at men's 100m and 200m at the 1948 Olympics, died in 1999?

12. In which year were the first New Zealand men's national championships held?

13. Mexico's first Olympic medal winner at athletics died in 1998. Who was he?

14. At what event has Lee Bong-ju been a Korean champion?

15. At what field event does German Peter Blank specialise?

LET GO!

ANSWERS 1. Christine Arron 2. Dominic Bannister 3. 10.04 4. Catherina McKiernan 5. Sri Lanka 6. Giacomo Leone 7. Brazil 8. 1973 9. Noureddine Morceli 10. Nigeria 11. Lloyd la Beach 12. 1887 13. José Pedraza 14. Marathon 15. Javelin.

Quiz 03 ATHLETICS

1. What was the unique about the first three finishers in the 1998 men's 200m at the European Championship?

2. In which country did the IAAF World Cup take place in September 1998?

3. Who set the women's javelin record at the 1987 IAAF World Championships?

4. Who was 1998 Japanese men's 100m champion?

5. What nationality is high jump champion Artur Partyka?

6. Who was men's 10,000m champion at the 1998 European Championships?

7. Who won the men's 100m & 200m at the 1998 IAAF World Junior Championships?

8. In which European country were the IAAF World Half-marathon Championships run in September 1998?

9. Who retained her European Championship shot title in 1998?

10. The 1972 Olympic men's shot champion died in 1998. Who was he?

11. Who retained the Rotterdam women's marathon title in 1998?

12. In which year was Jonathan Edwards born?

13. Who set a championship record at men's javelin at the 1998 IAAF World Cup?

14. In which U.S. city was hurdler Mark Crear born?

15. Who won the IAAF Combined Events Challenge 1998 at men's decathlon?

ANSWERS 1. They were all from the same country (Great Britain) 2. South Africa 3. Fatima Whitbread 4. Koji Ito 5. Poland 6. Antonio Pinto 7. Christian Malcolm 8. Switzerland 9. Vita Pavlysh 10. Wladyslaw Komar 11. Tegla Loroupe 12. 1966 13. Steve Backley 14. San Francisco 15. Erkki Nool.

THE ULTIMATE SPORTS FACT AND QUIZ BOOK

Quiz 04 ATHLETICS

1. Which Philadelphian sings with gospel group 'Kirk Franklin & The Family'?

2. Which country's runners filled the first three places in the men's marathon at the 1998 European Championships?

3. In which year was Sergey Bubka born?

4. The 1988 Olympic women's 100m winner died in 1998. Who was she?

5. Which country does 400m runner Davis Kamoga represent?

6. Who won the 1998 Hamburg women's marathon?

7. Which Briton won the male javelin event at the 1998 IAAF World Junior Championships?

8. Who won the men's 110m hurdles at the 1998 European Championships?

9. Which country does runner Susanthika Jayasinghe represent?

10. With 31,539 finishers, which city hosted 1998's largest marathon?

11. In which year were Spain's first men's national championships held?

12. Who won the girl's 3000m & 5000m at the 1998 IAAF World Junior Championships?

13. At which field event does Russian Ilya Konovalov compete?

14. Who in the 1998 London marathon became the first man to achieve ten sub 2:10:00 races?

15. In which city was Colin Jackson born?

Quiz 05 ATHLETICS

1. Who set a record of 17.99 for the men's triple jump at the 1998 European Championships?

2. At which event did Sarah Wilhelmy place at the 1998 IAAF World Junior Championships?

3. Which Briton won the women's heptathlon at the 1998 European Championships?

4. In which city was British high jumper Steve Smith born?

5. In which U.S. state was hurdler Roger Kingdom born?

6. At what field event does Romanian Bogdan Tudor compete?

7. At what ball game was javelin thrower Trini Hattestad a top player in Norway?

8. In which year were South Africa's first men's national championships?

9. Whose record did Iwan Thomas beat in winning the 1998 European Championships 400m event?

10. What age was Yelena Afanasyeva when she took the 800m title at the 1998 European Championships?

11. Which country won most golds at the 1998 Asian Championships?

12. Which country does shot champion Aleksandr Bagach represent?

13. Which men's team won the 1998 IAAF World Cup?

14. In which country were the 1998 Asian Games held?

15. How many nations took part in the 1997 IAAF World Championships?

ANSWERS 1. Jonathan Edwards 2. 200m 3. Denise Lewis 4. Liverpool 5. Georgia 6. Long jump 7. Handball 8. 1894 9. Roger Black 10. 31 11. China 12. Ukraine 13. Africa 14. Thailand 15. 198.

Quiz 06   ATHLETICS

1. Who holds the men's 200m and 400m records at the IAAF World Championships?

2. Which German won the men's discus at the 1998 European Championships?

3. Which Kenyan broke the world 10,000m record in July 1994?

4. In which country were the Central American and Caribbean Games held in 1998?

5. Which country won most golds at the 1998 European Championships?

6. What are the six European venues of the IAAF Golden League?

7. Which Japanese 1928 Olympic champion died in December 1998?

8. Which Briton finished runner-up to Steve Backley in the 1998 European Championships javelin competition?

9. Who set a record at the 1995 IAAF World Championships for men's 10,000m?

10. Which Romanian runner broke the women's world mile record in July 1989?

11. Who won the women's 5,000m & 10,000m at the 1998 European Championships?

12. What nationality is athlete Stephanie Graf?

13. Who was England's 1998 women's cross-country champion?

14. Of which country did Morocco-born Mohammed Mourhit become a citizen in 1997?

15. Who won the women's 100m & 200m at the 1998 Goodwill Games in New York?

ANSWERS 1. Michael Johnson 2. Lars Riedel 3. William Sigei 4. Venezuela 5. Great Britain 6. Oslo, Rome, Monaco, Zürich, Brussels & Berlin 7. Mikio Oda 8. Mick Hill 9. Haile Gebrselassie 10. Paula Ivan 11. Sonia O'Sullivan 12. Austrian 13. Mara Myers 14. Belgium 15. Marion Jones.

Quiz 07 ATHLETICS

1. Who won the men's 800m at the 1998 European Championships?

2. Which women's team won the 1998 IAAF World Cup?

3. Who set a record of 12.91 for the men's 110m hurdles at the 1993 IAAF World Championships?

4. Which country won gold and silver at the men's hammer in the 1998 European Championships?

5. Which country won most silvers at the 1998 Asian Championships?

6. The 1932 Olympic men's high jump champion died in 1998. Who was he?

7. Which American set a record of 47.18 for the 400m hurdles at the 1993 IAAF World Championships?

8. Which British hurdler broke the women's 400m world record in August 1993?

9. Who won her fourth long jump title at the European Championships in 1998?

10. What nationality is runner Sebastian Keitel?

11. What is the job of Ethiopian distance runner Worku Bikila?

12. Who was Scotland's 1998 women's cross-country champion?

13. Who won the 1990 & '98 women's 400m at the European Championships?

14. Which Briton finished fourth in the men's 1500m at the 1998 European Championships?

15. For which country did Mohammed Suleiman win gold at 1500m in the 1998 Asian Championships?

ANSWERS 1. Nils Schumann 2. U.S.A. 3. Colin Jackson 4. Hungary 5. Japan 6. Duncan McNaughton 7. Kevin Young 8. Sally Gunnell 9. Heike Drechsler 10. Chilean 11. Policeman 12. Fiona Lothian 13. Grit Breuer 14. Anthony Whiteman 15. Qatar.

SPORT IN THE MOVIES

Quiz 01 — SPORT IN THE MOVIES

Which sports are the following films about?

1. Winning (1969)

2. This Sporting Life (1963)

3. Players (1979)

4. Over the Top (1987)

5. Junior Bonner (1972)

6. When Saturday Comes (1996)

7. The Natural (1984)

8. Phar Lap (1983)

9. One on One (1977)

10. Trouble Along the Way (1953)

11. Downhill Racer (1969)

12. Man's Favourite Sport? (1964)

13. Personal Best (1982)

14. Slap Shot (1977)

15. Tin Cup (1996)

Quiz 02

SPORT IN THE MOVIES

Who starred as boxers in the following films?

1. Homeboy (1988)

2. The Champ (1931)

3. The Set-Up (1949)

4. Kid Galahad (1962)

5. The Main Event (1979)

6. Off Limits (1953)

7. The Harder They Fall (1956)

8. The Champion (1949)

9. Blonde Fist (1991)

10. Rocky (1976)

11. Kid Galahad (1937)

12. The Ring (1952)

13. Killer McCoy (1947)

14. The Champ (1979)

15. Body and Soul (1947)

ANSWERS **1.** Mickey Rourke **2.** Wallace Beery **3.** Robert Ryan **4.** Elvis Presley **5.** Ryan O'Neal **6.** Stanley Clements **7.** Mike Lane **8.** Kirk Douglas **9.** Margi Clarke **10.** Sylvester Stallone **11.** Wayne Morris **12.** Lalo Rios **13.** Mickey Rooney **14.** Jon Voight **15.** John Garfield.

Quiz 03

SPORT IN THE MOVIES

What sport are the following films about?

1. Ice Castles (1978)

2. The Great White Hope (1970)

3. ...All the Marbles (1981)

4. American Flyers (1985)

5. Angels in the Outfield (1951)

6. The Baltimore Bullet (1980)

7. Blue Chips (1994)

8. King of the Turf (1939)

9. The Mean Machine (1974)

10. Blue Juice (1995)

11. The Brave Bulls (1951)

12. By the Sword (1992)

13. Bronco Buster (1952)

14. The Club (1980)

15. Gregory's Girl (1982)

ANSWERS 1. Ice skating 2. Boxing 3. Wrestling 4. Bicycle racing 5. Baseball 6. Pool 7. Basketball 8. Horse racing 9. American Football 10. Surfing 11. Bullfighting 12. Fencing 13. Rodeo riding 14. Australian Rules Football 15. Football.

Quiz 04   SPORT IN THE MOVIES

About which sportsmen and women are the following film biographies?

1. Gentleman Jim (1942)

2. Man of Bronze (1951)

3. Somebody up there likes me (1956)

4. The Babe (1992)

5. Heart like a Wheel (1983)

6. The Pride of the Yankees (1942)

7. Dawn (1979)

8. Cobb (1994)

9. Chariots of Fire (1981)

10. Running Brave (1983)

11. Harmon of Michigan (1941)

12. Nadia (1984)

13. The Great John L. (1945)

14. Raging Bull (1980)

15. The Greatest (1977)

ANSWERS **1.** James J. Corbett **2.** Jim Thorpe **3.** Rocky Graziano **4.** Babe Ruth **5.** Shirley Muldowney **6.** Lou Gehrig **7.** Dawn Fraser **8.** Ty Cobb **9.** Harold Abrahams and Eric Liddell **10.** Billy Mills **11.** Tom Harmon **12.** Nadia Comaneci **13.** John L. Sullivan **14.** Jake LaMotta **15.** Muhammad Ali.

Quiz 05   SPORT IN THE MOVIES

Which sports are the following films about?

1. J.W. Coop (1971)

2. Knute Rockne All American (1940)

3. A League of Their Own (1992)

4. National Velvet (1944)

5. Requiem for a Heavyweight (1962)

6. Silver Dream Racer (1980)

7. Escape to Victory (1981)

8. Cool Runnings (1993)

9. The Cutting Edge (1992)

10. The Brave One (1956)

11. Eddie (1996)

12. Herbie Goes to Monte Carlo (1977)

13. The Hustler (1961)

14. Days of Thunder (1990)

15. The Crowd Roars (1932)

ANSWERS **1.** Rodeo riding **2.** American football **3.** Baseball **4.** Horse racing **5.** Boxing **6.** Motor cycle racing **7.** Football **8.** Bobsleigh **9.** Ice skating **10.** Bullfighting **11.** Basketball **12.** Rallying **13.** Pool **14.** Stock-car racing **15.** Motor racing.

COMMONWEALTH GAMES

Quiz 01 COMMONWEALTH GAMES

1. Where were the 1998 Commonwealth Games held?

2. Which Jamaican won the 1970 & '74 men's 200m?

3. Which country filled the medal positions in the 3,000m steeplechase in 1998?

4. Which Englishman won the 1986 5,000m event?

5. Which South African won the 1998 men's pole vault?

6. In which city were the 1974 Games held?

7. Which Englishman won silver at the 1998 hammer event?

8. Which Englishman won the 1970 400m hurdles?

9. Which team set a new Games record of 2:59.03 to win the 1998 men's 4 x 400m relay?

10. Which Englishman won three hammer titles from 1962-'70?

11. Which New Zealander collapsed whilst in the lead in the 1998 50km walk?

12. Which Malaysian won the 1990 & '94 men's singles badminton title?

13. Monica Twum was a finalist in the 1998 200m. Which country did she represent?

14. Which country did Frankie Lucas represent in winning the 1974 middleweight boxing title?

15. Esther Wanjiru won the 1998 women's 10,000m. Which country does she represent?

ANSWERS **1.** Kuala Lumpur, Malaysia **2.** Don Quarrie **3.** Kenya **4.** Steve Ovett **5.** Rianna Botha **6.** Christchurch **7.** Michael Jones **8.** John Sherwood **9.** Jamaica **10.** Howard Payne **11.** Craig Barrett **12.** Rashid Sidek **13.** Ghana **14.** St. Vincent **15.** Kenya.

Quiz 02 COMMONWEALTH GAMES

1. Who won the men's 100m at the 1998 Games?

2. Which Kenyan won the 1970 & '74 men's 400m?

3. Which Englishman won the 110m hurdles at the 1998 Games?

4. In which city were the 1966 Games held?

5. Who won the men's singles bowls title from 1962-'78?

6. Which South African finished second in the 1998 men's discus?

7. Which Australian won the men's pole vault in 1962 & '66?

8. Which Australian swimmer won the women's 110 yds freestyle in 1958 & '62?

9. Which South African won the 1998 men's javelin event?

10. Which country won the team foil, épée & sabre fencing events from 1958-'70?

11. Nick A'hern won the inaugural 20km walk in 1998. Which country did he represent?

12. Which Jamaican won the 1998 women's 400m event?

13. Where did England's Janine Whitlock place in the 1998 pole vault?

14. In what position did Darren Campbell finish in the men's 100m in 1998?

15. Which Englishwoman won the 1994 100m freestyle swimming title?

ANSWERS 1. Ato Boldon **2.** Charles Asati **3.** Anthony Jarrett **4.** Kingston **5.** David Bryant **6.** Frantz Kruger **7.** Trevor Bickle **8.** Dawn Fraser **9.** Marius Corbett **10.** England **11.** Australia **12.** Sandie Richards **13.** Fourth **14.** 5th **15.** Karen Pickering.

Quiz 03 COMMONWEALTH GAMES

1. In which city were the 1962 Games held?

2. At which gymnastics event did Brennon Dowrick win gold at the 1990 & '94 Games?

3. Japheth Kimutai won the 1998 men's 800m. Which country did he represent?

4. Which Englishman won the 1978 10,000m?

5. Which three Englishmen made the final of the 1998 5,000m?

6. Which Kenyan won the 1978 men's 800m?

7. Which South African won the 1998 women's high jump?

8. Which Canadian won the 1982 & '86 men's high jump?

9. Which Englishwoman won the 1998 long jump?

10. Which Jamaican won the 1982 & '90 women's 200m?

11. Which team won the 1998 women's 4 x 100m relay?

12. Which Australian won the 1990 men's 400m?

13. Which Australian won the 1986 & '90 women's marathon?

14. Which Australian made the finals of the 1998 men's 5,000m & 10,000m?

15. Which Englishman won the pole vault in 1954 & '58?

Quiz 04 COMMONWEALTH GAMES

1. Kersley Gardenne got a bronze in the 1998 men's pole vault - the first Commonwealth athletics medal for which country?

2. Which Welshman was 1986 featherweight weightlifting champion?

3. Which Welshman finished third in the shot in 1998?

4. Charles Gitonga won the 1994 men's 400m. Which country did he represent?

5. Which Australian won the 1982 women's 400m title?

6. Who took the inaugural women's pole vault gold at the 1998 Games?

7. Who won the 1982 women's 100m hurdles?

8. Françoise Mbango won the 1998 triple jump silver for which country?

9. Which Englishman won the 1986 800m?

10. Which two Englishwomen took gold & silver in the 1998 shot?

11. Billy Cole, Simon Williams & Matthew Simson each won which event for England from 1986-'94?

12. Who was the highest placed Englishwoman in the 1998 discus?

13. Who finished second in the 1998 men's 100m?

14. Which event did Stephanus du Plessis win for South Africa in 1954 & '58?

15. Which Englishwoman won the 1998 triple jump?

ANSWERS 1. Mauritius 2. Raymond Williams 3. Shaun Pickering 4. Kenya 5. Raelene Boyle 6. Emma George 7. Shirley Strong 8. Cameroon 9. Steve Cram 10. Judy Oakes & Myrtle Augee 11. Shot 12. Shelley Drew 13. Frankie Fredericks 14. Discus 15. Ashia Hansen.

Quiz 05 COMMONWEALTH GAMES

1. Which Englishman was 1970 & '74 lightweight weightlifting champion?

2. Which women's team won most athletics silvers at the 1998 Games?

3. Which Englishman won the 1986 10,000m?

4. Which Englishwoman won the 1998 heptathlon?

5. Which Englishman finished second to Iwan Thomas in the 1998 400m?

6. In which city were the 1950 Games held?

7. Who were England's two finalists in the 1998 men's 800m?

8. Which was the first city to host the Games twice?

9. Which Englishman finished second in the 1998 high jump?

10. In which year was archery first contested at the Games?

11. Which Jamaican won the men's 100m from 1970-'78?

12. Where did Scot Doug Walker finish in the 1998 men's 200m final?

13. Which Englishman won the 1978 1,500m?

14. Which two Englishmen finished in silver & bronze positions in the 1998 1,500m?

15. Which Canadian won the 1982 & '86 men's 110m hurdles?

ANSWERS 1. George Newton 2. England 3. Jonathan Solly 4. Denise Lewis 5. Mark Richardson 6. Auckland 7. Andy Hart & Bradley Donkin 8. Edinburgh 9. Ben Challenger 10. 1982 11. Don Quarrie 12. Eighth 13. David Moorcroft 14. John Maycock & Anthony Whiteman 15. Mark McKoy.

Quiz 06 COMMONWEALTH GAMES

1. Reny Limo finished third in the 1998 men's triple jump. Which country did he represent?

2. Who won the men's hammer event for England in 1974?

3. Which men's team won most athletics silvers at the 1998 Games?

4. Which Australian won the 1986 women's 400m?

5. Which Englishman retained his 1,500m title at the 1986 Games?

6. Which Scot won the 1970 women's 800m hurdles?

7. Which Englishman won the 1970 marathon?

8. What was Liz McColgan's maiden name, under which she won the 1986 10,000m title?

9. In which city were the 1982 Games held?

10. Which Kenyan won the 1998 women's 1,500m title?

11. Which Welshman won the 1978 110m hurdles title?

12. In which position did John Regis finish in the 1998 men's 200m final?

13. In which position did Jamie Baulch finish in the 1998 men's 400m final?

14. Who won the 1986 women's 800m for Wales?

15. Which country took the medals in the 1998 men's 5,000m?

ANSWERS 1. Kenya 2. Ian Chipchase 3. England 4. Debbie Flintoff 5. Steve Cram 6. Rosemary Stirling 7. Ron Hill 8. Liz Lynch 9. Brisbane 10. Jackline Maranga 11. Berwyn Price 12. Third 13. Fourth 14. Kirsty Wade 15. Kenya.

Quiz 07 COMMONWEALTH GAMES

1. Burger Lambrechts won the 1998 men's shot. Which country did he represent?

2. In which city were the 1990 Games held?

3. Which Australian won the inaugural women's 5,000m event in 1998?

4. Which Scot won the 1994 women's 10,000m title?

5. Who won the 1982 & '86 women's 400m hurdles?

6. Who won the women's 100m at the 1998 Games?

7. How often are the Commonwealth Games contested?

8. How many athletics medals did England win at the 1998 Games?

9. In which city were the 1938 Games held?

10. Who won the 1982 men's 100m?

11. How many athletics medals did the women's team win for Wales in 1998?

12. Which Englishman won the 1994 5,000m event?

13. How old was Kenyan medal-winning runner Richard Limo at the 1998 Games?

14. Which Kenyan won the 1978 3,000m steeplechase?

15. In the 1998 men's 110m hurdles final, how many of the eight were Britons?

ANSWERS 1. South Africa 2. Auckland 3. Katie Anderson 4. Yvonne Murray 5. Debbie Flintoff 6. Chandra Sturrup 7. Every four years 8. 33 9. Sydney 10. Allan Wells 11. None 12. Rob Denmark 13. 17 14. Henry Rono 15. Four.

Quiz 08 COMMONWEALTH GAMES

1. How many teams participated at the first Games in 1930?

2. Who in 1998 became the first Briton to win the men's high jump?

3. Which Tanzanian won the 1974 men's 1,500m?

4. Which Scot won the 1970 men's 10,000m?

5. Which Australian won the 1998 women's 200m?

6. Which Jamaican won the 1954 & '58 men's 120yd hurdles?

7. Which Englishwoman was runner-up in the inaugural women's hammer event in 1998?

8. In which year did women first compete at athletics at the Games?

9. Dinsdale Morgan won the men's 400m hurdles in 1998. Which country did he represent?

10. Which Englishman was the 1974 400m hurdles winner?

11. Which country did Govindaswamy Saravanan represent in winning the 50km walk at the 1998 Games?

12. Which men's fencer won nine golds from 1958-'70?

13. Which Sri Lankan won a women's 400m semi-final heat in 1998 but only placed fourth in the final?

14. Which Australian swimmer won nine golds from 1966-'74?

15. In which year was judo first included in the Games?

ANSWERS 1. Eleven 2. Dalton Grant 3. Filbert Bayi 4. Lachie Stewart 5. Nova Peris-Kneebone 6. Keith Gardner 7. Lorraine Shaw 8. 1934 9. Jamaica 10. Alan Pascoe 11. Malaysia 12. Bill Hoskyns 13. Damayanthi Darsha 14. Michael Wenden 15. 1990.

Quiz 09 COMMONWEALTH GAMES

1. Which medal did Diane Modahl win in the 1998 800m?

2. Which Englishman won the 1994 men's 200m breaststroke swimming title?

3. Beatrice Faumuina won the 1998 women's discus event. Which country did she represent?

4. Which Englishwomen placed second and third in the 1998 javelin?

5. Which Englishwoman was the 1982 100m & 200m freestyle swimming champion?

6. Who won the 1958 bantamweight boxing title?

7. Which Englishwoman was the 1986 400m & 800m freestyle swimming champion?

8. Which Kenyan won the men's 10,000m at the 1998 Games?

9. Which Canadian was heavyweight weightlifting champion from 1970-'78?

10. Who was middleweight weightlifting champion in 1982?

11. Which three Englishmen finished in second, third and fourth positions in the 1998 javelin?

12. Which country won the most medals from 1930-'94?

13. Which Australian won the 1998 men's decathlon?

14. Who was England's highest placed finisher in the 1998 women's 10,000m?

15. How many children does 1998 women's marathon winner Heather Tupland have?

ANSWERS 1. Bronze 2. Nick Gillingham 3. New Zealand 4. Karen Martin & Kirsty Morrison 5. June Croft 6. Howard Winstone 7. Susan Hardcastle 8. Simon Maina 9. Russell Prior 10. Stephen Pinsent 11. Steve Backley, Mick Hill & Mark Roberson 12. Australia 13. Jagan Hames 14. Sarah Bentley 15. Four.

THE ULTIMATE SPORTS FACT AND QUIZ BOOK

Quiz 10 COMMONWEALTH GAMES

1. Which Englishman won the 1986 men's 400m?

2. Which Australian won the inaugural women's hammer event in 1998?

3. Which men's decathlete finished seventh for England in the 1998 event?

4. Which Australian won the 1958 & '62 triple jump?

5. Which Englishwoman won the 1958 110yds backstroke swimming title?

6. Which men's team set a new Games record in 1998 of 38.20 to win the 4x100m relay?

7. Which Englishwoman finished fourth in the 1998 women's marathon?

8. Which men's team won most athletics golds at the 1998 Games?

9. Which Englishwoman won the 1970 long jump?

10. Which Welshman was 1986 & '90 light-heavyweight weightlifting champion?

11. Who broke the Games record in winning the 1998 women's 100m hurdles?

12. Which Englishwoman won the 1962 & '66 110 & 220yds backstroke swimming titles?

13. Which Australian won the 1998 women's javelin event?

14. Who finished runner-up to Julian Golding in the 1998 men's 200m final?

15. In which year was cricket included in the Commonwealth games for the first time?

Quiz 11 COMMONWEALTH GAMES

1. Who broke the women's 800m Games record in winning the 1998 event?

2. Which Englishman won the 1974 long jump?

3. Which South African was disqualified from the 1998 100m hurdles final for two false starts?

4. Which Englishman won the 1986 bantamweight boxing title?

5. Which Englishman won the 1990 1500m title?

6. Anthony Mosse won the 1986 & '90 men's 200m butterfly swimming titles. Which country did he represent?

7. Which Australian won the 1962 & '66 men's 440 yds hurdles titles?

8. Which Englishman was 1962 & '66 springboard diving champion?

9. Which South African finished third in the 1998 men's 800m?

10. What time did Iwan Thomas run to win the 1998 men's 400m?

11. Which Australian won the 1970 & '74 women's javelin?

12. Which New Zealander tested positive for steroids after the 1998 men's pole vault final?

13. Which Englishman won the 1954 mile event?

14. Which Australian won the 1998 men's long jump?

15. Which Englishman won the 1954 three mile event?

ANSWERS 1. Maria Mutola 2. Alan Lerwill 3. Corien Botha 4. Sean Murphy 5. Peter Elliott 6. New Zealand 7. Ken Roche 8. Brian Phelps 9. Johan Botha 10. 44.52 11. Petra Rivers 12. Denis Petushinskiy 13. Roger Bannister 14. Peter Burge 15. Chris Chataway.

Quiz 12 COMMONWEALTH GAMES

1. Which Englishwoman finished second in the 1998 1,500m?

2. Which Northern Ireland athlete won the 1970 men's pole vault?

3. Which country did Andrea Blackett represent in winning the 1998 400m hurdles?

4. Which Englishman won the 1974 200m butterfly swimming title?

5. Which Englishwoman finished third in the 1998 triple jump?

6. Which Australian won the 1982 & '86 men's long jump?

7. Which Englishman won the 1962 marathon?

8. Which Ghanaian boxer won the 1978 featherweight title?

9. Which Kenyan won the 1998 men's 1,500m title?

10. Which Briton won the 1982 men's 5,000m?

11. Which field event did Malcolm Nokes win for England in 1930 & '34?

12. Who in 1998 at the age of 40 years and 217 days became the oldest ever women's commonwealth champion?

13. Which woman won the 1962 & '66 shot and discus titles for New Zealand?

14. In which three years did Tessa Sanderson win the javelin event?

15. Which Scottish men's swimmer was the 1974 200m individual medley winner?

ANSWERS **1.** Kelly Holmes **2.** Mike Bull **3.** Barbados **4.** Brian Brinkley **5.** Connie Henry **6.** Gary Honey **7.** Brian Kilby **8.** Azumah Nelson **9.** Laban Rotich **10.** David Moorcroft **11.** Hammer **12.** Judy Oakes **13.** Valerie Young **14.** 1978, '86 & '90 **15.** David Wilkie.

Quiz 13 COMMONWEALTH GAMES

1. In which city were the 1954 Games held?

2. Which Kenyan finished second in the 1998 men's 10,000m?

3. Which two Britons tied the 1982 men's 200m?

4. Whose record did Dinsdale Morgan beat in winning the 1998 men's 400m?

5. Which Australian won the 1958 men's 880 yards?

6. Shane Hair finished fourth in the 1998 men's long jump. Which country did he represent?

7. Which Scot won the 1970 5,000m event?

8. In which city were the 1958 Games held?

9. Which Welshman won the 1994 pole vault?

10. Who was the only Briton in the top eight of the 1998 men's marathon?

11. Which Englishman won the 1990 200m?

12. Which Englishwoman finished second in the 1998 400m hurdles?

13. Which New Zealander won the 1962 men's 880 yards?

14. Which Kenyan won the 1970 men's 1,500m?

15. Who won the 1982 & '86 women's badminton singles title?

ANSWERS **1.** Vancouver **2.** William Kalya **3.** Allan Wells & Mike McFarlane **4.** Samuel Matete **5.** Herb Elliott **6.** Australia **7.** Ian Stewart **8.** Cardiff **9.** Nick Winter **10.** David Taylor **11.** Marcus Adam **12.** Gowry Retchakan **13.** Peter Snell **14.** Kip Keino **15.** Helen Troke.

Quiz 14 COMMONWEALTH GAMES

1. What birthday did Jo Jennings celebrate by taking the high jump silver in 1998?

2. Which New Zealander won the 1958 & '62 men's three mile event?

3. Which Kenyan won the 1994 men's 800m?

4. Who won the 1982 women's 1,500m title for England?

5. Who won the 1978 bantamweight boxing title?

6. Which Scot won the 1990 light-welterweight boxing title?

7. Thabiso Moghali won the 1998 men's marathon. Which country did he represent?

8. Who was 1966 & '70 bantamweight weightlifting champion?

9. How many Britons were in the 1998 men's 400m hurdles final?

10. Fine Sani won the 1982 light-heavyweight boxing title. Which country did he represent?

11. The 1994 world junior champion won the 1998 men's triple jump. Who is he?

12. Which Canadian swimmer won six golds at the 1978 Games?

13. Aaron Neighbour finished fifth in the men's shot in 1998. Which country did he represent?

14. Which Australian athlete won five golds at the 1938 Games?

15. Which Canadian won the 1990 & '94 women's 3,000m titles?

ANSWERS 1. 29th 2. Murray Halberg 3. Patrick Konchellah 4. Christina Boxer 5. Barry McGuigan 6. Charlie Kane 7. Lesotho 8. Precious Mackenzie 9. None 10. Fiji 11. Onochie Achike 12. Graham Smith 13. Australia 14. Decima Norman 15. Angela Charles.

Quiz 15 COMMONWEALTH GAMES

1. Which Englishwoman won the 1990 shot title?

2. Which Canadian swimmer won eight medals at the 1966 Games?

3. Which Englishwoman won the 1978 200m & 400m individual swimming medleys?

4. What age was Robert Weir when he won the 1998 discus title?

5. Who won the men's 1986 100m?

6. Which Englishman placed second in the 1998 5,000m?

7. Which English swimmer was men's 200m backstroke champion in 1994?

8. Which Australian finished second in the 1998 women's 10,000m?

9. Which women's team won most athletics golds at the 1998 Games?

10. How many athletics golds did Kenya win at the 1998 Games?

11. Who won the 1990 & '94 men's 100m?

12. From which event was Malaysia's Yuan Yufang disqualified at the 1998 Games?

13. Which team won the 1998 women's 4 x 400m relay?

14. Which Canadian won the 1966 & '70 men's shot?

15. Which Englishman won the 1982 & '90 100m breaststroke swimming titles?

15. Adrian Moorhouse.
10. Seven 11. Linford Christie 12. 10km walk 13. Australia 14. David Steen
Johnson 6. Andrew Whitcombe 7. Adam Ruckwood 8. Kylie Risk 9. Australia
ANSWERS 1. Myrtle Augee 2. Ralph Hutton 3. Sharron Davies 4. 37 5. Ben

Quiz 16 COMMONWEALTH GAMES

1. Which Northern Ireland athlete won the 1970 & '74 pentathlons?

2. Which English athlete won the 1986 heptathlon event?

3. Which team were men's 4 x 200m freestyle relay swimming champions from 1970-'94?

4. Which English swimmer won the women's 110yds & 220yds breaststroke in 1962?

5. Which English swimmer won the 1986 women's 100m butterfly title?

6. Which Englishman won the 1974 & '78 men's shot events?

7. Which Englishman won the 1974 marathon?

8. Which Australian won the women's 100yds in 1950 & '54?

9. Who won the men's 4 x 400m relay from 1970-'78?

10. Which English boxer was 1990 light-middleweight champion?

11. Which South African won the men's high jump in 1934 & '38?

12. Which Australian won the men's sprint cycling title from 1986-'94?

13. Which Englishman won the 1978 & '82 triple jump?

14. Who was men's open judo champion in 1990?

15. Which Australian won the 1990 & '94 men's hammer events?

Quiz 17 COMMONWEALTH GAMES

1. Who was men's 100m freestyle swimming champion in 1970 & '74?

2. Who was Northern Ireland's 1974 decathlon champion at the Games?

3. Which Englishman was the 1982 200m & 400m freestyle swimming champion?

4. Which country did Lennox Lewis represent in winning the 1986 super-heavyweight boxing title?

5. Which Australian won the men's marathon in 1982 & '86?

6. Who won the 1994 men's 4 x 400m relay?

7. Which Australian won the men's high jump in 1966 & '70?

8. Which event did Charles Clover win for England in 1974?

9. How many points did Daley Thompson score in winning the 1986 decathlon?

10. Which Australian won the women's 100m in 1970 & '74?

11. Which Australian cyclist won the women's road race in 1990 & '94?

12. Which women's team won the 4 x 100m relay from 1978-'86?

13. Which Englishwoman won the 1986 100m?

14. Who was women's judo champion in 1990?

15. Which Canadian won the 1970 & '82 women's high jump?

ANSWERS **1.** Mike Wenden **2.** Mike Bull **3.** Andrew Astbury **4.** Canada **5.** Rob de Castella **6.** England **7.** Laurie Peckham **8.** Javelin **9.** 8663 **10.** Raelene Boyle **11.** Kathy Watt **12.** England **13.** Heather Oakes **14.** Sharon Lee **15.** Debbie Brill.

THE ULTIMATE SPORTS FACT AND QUIZ BOOK

Quiz 18 COMMONWEALTH GAMES

1. Which Australian was the 1978 & '82 men's 1,500m freestyle swimming champion?

2. Which Englishman was the 1970 middleweight boxing champion?

3. Which Australian won the 1994 men's marathon?

4. Marios Hadjiandreou won the 1990 men's triple jump. Which country did he represent?

5. Which women's team won the 4 x 400m relay in 1982 & '86?

6. Which team were men's 4 x 100m freestyle swimming champions from 1982-'94?

7. Which Kenyan won the 1974 men's 5,000m event?

8. Which Northern Ireland athlete won the 1970 women's shot?

9. Which Kenyan won the 1974 3,000m steeplechase?

10. Which Englishman was the 1978 & '82 springboard diving champion?

11. Which Englishman won the 1990 400m hurdles title?

12. Which Australian swimmer won five golds at the 1990 Games?

13. Which Australian won the 1950 & '54 women's long jump?

14. Which Englishman won the 1994 light-welterweight boxing title?

15. Which team won the men's 4 x 100m relay in 1986 & '94?

ANSWERS 1. Max Metzker 2. John Conteh 3. Steve Moneghetti 4. Cyprus 5. Canada 6. Australia 7. Ben Jipcho 8. Mary Peters 9. Ben Jipcho 10. Chris Snode 11. Kriss Akabusi 12. Hayley Lewis 13. Yvette Williams 14. Peter Richardson 15. Canada.

Quiz 19 COMMONWEALTH GAMES

1. At what sport did Sudesh Kumar win medals in 1970 & '74?

2. At which two Games did Mary Glen-Haig win medals for individual foil in fencing?

3. At what sport did Oliver Orok win a medal in 1982?

4. Which country did Densign White represent in winning the 1990 86kg judo gold?

5. In which sport did Elaine Tanner win medals at the 1966 Games?

6. Which Northern Ireland boxer won the 1990 flyweight title?

7. Which pair won the women's badminton doubles in 1990?

8. Phineas Danilowitz won the 1958 men's singles bowls. Which country did he represent?

9. Who won the 1934 women's javelin?

10. Who was the 1978 women's 3,000m winner?

11. Who was the 1970 women's 400m champion?

12. Which Pakistani won the 1966 men's hammer?

13. Samuel Igun won the 1966 triple jump. For which country?

14. Which country won the 1982 men's 4 x 100m relay?

15. At what shooting event did Fotini Theofanous win gold in 1994?

ANSWERS 1. Wrestling 2. 1950 & '54 3. Weightlifting 4. England 5. Swimming 6. Wayne McCullogh 7. Fiona Smith & Sara Sankey 8. South Africa 9. Gladys Lunn 10. Paula Fudge 11. Marilyn Neufville 12. Mohammad Iqbal 13. Nigeria 14. Nigeria 15. Air rifle.

ACROSS THE POND

THE ULTIMATE SPORTS FACT AND QUIZ BOOK

Quiz 01 ACROSS THE POND

1. Which baseball team headed the National League Eastern Division in 1998?

2. Who was Detroit's coach in their N.B.A. championship wins in 1989 & '90?

3. What is the name of Baltimore's A.F.C. team in American Football?

4. Which team won the Stanley Cup in 1994/5?

5. For which side did Ken Griffey Jr. hit 56 home runs in 1998?

6. What is the name of Charlotte's N.B.A. team?

7. How many touchdown passes did Johnny Unitas make in his career?

8. What is the name of Arizona's National League baseball team?

9. For which team was Hakeem Olajuwon the N.B.A. Finals M.V.P. in 1994 & '95?

10. What is the name of Denver's N.B.A. team?

11. Who scored all 40 points for Chicago Cardinals against Chicago Bears in a 1929 win?

12. What is the name of Jacksonville's A.F.C. team in American Football?

13. Who were N.B.A. runners-up seven times from 1962-70?

14. Which baseball team headed the National League Western Division in 1998?

15. What is the name of Detroit's N.B.A. team?

ANSWERS 1. Atlanta **2.** Chuck Daly **3.** Baltimore Ravens **4.** New Jersey Devils **5.** Seattle **6.** Charlotte Hornets **7.** 290 **8.** Arizona Diamondbacks **9.** Houston **10.** Denver Nuggets **11.** Ernie Nevers **12.** Jacksonville Jaguars **13.** L.A. Lakers **14.** San Diego **15.** Detroit Pistons.

Quiz 02   ACROSS THE POND

1. Who won the Stanley Cup in 1992/3?

2. Who was N.B.A. Defensive Player of the Year in 1996/7 & 1997/8?

3. What is the name of Colorado's National League baseball team?

4. When did Detroit last win the World Series in baseball?

5. Who kicked seven field goals for Minnesota versus L.A. Rams in a 1989 NFL game?

6. How many touchdown passes did Joe Montana make in his career?

7. For which team did Albert Belle hit 49 homers in the American League in 1998?

8. What are the names of Los Angeles's two N.B.A. teams?

9. What is the name of Tennessee's A.F.C. team in American Football?

10. How many home runs did Mark McGwire hit in 1998?

11. What is the name of Seattle's N.B.A. team?

12. Who holds the record of touchdowns in a career in American Football?

13. When did Oakland last appear in the final of the World Series?

14. How many goals did Wayne Gretzky score in the 1981/2 N.H.L. season?

15. What is the name of Calgary's N.H.L. ice hockey team?

ANSWERS 1. Montreal Canadiens 2. Dikembe Mutombo 3. Colorado Rockies 4. 1984 5. Rich Karlis 6. 273 7. Chicago 8. Los Angeles Lakers & Los Angeles Clippers 9. Tennessee Oilers 10. 70 11. Seattle SuperSonics 12. Jerry Rice 13. 1990 14. 92 15. Calgary Flames.

Quiz 03 ACROSS THE POND

1. Which city's American League baseball team is called the 'Red Sox'?

2. Which baseball team headed the American League Eastern Division in 1998?

3. How many touchdowns did Emmitt Smith score for Dallas in the 1995 season?

4. What is the name of Chicago's N.H.L. ice hockey team?

5. What is the name of Milwaukee's National League Baseball Team?

6. What are the names of the two conferences in the Eastern Conference in the N.H.L.?

7. What is the name of Utah's N.B.A. team?

8. What is the name of Washington's N.F.C. team in American Football?

9. Who batted .339 for New York in the American League in 1998 to head the averages?

10. Who scored 24 touchdowns for Washington in the 1983 season?

11. What is the name of Florida's N.H.L. ice hockey team?

12. Which team have won the N.H.L. most times?

13. What is the name of Anaheim's American League baseball team?

14. Who kicked 35 field goals in the 1993 season for the L.A. Raiders?

15. Who holds the record for most field goals in a career in American Football?

ANSWERS 1. Boston 2. New York 3. 25 4. Chicago Blackhawks 5. Milwaukee Brewers 6. Northeast and Atlantic 7. Utah Jazz 8. Washington Redskins 9. Bernie Williams 10. John Riggins 11. Florida Panthers 12. Montreal Canadiens 13. Anaheim Angels 14. Jeff Jaeger 15. Nick Lowery.

THE ULTIMATE SPORTS FACT AND QUIZ BOOK

Quiz 04   ACROSS THE POND

1. Who scored seven goals for Quebec Bulldogs versus Toronto St. Patrick's in a 1920 N.H.L. game?

2. When did Kansas City last win the World Series in baseball?

3. What is the name of Vancouver's N.B.A. team?

4. What is the name of Tampa Bay's American League baseball team?

5. Who batted .363 for Colorado in the National League in 1998 to head the averages?

6. In which sport are the Vezina Trophy and Art Ross Trophy awarded?

7. What is the name of San Jose's N.H.L. team?

8. How many times have the New York Knicks been N.B.A. champions?

9. In which year was the N.H.L. founded?

10. How many home runs did Mel Ott hit in his career?

11. Which team won the N.H.L. in 1915?

12. Which American Football player gained 275 yards rushing for Chicago versus Minnesota in a 1977 game?

13. What is the name of Houston's National League baseball team?

14. What is the name of Arizona's N.F.C. team in American Football?

15. Before 1998, when was the last whitewash in the World Series?

Arizona Cardinals **15.** 1990.
11. Vancouver Millionaires **12.** Walter Payton **13.** Houston Astros **14.**
511 **11.** Vancouver Millionaires **12.** Walter Payton **13.** Houston Astros **14.**
Rays **5.** Larry Walker **6.** Ice hockey **7.** San Jose Sharks **8.** Twice **9.** 1917 **10.**
ANSWERS **1.** Joe Malone **2.** 1985 **3.** Vancouver Grizzlies **4.** Tampa Bay Devil

THE ULTIMATE SPORTS FACT AND QUIZ BOOK

Quiz 05 ACROSS THE POND

1. For which N.B.A. team did George Gervin play when he was leading scorer from 1978-80?

2. Which team won the N.H.L. in 1925?

3. What is the name of Minnesota's N.B.A. team?

4. How many home runs did Sammy Sosa hit for Chicago in 1998?

5. What are the names of the two conferences in the Western Conference in the N.H.L.?

6. Who holds the record for 2,002 career points in American football?

7. What is the name of Pittsburgh's N.H.L. ice hockey team?

8. Which baseball player holds the record of 4,256 career hits?

9. What is the name of Phoenix's N.B.A. team?

10. Which baseball team headed the American League Western Division in 1998?

11. What is the name of Phoenix's N.H.L. ice hockey team?

12. Which city's American League baseball team is the 'White Sox'?

13. What is the name of St. Louis's N.F.C. team in American Football?

14. Who scored five touchdowns for Cleveland versus Baltimore Colts in a 1959 game?

15. Which team won the N.H.L. in 1996?

ANSWERS 1. San Antonio 2. Victoria Cougars 3. Minnesota Timberwolves 4. 66 5. Central & Pacific 6. George Blanda 7. Pittsburgh Penguins 8. Pete Rose 9. Phoenix Suns 10. Texas 11. Phoenix Coyotes 12. Chicago 13. St. Louis Rams 14. Jim Brown 15. Colorado Avalanche.

CRICKET WORLD CUP

THE ULTIMATE SPORTS FACT AND QUIZ BOOK

Quiz 01 CRICKET WORLD CUP

1. Who scored 137 for England versus India in the 1975 World Cup?

2. Who scored 461 runs for India in the 1999 World Cup?

3. Which England opener was l.b.w. for 1 against Australia in a 1979 group game?

4. Who took 4 for 42 for Zimbabwe against Kenya in 1999?

5. Against whom did David Gower hit 130 in the 1983 World Cup?

6. Where was the 1999 fixture between Australia and Scotland played?

7. Alec Stewart was England's highest scorer in 1992 against Zimbabwe. How many did he score?

8. Who took 5 for 21 for South Africa against Kenya in 1999?

9. Who won the 1996 fixture between India & the West Indies?

10. Who took 4 for 31 for England against Australia in 1992?

11. Who scored 113 n.o. for Pakistan in their 1999 semi-final against New Zealand?

12. By how many runs did Australia beat New Zealand in their first meeting in 1987?

13. Darren Gough was England's top bowler in the 1999 World Cup. How many wickets did he take?

14. Which two players scored 100 in the 1992 New Zealand versus Australia game?

15. Who scored 103 n.o. for Pakistan versus New Zealand in their 1983 World Cup game at Trent Bridge?

ANSWERS 1. Dennis Amiss 2. Rahul Dravid 3. Geoffrey Boycott 4. Neil Johnson 5. Sri Lanka 6. Worcester 7. 29 8. Lance Klusener 9. India 10. Ian Botham 11. Saeed Anwar 12. Three 13. Eleven 14. Martin Crowe & David Boon 15. Zaheer Abbas.

THE ULTIMATE SPORTS FACT AND QUIZ BOOK

Quiz 02   CRICKET WORLD CUP

1. Who hit 100 for Australia against the West Indies in 1992?

2. Who scored 171 n.o. for New Zealand versus East Africa in the 1975 World Cup?

3. How many did Scotland score against West Indies in 1999?

4. Who was captain and wicketkeeper for Canada in their 1979 World Cup appearance?

5. Who took 4 for 40 for Zimbabwe against West Indies in 1996?

6. Against whom were Pakistan 0 for 3 at one stage in the 1983 World Cup?

7. Who hit 73 n.o. for England against Sri Lanka in 1999?

8. Who scored 104 n.o. for England against Holland in 1996?

9. Which England opener scored 75 against Pakistan in their 1996 group game?

10. By how many runs did Australia beat West Indies in a 1996 semi-final?

11. Who hit 81 for India against Zimbabwe in 1992 and received the match award?

12. Who scored 77 for West Indies against Pakistan in 1999?

13. Who hit 113 for Pakistan against England in Karachi in 1987?

14. Who took 4 for 20 for India against Australia in their 1983 game at Chelmsford?

15. By how many runs did England beat India in their 1992 game?

ANSWERS 1. David Boon 2. Glenn Turner 3. 68 4. B.M. Mauricette 5. Paul Strang 6. New Zealand 7. Graeme Hick 8. Graeme Hick 9. Robin Smith 10. Five 11. Sachin Tendulkar 12. Shivnarine Chanderpaul 13. Ramiz Raja 14. Madan Lal 15. Nine.

Quiz 03   CRICKET WORLD CUP

1. Who high-scored in the 1992 semi-final between New Zealand & Pakistan but ended on the losing side?

2. Who was Pakistan's leading bowler in 1999?

3. Who took 5 for 34 for Australia against Pakistan in the 1975 World Cup?

4. Who took 4 for 29 for Australia in their 1999 semi-final against South Africa?

5. Which Group B game in 1979 was abandoned without a ball being bowled?

6. Who won the match award in the 1999 Super Six game between New Zealand & India?

7. Who took 7 for 51 for West Indies against Australia at Headingley in 1983?

8. Who was Zimbabwe's leading bowler in the 1999 World Cup?

9. Who scored 130 for Australia against Kenya in 1996?

10. Who captained Australia in their 1992 match against Sri Lanka?

11. What were Shane Warne's figures in the 1999 World Cup final?

12. Zimbabwe's wicketkeeper scored 115 n.o. versus Sri Lanka in 1992. Who was he?

13. Who scored 56 n.o. for Australia against Bangladesh in 1999?

14. Who scored 65 off 66 balls for West Indies against Sri Lanka at Kanpur in 1987?

15. Who took 3 for 28 for West Indies against Zimbabwe at Edgbaston in 1983?

ANSWERS 1. Martin Crowe 2. Saqlain Mushtaq 3. Dennis Lillee 4. Shane Warne 5. West Indies versus Sri Lanka 6. Roger Twose 7. W.W. Davis 8. Neil Johnson 9. Mark Waugh 10. Allan Border 11. 4 for 33 12. Andrew Flower 13. Tom Moody 14. Gus Logie 15. Wayne Daniel.

Quiz 04   CRICKET WORLD CUP

1. How many overs did Pakistan take to beat the U.A.E. total of 109 in a 1996 game?

2. Who scored 88 for West Indies against Pakistan in 1992 before retiring hurt?

3. By how many runs did Bangladesh beat Scotland in their 1999 Group B game?

4. What did the West Indies score in defeating Sri Lanka in 1975?

5. How many sixes did Lance Klusener hit in the 1999 finals?

6. Where was the 1979 Group B game between New Zealand & India played?

7. Who took 4 for 34 for Australia against Zimbabwe in 1996?

8. Where was the first 1983 encounter between Zimbabwe & India played?

9. Which Kenyan bowler's figures for the 1999 World Cup were 1 for 210?

10. Who scored 81 n.o. for New Zealand in their 1992 win against West Indies?

11. Which team did Asim Butt represent in the 1999 World Cup?

12. Who scored 102 for Australia in their 1996 game against West Indies before being run out?

13. Who hit 62 for England against Zimbabwe in 1999?

14. Who beat England in a 1983 World Cup semi-final?

15. Who scored 54 off 45 balls for India against Australia in 1987 in Delhi?

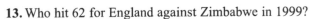

ANSWERS 1. 18 2. Brian Lara 3. 22 4. 87 5. Ten 6. Headingley 7. Shane Warne 8. Leicester 9. Asif Karim 10. Martin Crowe 11. Scotland 12. Ricky Ponting 13. Graham Thorpe 14. India 15. Mohammed Azharuddin.

Quiz 05   CRICKET WORLD CUP

1. Who scored 88 n.o. for New Zealand against Zimbabwe in Calcutta in 1987?

2. Which associate members team played their first World Cup fixture in 1996 against New Zealand?

3. Who won the match award for New Zealand for his 65 n.o. against Sri Lanka in 1992?

4. By how many wickets did Australia beat South Africa in their 1999 Super Six game?

5. Who scored 131 for England in their 1975 World Cup win against New Zealand?

6. Who hit 96 for South Africa against India in 1999?

7. Which two players hit 61 for Pakistan in their 1979 victory against Australia?

8. How many did Bangladesh score in their 1999 game against New Zealand?

9. Who scored 78 n.o. for England in their 1983 defeat of Pakistan at Lords?

10. Who scored 127 n.o. for India against Kenya in 1996?

11. Who scored a duck in the 1996 England versus South Africa fixture?

12. Who won the 1996 fixture between Holland and the United Arab Emirates?

13. Who scored 80 n.o. for West Indies in their 1983 semi-final against Pakistan?

14. Who was India's top bowler in the 1999 World Cup?

15. In which Australian city was the 1992 fixture between South Africa and Pakistan played?

ANSWERS 1. J.J. Crowe 2. Holland 3. K. R. Rutherford 4. Five 5. Keith Fletcher 6. Jacques Kallis 7. Majid Khan & Asif Iqbal 8. 116 9. Graeme Fowler 10. Sachin Tendulkar 11. Mike Atherton 12. U.A.E. 13. Viv Richards 14. Javangal Srinath 15. Brisbane.

Quiz 06 CRICKET WORLD CUP

1. Who scored 100 for Pakistan versus Sri Lanka in 1987 at Faislabad?

2. Who was the only player to score a duck in the 1983 World Cup final?

3. How many did Sourav Ganguly hit for India against Sri Lanka in 1999?

4. Which South African opener scored 81 n.o. against Australia in 1992?

5. By how many wickets did England beat Kenya in their 1999 Group A game?

6. Who were the two India openers in their 1975 defeat of East Africa?

7. Who took 4 for 64 for New Zealand against Pakistan in 1999?

8. Which England bowler took 4 for 8 in their 1979 humbling of Canada?

9. Who was England captain in their 1996 fixture against the United Arab Emirates?

10. Which New Zealand bowler took 5 for 25 against Sri Lanka at Bristol in 1983?

11. Which Sri Lankan bowler's figures for the 1999 World Cup were 1 for 168?

12. Who took 4 for 26 for Pakistan against Holland in 1996?

13. What did Holland score in reply to South Africa's 328 in their 1996 fixture?

14. Who was the West Indies top bowler in 1999?

15. Who took 4 for 30 for England in their 1992 win against Sri Lanka?

ANSWERS 1. Salim Malik 2. K. Azad 3. 183 4. K. Wessels 5. Nine 6. Gavaskar & Engineer 7. Geoffrey Allott 8. Chris Old 9. Mike Atherton 10. Richard Hadlee 11. Eric Upashantha 12. Waqar Younis 13. 168 14. Courtney Walsh 15. Chris Lewis.

Quiz 07   CRICKET WORLD CUP

1. What was the opening match of the 1987 World Cup?

2. Who took 3 for 28 for England against West Indies in Jaipur in 1987?

3. Who won the 1999 Super Six game between India and Pakistan?

4. Which Pakistan opener scored 114 against Zimbabwe in 1992?

5. Where was the 1999 Super Six game between South Africa & New Zealand played?

6. The match between Kenya and Zimbabwe in 1996 was declared void and replayed. Who won the replay?

7. Who hit 101 for Australia in their 1975 defeat of Sri Lanka?

8. Who took 3 for 34 against New Zealand for South Africa in their 1996 fixture?

9. Where was the 1979 Group B game between India and Sri Lanka played?

10. How many did Sri Lanka score in reply to South Africa's 199 in 1999?

11. Who scored 110 for Australia versus India at Trent Bridge in 1983?

12. Who took 3 for 60 for Zimbabwe against Sri Lanka in 1996?

13. Who scored 106 for India against Zimbabwe in their 1996 fixture?

14. Who hit 107 n.o. for Sri Lanka in the 1996 World Cup final?

15. Where in New Zealand was the 1992 fixture between West Indies & India played?

THE ULTIMATE SPORTS FACT AND QUIZ BOOK

Quiz 08 CRICKET WORLD CUP

1. Who took 10 wickets for Scotland in the 1999 World Cup?

2. How many did England make in 1999 in reply to India's 232?

3. Who hit 137 for India against Sri Lanka in their 1996 group match?

4. Who hit three sixes in his 41 for India against Zimbabwe at Ahmedabad in 1987?

5. By how many wickets did England beat West Indies in their opening encounter in 1987?

6. Who took 3 for 30 in 8.2. overs for England against West Indies in 1992?

7. Who scored 145 for Sri Lanka against Kenya in 1996?

8. Which West Indies batsmen made a last wicket stand of 64 to defeat Pakistan by one wicket in 1975?

9. Which West Indies bowler took 3 for 43 against New Zealand in their 1979 Group B game?

10. Who hit 132 n.o. for Zimbabwe against Australia in their 1999 game?

11. Who hit 105 n.o. for West Indies against Zimbabwe at Worcester in 1983?

12. Who scored 92 for New Zealand in 1996 against United Arab Emirates?

13. Who scored 62 n.o. and took 3 for 31 for South Africa versus Zimbabwe in 1992?

14. Who scored 126 n.o. for Australia against New Zealand at Chandigarh in 1987?

15. How many did Zimbabwe score in reply to Pakistan's 271 in their 1999 Super Six game?

ANSWERS 1. John Blain 2. 169 3. Sachin Tendulkar 4. Kapil Dev 5. Two 6. Chris Lewis 7. Aravinda de Silva 8. Andy Roberts & Deryck Murray 9. Andy Roberts 10. Neil Johnson 11. Gordon Greenidge 12. Roger Twose 13. P.N. Kirsten 14. Geoff Marsh 15. 123.

Quiz 09 — CRICKET WORLD CUP

1. By how many runs did Australia beat India in their opening encounter of the 1987 tournament?

2. Who scored the only run in the 1992 match betwen India & Sri Lanka?

3. Who hit 126 n.o. for Australia against India in 1996?

4. Who took 4 for 11 for England in 1975 in their defeat of East Africa?

5. Where was the 1979 Group A game between Australia & Canada played?

6. Which England bowler took 4 for 42 against New Zealand at Edgbaston in 1983 but still ended on the losing side?

7. Who took 2 for 41 and scored 55 n.o. for Pakistan against New Zealand in 1996?

8. Who was wicketkeeper for Pakistan in the 1992 World Cup?

9. What relation is current South African player G. Kirsten to P.N. Kirsten, top scorer in a 1992 World Cup game against New Zealand?

10. Which Scot scored 217 runs in the 1999 World Cup?

11. Who scored 142 for Zimbabwe versus New Zealand in Hyderabad in 1987?

12. Who was New Zealand's top wicket taker in the 1999 World Cup?

13. How many did West Indies score in their 1996 humiliation by Kenya?

14. Who hit 140 n.o. for India against Kenya in their 1999 Group A game?

15. Who did England play in the quarter-final of the 1996 World Cup?

ANSWERS 1. One 2. K. Srikkanth 3. Mark Waugh 4. John Snow 5. Edgbaston 6. Bob Willis 7. Salim Malik 8. Moin Khan 9. Brother 10. Gavin Hamilton 11. David Houghton 12. Geoffrey Allott 13. 93 14. Sachin Tendulkar 15. Sri Lanka.

Quiz 10   CRICKET WORLD CUP

1. What is the job of Scotland's batsman Bruce Patterson?

2. Who hit 114 n.o. for New Zealand in 1975 to help defeat India?

3. Which England opener went for a duck in 1979 against Pakistan?

4. Who hit 119 for West Indies versus India at the Oval in 1983?

5. How many of the Australian team bowled against Zimbabwe in their second encounter in 1987?

6. Who hit 84 for India against New Zealand in 1992 but ended up on the losing side?

7. Who was West Indies top scorer, with 205 runs, in the 1999 World Cup?

8. Which future captain scored 72 for West Indies against Zimbabwe in 1992?

9. Who took 4 for 31 against England for Pakistan in their first meeting in 1987?

10. Who was South Africa's top wicket taker in the 1999 World Cup?

11. By how many runs did Pakistan beat England in the 1992 World Cup final?

12. By how many runs did Pakistan beat Australia in their 1999 Group B game?

13. Who scored 78 for West Indies against Australia in 1975 to take the match award in their Group B game?

14. Which England player made his Limited OversInternational debut against New Zealand in a 1979 semi-final?

15. Who took 5 for 44 against Sri Lanka for Pakistan in their 1983 game at Headingley?

Quiz 11   CRICKET WORLD CUP

1. Which Australian bowler took 3-40 against Zimbabwe at Southampton in 1983?

2. Nasser Hussain was England's top scorer in the 1999 World Cup. How many runs did he make?

3. Of the four England batsmen who took the field against Australia at Poona in 1987, who low-scored with 40?

4. Who took 4 for 46 for West Indies versus New Zealand in their 1999 group game?

5. Who won the match award in the initial Australia versus Zimbabwe fixture in 1987?

6. Who did Pakistan play in the quarter-finals of the 1996 World Cup?

7. Who captained England against South Africa in 1992 and hit 77?

8. Who hit 97 for Pakistan against Sri Lanka in their 1975 game?

9. Who scored 93 for Pakistan against West Indies in a 1979 semi-final?

10. By how many runs did Australia beat India in 1992?

11. Who scored 110 for West Indies versus Pakistan at Karachi in 1987?

12. Who hit 42 off 52 balls for Pakistan versus England in their 2nd meeting in 1983?

13. Who was Australia's top batsman in 1999?

14. Who scored 110 for West Indies against Sri Lanka in 1992?

15. Who scored 367 runs for Zimbabwe in 1999?

Quiz 12   CRICKET WORLD CUP

1. Who scored 81 n.o. for Pakistan versus Scotland in 1999?

2. Which two West Indies players hit centuries versus Sri Lanka in their initial meeting in 1987?

3. Who took 5 for 35 for Pakistan against Bangladesh in 1999?

4. Who did South Africa play in a quarter-final of the 1996 World Cup?

5. Who scored 100 n.o. for India in their 1999 Super Six game against Australia?

6. Which England bowler took 3 for 8 in 8.2 overs against Pakistan in 1992 before the match was declared a no-result?

7. Which Australian bowler demolished England in a 1975 semi-final, taking 6-14?

8. Viv Richards scored 138 n.o. for the West Indies in the 1979 World Cup final. Who scored 86 for them in the same game?

9. Who scored 102 for England in their first 1983 game against New Zealand?

10. Who was Pakistan's top batsman in the 1999 World Cup?

11. Against which team did Sri Lanka register their only win of the 1983 World Cup?

12. Who scored 103 for India against New Zealand at Nagpur in 1987?

13. Who took 4 for 7 for New Zealand against Scotland in 1999?

14. By how many runs did Australia beat Pakistan in their 1987 semi-final?

15. Who was New Zealand's top batsman in 1999?

ANSWERS 1. Yousuf Youhana 2. Viv Richards & Desmond Haynes 3. Saqlain Mushtaq 4. West Indies 5. Ajaysinhji Jadeja 6. Derek Pringle 7. Gary Gilmour 8. Collis King 9. Allan Lamb 10. Saeed Anwar 11. New Zealand 12. Sunil Gavaskar 13. Chris Harris 14. 18 15. Roger Twose.

Quiz 13   CRICKET WORLD CUP

1. How many runs did Herschelle Gibbs score for South Africa in 1999?

2. Who scored 64 n.o. and took 2 for 26 for Sri Lanka against South Africa in 1992?

3. Which match in the 1999 Super Sixes was abandoned?

4. Where was the 1975 semi-final between West Indies and New Zealand played?

5. Where was the 1999 Super Six game between South Africa & Pakistan played?

6. Who scored 73 n.o. for New Zealand in their 1992 victory over England?

7. Which two Pakistan batsmen each scored 82 against Sri Lanka in their first 1983 game?

8. Which two West Indies batsmen got into the 90's in beating Australia by seven wickets at Lord's in 1983?

9. Who hit 84 for South Africa against India in 1992?

10. Who hit 130 for New Zealand against Australia in a 1996 quarter-final?

11. Which former England bowler was Scotland's bowling coach for the 1999 World Cup?

12. Which New Zealander took 3 for 15 against Zimbabwe in 1992?

13. Where did the 1999 game between West Indies and Bangladesh take place?

14. Both India's openers against New Zealand at Bangalore in 1987 were run out. Who were they?

15. Who hit 66 runs off 39 balls for Australia in 1992 against Zimbabwe?

Quiz 14   CRICKET WORLD CUP

1. Which West Indies batsman hit 102 to help defeat Australia in the first World Cup Final?

2. Who hit 106 n.o. for West Indies against India in 1979?

3. Who hit 82 for Kenya against Sri Lanka in their 1999 Group A game?

4. By how many runs did Zimbabwe beat Australia in their first 1983 meeting?

5. Which team did Eddo Brandes represent in the 1999 World Cup?

6. Who scored 175 n.o. for India against Zimbabwe in their second meeting in 1983?

7. What relationship are Zimbabwe's Andrew Flower and Grant Flower to each other?

8. What were Allan Donald's figures for South Africa in the 1999 Group A game against England?

9. How many of England's XI bowled in their first match against Sri Lanka in 1987?

10. Who scored 51 off 66 balls for Pakistan in their 1992 win against Sri Lanka?

11. Who scored 54 n.o. and took 1 for 37 for India versus Pakistan in 1992?

12. Who hit 115 for England in their 1987 semi-final against India?

13. Which England opener scored a duck in the 1987 final?

14. Where was the 1979 Group B game between New Zealand & Sri Lanka played?

15. Who hit 89 for India against West Indies in their first 1983 encounter?

ANSWERS 1. Clive Lloyd 2. Gordon Greenidge 3. Maurice Odumbe 4. 13 5. Zimbabwe 6. Kapil Dev 7. Brothers 8. 4 for 17 9. Nine 10. Salim Malik 11. Sachin Tendulkar 12. Graham Gooch 13. Tim Robinson 14. Trent Bridge 15. Yashpal Sharma.

Quiz 15   CRICKET WORLD CUP

1. By how many runs did England beat South Africa in a 1992 semi-final?

2. Who took 5 for 14 for Australia against the West Indies in 1999?

3. Who scored 61 for the West Indies against South Africa in 1992?

4. Who took 4 for 19 for India against Zimbabwe in their first meeting in 1987?

5. What team did Anil Kumble represent in the 1999 World Cup?

6. By how many runs did Zimbabwe beat India in their 1999 Group A game?

7. Which England bowler took 1 for 9 off 9 overs against Sri Lanka at Headingley in 1983?

8. Who scored 119 n.o. for Pakistan against New Zealand in 1992?

9. Who hit 101 for New Zealand versus England in their 1996 win?

10. Who scored 45 n.o. and took 2 wickets for South Africa against Pakistan in 1996?

11. Who was 80 n.o. for New Zealand in 1999 in their Group B game versus Australia?

12. Who won the 1999 Group A game between Sri Lanka & Zimbabwe?

13. By how many runs did Zimbabwe beat South Africa in their 1999 Group A game?

14. Who did Sri Lanka play in a 1996 semi-final?

15. Against whom did the United Arab Emirates play their first game in 1996?

ANSWERS 1. 19 2. Glenn McGrath 3. Gus Logie 4. M. Prabhakar 5. India 6. Three 7. Bob Willis 8. Ramiz Raja 9. Nathan Astle 10. Hansie Cronje 11. Roger Twose 12. Sri Lanka 13. 48 runs 14. India 15. South Africa.

MIXED BAG

Quiz 01   MIXED BAG

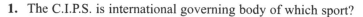

1. The C.I.P.S. is international governing body of which sport?

2. When were the world figure skating championships in roller skating first held?

3. Which town in England is home to the International Badminton Federation?

4. Who has won most University Boat races - Oxford or Cambridge?

5. Who was the men's 20km biathlon world champion in 1997?

6. Which Russian won the men's 100m freestyle at the 1994 & '98 world swimming championships?

7. In which year did Fred Davis win his last world professional billiards title?

8. At what sport was Paul Luxon the 1972 individual world champion?

9. Which Englishwoman was the 1996 & '97 world nine-ball pool champion?

10. Who was the first man to win the B.B.C. Sports Personality of the Year award twice?

11. Who was the 1995 world individual women's tenpin bowling champion?

12. In which year was skater Aleksandr Zaitsev born?

13. Which Belgian cyclist had 13 stage wins in the Vuelta A España in 1977?

14. Which world badminton champion coached the Malaysian team that won the 1992 Thomas Cup?

15. Which team lost 1995's World Bowl in American Football?

ANSWERS 1. Angling 2. 1947 3. Cheltenham 4. Cambridge 5. Ricco Gross 6. Aleksandr Popov 7. 1980 8. Trampolining 9. Allison Fisher 10. Henry Cooper 11. Debby Ship 12. 1952 13. Freddy Maertens 14. Yang Yang 15. Amsterdam Admirals.

THE ULTIMATE SPORTS FACT AND QUIZ BOOK

Quiz 02   MIXED BAG

1. Which Briton won the men's 200m breaststoke at the 1973 & '75 swimming world championships?

2. Who was the men's individual World Fresh Water angling champion in 1990 & '91?

3. Only once has the B.B.C. Sports Personality of the Year been won by two people. Which couple?

4. Where is the Cresta Run?

5. In which year did judo's Yasuhiro Yamashita retire, after winning 203 successive contests from 1977?

6. Which South African was 1976 world outdoor bowls men's singles champion?

7. What nationality was rower Mervyn Wood?

8. Which two countries contest the Strathcona Cup series in curling?

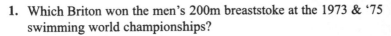

9. In which year was figure skater Katarina Witt born?

10. Which show jumper won the 1974 men's individual championship?

11. In which year was German equestrian Hans Günter Winkler born?

12. In which year were the Three-Day Eventing individual World Championships inaugurated?

13. What was the venue for the first World Championships in rowing in 1962?

14. The F.I.P.V. is the international governing body of which sport?

15. Torbjörn Blomdahl was the 1997 world three-cushion billiards champion. Which country did he represent?

ANSWERS 1. David Wilkie **2.** Bob Nudd **3.** Torvill & Dean **4.** St. Moritz **5.** 1985 **6.** Doug Watson **7.** Australian **8.** Scotland & Canada **9.** 1965 **10.** Hartwig Steenken **11.** 1926 **12.** 1966 **13.** Lucerne **14.** Pelota **15.** Sweden.

Quiz 03

MIXED BAG

1. Which Finnish team were the 1988 Eurobowl winners in American Football?

2. From which country is ex-world professional billards champion Robbie Foldvari?

3. Who was skipper of the 1998 Whitbread Round-the-World race-winning yacht *E F Language*?

4. In which sport would you compete for the Sam Maguire Cup?

5. Which Englishman was the 1995 world individual fly-fishing champion?

6. How many players are there in a shinty team?

7. In which year was the F.I.S., the international governing body of skiing, founded?

8. How many players are there in a team in Australian Rules Football?

9. In which country were the first modern rules of badminton codified?

10. Up to 1997, which two countries had won the Swaythling Cup in table tennis 12 times each?

11. In bobsleighing, why were the world four-man bob championships not held in 1967?

12. In which year was the first official tournament in beach volleyball?

13. Who scored a perfect game of 300 in the 1987 world tenpin bowling championship?

14. In which year was darts player Jocky Wilson born?

15. When were the alpine skiing world championships first held?

ANSWERS 1. Helsinki Roosters 2. Australia 3. Paul Cayard 4. Gaelic football 5. Jeremy Hermann 6. 12 7. 1924 8. 18 9. India 10. Hungary & China 11. Because of a thaw 12. 1948 13. Rick Steelsmith 14. 1950 15. 1931.

Quiz 04 MIXED BAG

1. At which cricket ground is Australian Rules Football's Grand Final played?

2. What is the international governing body of archery?

3. Which country is home to the international governing body of basketball, F.I.B.A.?

4. Who was the last Englishman to win the world men's singles table tennis championships?

5. Andrey Tchmil won the 1994 Paris - Roubaix cycle race. Which country did he represent?

6. In which year was billiards player Rex Williams born?

7. From which country do the men's handball team Metaloplastika Sabac come?

8. In which country was swimmer David Wilkie born?

9. Which country won the 1998 men's hockey World Cup?

10. What nationality is swimmer Tracey Wickham?

11. What distance is swum in the swimming discipline of modern pentathlon?

12. In which year was show jumper John Whitaker born?

13. Why were the 1995 alpine skiing championships cancelled?

14. In which country was alpine skier Hanni Wenzel born?

15. Which Briton won the 1968 women's European Championship in show jumping?

ANSWERS 1. Melbourne **2.** F.I.T.A. **3.** Germany **4.** Johnny Leach **5.** Moldova **6.** 1933 **7.** Yugoslavia **8.** Sri Lanka **9.** Netherlands **10.** Australian **11.** 300m **12.** 1955 **13.** Lack of snow **14.** Germany **15.** Anneli Drummond-Hay.

Quiz 05   MIXED BAG

1. There are three bow divisions in world field archery. What are they?

2. At what sport does Canada's Ed Werenich excel?

3. How often is the Thomas Cup for men's badminton teams held?

4. In which year did swimmer Johnny Weissmuller die?

5. Which Dane won the Flèche Wallonne in cycling in 1998?

6. In which U.S. state was highboard diver Robert Webster born?

7. Tom Stiansen won the 1997 men's alpine skiing slalom world championships. Which country does he represent?

8. On which horse did Virginia Leng win the 1993 Badminton Horse Trials?

9. At which sport was Simon Fairweather world individual men's champion in 1991?

10. What is the weight in kilograms of the rifle used in the biathlon?

11. In which year was the World Croquet Federation formed?

12. How many players are in a netball team?

13. Lucien van Impe won the 1976 Tour de France. Which country did he represent?

14. In which year was the American Powerboat Association formed?

15. In which sport did Labegarce win the 1997 British Open?

ANSWERS 1. Bare bow, recurve & compound 2. Curling 3. Every two years 4. 1984 5. Bo Hamburger 6. California 7. Norway 8. Houdini 9. Archery 10. 4.54 kg 11. 1986 12. Seven 13. Belgium 14. 1903 15. Polo.

Quiz 06   MIXED BAG

1. As what was the Australian Football League, which covers Australian Rules Football, known until 1990?

2. When was the European Badminton Union formed?

3. In basketball which men's club team has won the European Championships most times?

4. In which sport is the Leonard Trophy awarded?

5. Who won the canoe sailing world championships in 1993 & '96?

6. What is the name of the curved stick in shinty?

7. What is the nickname of the Paris-Roubaix cycle race?

8. In which year was the first boardsailing world championship?

9. Which Irish show jumper won the 1995 European Championships?

10. In what sport is the St. Bride Vase awarded?

11. Which Russian gymnast was women's horse vault winner at the 1978 world championship?

12. In which year were the first official world championships in beach volleyball?

13. On which horse did Mark Phillips win the 1981 Badminton Horse Trials?

14. Which Briton won the Volvo World Cup in show jumping in 1991?

15. How many players are in a bandy team?

ANSWERS 1. Victorian Football League **2.** 1967 **3.** Real Madrid **4.** Bowls **5.** Robin Wood **6.** The caman **7.** The Hell of the North **8.** 1973 **9.** Peter Charles **10.** Table tennis **11.** Nelli Kim **12.** 1997 **13.** Lincoln **14.** John Whitaker **15.** Eleven.

Quiz 07   MIXED BAG

1. How many shooting competitions are there in the men's 10km biathlon?

2. Who was world indoor bowls women's singles champion in 1973 & '77?

3. In which year did Gastone Nencini win the Tour de France?

4. Which Briton won the 1973 men's show jumping European Championship?

5. In which country is I.P.F., the international governing body of powerlifting, based?

6. Athletic Terrassa won the 1998 European Cup in men's hockey. Which country are they from?

7. At what sport did Osamu Watanabe excel?

8. In which year were the women's world championships in modern pentathlon first held?

9. When were the Badminton Horse Trials first held?

10. What nationality is alpine skier Maria Walliser?

11. In which sport are Daugava Riga the most successful European women's team?

12. Which Briton won the 1960 single-handed transatlantic yacht race?

13. Until 1997, the USSR had won the women's European basketball championship 21 times. How many times had the next most successful team won it?

14. What nationality was cyclist Rik van Looy?

15. Where in Surrey are the BDO world professional darts championships held?

ANSWERS 1. Two 2. Elsie Wilke 3. 1960 4. Paddy McMahon 5. Sweden 6. Spain 7. Wrestling 8. 1981 9. 1949 10. Swiss 11. Basketball 12. Francis Chichester 13. Once 14. Belgian 15. Lakeside Country Club, Frimley Green.

Quiz 08   MIXED BAG

1. What did Yuriy Vlasov become famous as on retiring from weightlifting?

2. At which sport was Kim Du-ri world women's individual champion in 1997?

3. In which year were the canoe slalom world championships first held?

4. Which country won the men's 4 x 100m medley relay at the world swimming championships from 1973-'94?

5. Which Swiss rider won the 1975 & '77 individual dressage European Championships?

6. In which year was the Vuelta a España cycling race first held?

7. What was the Hundred Guinea Cup a forerunner of?

8. In which year was the British Cyclo-Cross Association formed?

9. Sue Shotton was women's individual champion at which sport in 1984?

10. What was the maiden name of show jumper Jean Davenport?

11. Which three events comprise the triathlon?

12. In which year was show jumping's Queen Elizabeth II Cup inaugurated?

13. Which Briton won newspaper *L'Equipe*'s sportsperson of the year award, the Champion des Champions, in 1995?

14. Which Welshman was the 1995 B.DO. world professional darts champion?

15. Which British woman rode 47.411 km in breaking the 1 hour record in cycling in 1995?

ANSWERS 1. A poet 2. Archery 3. 1949 4. U.S.A. 5. Christine Stückelberger 6. 1935 7. The America's Cup 8. 1954 9. 1949 10. Jean Goodwin 11. Swimming, cycling & running 12. 1949 13. Jonathan Edwards 14. Richie Burnett 15. Yvonne McGregor.

THE ULTIMATE SPORTS FACT AND QUIZ BOOK

Quiz 09

MIXED BAG

1. Bury Fen and Haarlem contested the first international match, in 1891, of which sport?

2. Who was the men's K1 slalom world champion in canoeing from 1981-'85?

3. Which Scot was the 1997 B.D.O. world professional darts champion?

4. What is the target area in épée fencing?

5. Which show jumper won the 1990 world individual world championships?

6. Which American won the men's springboard diving event from 1973-'78 at the world swimming championships?

7. In which city was the first European judo club formed?

8. Which boat won the 1995 America's Cup?

9. In which year were the first karate world championships held?

10. When were the triathlon world championships inaugurated?

11. In which sport is a chistera attached to the arm?

12. In which U.S. city was swimmer Chris von Saltza born?

13. In which year was the Henley Royal Regatta inaugurated?

14. How often is the Whitbread Round-the-World race held in sailing?

15. Where is the British show jumping derby held?

ANSWERS 1. Bandy 2. Richard Fox 3. Les Wallace 4. The whole body 5. Eric Navet 6. Phil Boggs 7. London 8. Black Magic 9. 1970 10. 1989 11. Pelota 12. San Francisco 13. 1839 14. Every four years 15. Hickstead.

Quiz 10   MIXED BAG

1. Up to 1997, the U.S.S.R. had won the men's European basketball championship 14 times. Which country had won it seven times?

2. In which year did Susi Susanti first win the world badminton women's singles title?

3. In which South American country were the 1982 swimming world championships held?

4. In which year were the world indoor bowls singles championships for men instituted?

5. At which sport was Briton Stewart Matthews individual world champion in 1980?

6. In which year was the first curling club formed in the U.S.?

7. Which ice skater was the 1976 B.B.C. Sports Personality of the Year?

8. On which horse did David Broome win the 1966 King George V Gold Cup?

9. Which America's Cup-winning skipper invented Contract Bridge?

10. Great Britain won the team dressage at the 1963 European Championship. Which team has won it since?

11. At which sport did Bohumil Vana excel?

12. Rüsselsheimer won the 1998 European Cup in women's hockey. Which country are they from?

13. At which sport did Jean Urruty excel?

14. In what sport has the Little Brown Jug race been run since 1946?

15. In which Italian city was cycling's Grand Prix des Nations held in 1991?

ANSWERS 1. Yugoslavia 2. 1993 3. Ecuador 4. 1979 5. Trampolining 6. 1832 7. John Curry 8. Mister Softee 9. Harold Vanderbilt 10. Germany 11. Table tennis 12. Germany 13. Pelota 14. Harness racing 15. Pisa.

Quiz 11   MIXED BAG

1. How many pockets are there on a three-cushion billiards table?

2. In canoeing what does K, as in K1, stand for?

3. Of the six world croquet championships between 1990-'97, how many did Robert Fulford win?

4. At what sport did Frank Urso excel?

5. In which county is Cowdray Park, home of polo's British Open?

6. In which German city was dressage rider Nicole Uphoff born?

7. At which sport did Robert Fahey become world champion in 1994?

8. Which Chinaman won the 1998 All-England badminton singles title?

9. In which country was hockey player Udam Singh born?

10. Raymond Poulidor never won the Tour de France. How many times did he finish second?

11. Which country did Nordic skier Vegard Ulvang represent?

12. In which year were there two University Boat Races?

13. Which ice skater was the 1980 B.B.C. Sports Personality of the Year?

14. What game was originally known as 'kitten-ball' or 'mush-ball'?

15. In which Australian city were the 1998 swimming world championships held?

Quiz 12 — MIXED BAG

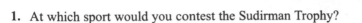

1. At which sport would you contest the Sudirman Trophy?

2. In the six competitions in the men's C1 canoe slalom at the world championships from 1979-'89, how many did Jon Lugbill win?

3. In which sport is the MacRobertson International Shield played for?

4. What is the starting point of the single-handed transatlantic yacht race?

5. Which show jumper rode Towerlands Anglezark to victory in the 1985 & '87 King George V Gold Cup?

6. Pok-ta-Pok was a 10c B.C. version of which modern ball game?

7. Which country houses the International Biathlon Union, the sport's international governing body?

8. How often are the world outdoor bowls championships held?

9. Which Briton won the men's 100m butterfly at the 1987 European Championships in swimming?

10. Who holds the record for most career stage wins in the Tour de France?

11. When was the English Table Tennis Association formed?

12. How long in metres is the beam in women's gymnastics?

13. In which sport is the Hawaii Ironman competition held?

14. What is the game of pelota called in the U.S.A.?

15. Which country won the men's volleyball title at the 1997 European Championships?

ANSWERS 1. Badminton 2. Five 3. Croquet 4. Plymouth, England 5. Malcolm Pyrah 6. Basketball 7. Austria 8. Every four years 9. Andrew Jameson 10. Eddy Merckx 11. 1927 12. 5 metres 13. Triathlon 14. Jai-alai 15. Netherlands.

Quiz 13   MIXED BAG

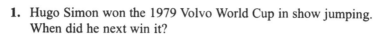

1. Hugo Simon won the 1979 Volvo World Cup in show jumping. When did he next win it?

2. Which two countries contest the Gordon International Medal series in curling?

3. Which country houses the headquarters of the International Bandy Federation?

4. Which Welshman was the 1972 world outdoor bowls men's singles champion?

5. When was the world professional billiards championship first held?

6. Which Irishman won the Milan - San Remo cycle race in 1986 & '92?

7. Who won the 1995 Individual European Championships in Three-Day Eventing?

8. Which country has won the Corbillon Cup, for women's table tennis, the most?

9. In which European country is the home of the International Korfball Federation?

10. In which U.S. state was cyclist Rebecca Twigg born?

11. The Camanachd Cup is the premier competition in which sport?

12. In which sport might you see a Tsukahara?

13. Who won the 1997 men's alpine skiing giant slalom at the world championships?

14. In which year was U.S. swimmer Mike Troy born?

15. Sam Allen and Jeremy Henry were world outdoor bowls men's pairs champions in 1996. Which country did they represent?

ANSWERS 1. 1996 2. Canada & the U.S. 3. Sweden 4. Malwyn Evans 5. 1870 6. Sean Kelly 7. Lucy Thompson 8. China 9. Netherlands 10. Hawaii 11. Shinty 12. Gymnastics 13. Michael von Grünigen 14. 1940 15. Ireland.

Quiz 14   MIXED BAG

1. How often are the world basketball championships held?

2. Margaret Johnston and Phyllis Nolan were world outdoor bowls pairs champions in 1988, '92 & '96. Which country did they represent?

3. When was the national rifle association formed in the U.S.A.?

4. Which country won the men's volleyball titles at the 1993 & '95 European Championships?

5. When was the super-giant slalom first contested at the alpine skiing world championships?

6. In which year was skater Jayne Torvill born?

7. Who was the first man to win the downhill alpine skiing world championships twice?

8. What was the maiden name of equestrian Janou Tissot?

9. In which year were the first kendo world championships held?

10. Mark Kirchner was the men's world 10km & 20km biathlon champion in 1991. Which country did he represent?

11. Which German won the men's 1,500m freestyle at the European Championships in swimming from 1989-'95?

12. Which country has won the men's curling world championships the most?

13. How many players are on a water polo team?

14. Hugo Koblet won the 1951 Tour de France. Which country did he represent?

15. Which swimmer was the 1962 B.B.C. Sports Personality of the Year?

ANSWERS 1. Every four years 2. Ireland 3. 1871 4. Italy 5. 1987 6. 1957 7. Walter Prager 8. Janou Lefèbvre 9. 1970 10. Germany 11. Jörg Hoffmann 12. Canada 13. Seven 14. Switzerland 15. Anita Lonsbrough.

Quiz 15   MIXED BAG

1. In which year was bandy included as a demonstration sport at the winter Olympics?

2. In canoeing what does C, as in C1, stand for?

3. How many hoops are there in a game of croquet?

4. Who was the first non-Frenchman to win the Tour de France?

5. Which Briton won the men's 100m breaststroke at the European Championships in swimming from 1985-'89?

6. The Giro d'Italia cycle race was first held in 1909. When did a non-Italian first win it?

7. Which Briton was world individual men's triathlon champion in 1993 & '94?

8. Who was 1995 & '97 world matchplay darts champion?

9. Which cyclist won the 1965 B.B.C. Sports Personality of the Year award?

10. Eric Srecki was a 1995 & '97 world fencing champion. In which discipline?

11. Which country have been men's water polo European champions most times?

12. Which Irishman won the 1998 British show jumping derby?

13. Which Irishwoman won the 1986 individual world championships in show jumping?

14. Which Briton won cycling's Grand Prix des Nations in 1996?

15. Which country houses the W.C.B.S., the international governing body of billiards?

ANSWERS 1. 1952 2. Canadian canoe 3. Six 4. Francois Faber 5. Adrian Moorhouse 6. 1950 7. Spencer Smith 8. Phil Taylor 9. Tommy Simpson 10. Épée 11. Hungary 12. Eric Holstein 13. Gail Greenhough 14. Chris Boardman 15. Malaysia.

Quiz 16   MIXED BAG

1. Joop Zoetemelk won the 1980 Tour de France. Which country did he represent?

2. In which year were the canoe racing world championships first held?

3. How many miles long was the 1926 Tour de France?

4. Which Briton won the men's 200m breaststroke at the European Championships in swimming from 1989-'93?

5. How many players are there in a Gaelic football team?

6. In which year were the water-skiing world championships first held?

7. Who did Natalya Bestemianova & Andrey Bukin succeed in 1985 as world ice dance figure skating champions?

8. What are the two forms of wrestling at international level?

9. What colour belt does a 12th Dan wear in judo?

10. Which three-day eventer was the 1971 B.B.C. Sports Personality of the Year?

11. The French game of Jeu Provençal was the forerunner of which game?

12. What nationality is cyclist Guillermo Timoner?

13. Who won the Paris - Nice cycle race from 1982-'88?

14. In which year were the world target archery championships first held?

15. Who was the first president of the English Bowling Association?

ANSWERS 1. Netherlands 2. 1938 3. 3,569 miles 4. Nick Gillingham 5. 15 6. 1949 7. Torvill & Dean 8. Freestyle & Greco-Roman 9. White 10. Princess Anne 11. Pétanque (Boules) 12. Spanish 13. Sean Kelly 14. 1931 15. W.G. Grace.

Quiz 17   MIXED BAG

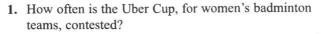

1. How often is the Uber Cup, for women's badminton teams, contested?

2. The W.S.F., W.P.A. & U.M.B. are divisions of which sport's governing body?

3. Who was the 1995 men's individual tenpin bowling champion?

4. In which year was the Liverpool Velocipede Club formed?

5. Which countries met in September 1925 in the first international handball fixture?

6. Which Briton won the 1973 women's European championship in show jumping?

7. Who were men's world coxless pairs rowing champions from 1991-'95?

8. Which Russian gymnast was women's horse vault winner at the 1974 world championships?

9. Which Briton won the 1998 British Open squash tournament?

10. When did India last win the men's hockey World Cup?

11. When were the world professional surfing championships first held?

12. On which horse did Mark Phillips win the 1974 Badminton Horse Trials?

13. What cup is awarded to the winners of the men's doubles table tennis title at the world championships?

14. In which country is the Tour of Flanders cycle race held?

15. How many points are in a set in a single F.I.T.A. round in archery?

ANSWERS 1. Every two years 2. Billiards 3. Marc Doi 4. 1867 5. Austria & Germany 6. Ann Moore 7. Steven Redgrave & Matthew Pinsent 8. Olga Korbut 9. Peter Nicol 10. 1975 11. 1970 12. Columbus 13. The Iran Cup 14. Belgium 15. 360.

THE ULTIMATE SPORTS FACT AND QUIZ BOOK

Quiz 18 MIXED BAG

1. The Union Cycliste International, world cycling's governing body, is based in which country?

2. Joyce Cave won the 1922 women's British Open squash tournament. Who won it in 1923?

3. Which Russian gymnast was the women's 1970 & '74 floor exercise champion at the world championships?

4. Which country were men's volleyball world champions in 1990 & '94?

5. Who was the first president of the International Amateur Handball Federation?

6. At what team sport does American Steve Timmons excel?

7. Who won the 1998 women's hockey World Cup?

8. What nationality is swimmer Petra Thümer?

9. In which year were the men's world championships in modern pentathlon first held?

10. Who was America's first world champion in gymnastics?

11. Which two teams compete for the Cup of the Americas in polo?

12. What nationality is cyclist Lothar Thoms?

13. Who was the 1995 & '97 world women's real tennis singles champion?

14. Why was Eugene Christophe delayed by three hours in the 1913 Tour de France, causing him to lose the race?

15. Which team has won the men's European championship in roller hockey the most times?

ANSWERS 1. Switzerland **2.** Nancy Cave **3.** Lyudmila Tourischeva **4.** Italy **5.** Avery Brundage **6.** Volleyball **7.** Australia **8.** German **9.** 1949 **10.** Kurt Thomas **11.** U.S.A. & Argentina **12.** German **13.** Penny Lumley **14.** He had to repair his bike **15.** Portugal.

Quiz 19

MIXED BAG

1. In which year was the Tour de France first held?

2. Which Frenchman won the 1964 & '76 single-handed transatlantic yacht races?

3. What are the initials of the international governing body of tenpin bowling?

4. When was the United States Squash Racquets Association formed?

5. Which Irish show jumper won the 1969 European championship for women?

6. In what sport is the G. Geist Prize awarded?

7. On which horse did Mark Phillips win the 1973 Burghley Horse Trials?

8. The Netherlands-based T.W.I.F. is the international governing body of which sport?

9. Which men's handball team won the European Cup from 1996-'8?

10. Who became world chess champion in 1960?

11. In what sport is the Hambletonian Stakes run?

12. At what sport was Toshiaki Tanaka a world champion?

13. In which country are the headquarters of F.I.H., the international governing body of hockey?

14. On which horse did Luigi Cartesegna win the 1955 King George V Gold Cup in show jumping?

15. What sport did Major Ernst Killander devise in 1918?

ANSWERS 1. 1903 2. Eric Tabarly 3. F.I.Q. 4. 1907 5. Iris Kellett 6. Table tennis 7. Maid Marion 8. Tug-of-war 9. F.C. Barcelona 10. Mikhail Tal 11. Harness racing 12. Table tennis 13. Belgium 14. Brando 15. Orienteering.

THE ULTIMATE SPORTS FACT AND QUIZ BOOK

Quiz 20 MIXED BAG

1. Which is the oldest of the Belgian classic cycle races?

2. When was the world open championships in squash first held?

3. When were the individual dressage world championships inaugurated?

4. What sport developed from the game of mintonette?

5. Which team has won the women's handball European Cup most times?

6. At what sport was Koki Taiho considered the greatest exponent?

7. How often is the men's hockey World Cup held?

8. What nationality is gymnast Ecaterina Szabo?

9. In which city were the first men's lacrosse world championships held?

10. What nationality is Nordic skier Gunde Svan?

11. What distance is run in the cross-country section of modern pentathlon?

12. In which German city was swimmer Astrid Strauss born?

13. Which country won the 1995 netball world championships?

14. At what sport was Øyvin Thon a world champion?

15. What was the nickname of swimmer Elaine Tanner?

Quiz 21

MIXED BAG

1. Which Australian won the 1997 men's world open squash championship?

2. Which cycle race is known as 'The Race of Falling Leaves'?

3. Which Frenchman won the 1992 & '96 single-handed transatlantic yacht races?

4. How often are the European dressage championships held?

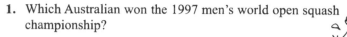

5. Which race is the culmination of the Admiral's Cup in sailing?

6. How many a side are there in the game of polo?

7. Who has won the President's Cup in croquet most times?

8. Which team has won the All-Ireland championships in Gaelic football most times?

9. Which Irishman won the 1988 Vuelta A España?

10. In gymnastics, how long in centimetres are the parallel bars?

11. Which British show jumper won the 1995 Volvo World Cup?

12. Which Russian won the men's highboard platform diving event at the 1994 & '98 world swimming championships?

13. Who has won the men's figure skating world championships most times?

14. Which Briton was the world men's individual triathlon champion in 1992 & '96?

15. Which Briton won the 1970 Three-Day Event individual world championships?

ANSWERS 1. Rodney Eyles 2. Tour of Lombardy 3. Loïck Peyron 4. Every two years 5. The Fastnet Race 6. Four 7. Nigel Aspinall 8. Kerry 9. Sean Kelly 10. 350 cm 11. Nick Skelton 12. Dmitriy Sautin 13. Ulrich Salchow 14. Simon Lessing 15. Mary Gordon-Watson.

Quiz 22   MIXED BAG

1. Which American woman won the 400m & 800m freestyle events at the 1991 swimming world championships?

2. Which sport is known as 'the roaring game'?

3. Fu Mingxia won the women's highboard platform diving event at the 1991 & '94 swiming world championships. Which country did she represent?

4. Which two teams contested the Westchester Cup in polo in 1886?

5. What is the Milan - San Remo cycling race known as in Italy?

6. What game was originally known as 'football in the water'?

7. Which item of sports equipment did Belgian Joseph Merlin invent in the mid 18th century?

8. Which swimmer was 1958 B.B.C. Sports Personality of the Year?

9. Who was the first man to win the alpine combination competition twice at the skiing world championship?

10. What nationality is cyclist Jean Stablinski?

11. What is the area of the mat in gymnastics floor exercises?

12. What nationality is biathlon expert Magnar Solberg?

13. What are the three activities in freestyle skiing?

14. At which public school was croquet player John Solomon when he made his tournament debut?

15. Who won the women's world figure skating championship titles in 1996 & '98?

ANSWERS 1. Janet Evans 2. Curling 3. China 4. U.S.A. & Great Britain 5. The Primavera 6. Water polo 7. Roller skate 8. Ian Black 9. Anton Seelos 10. French 11. 144 sq. metres 12. Norwegian 13. Aerials, ballet and moguls 14. Charterhouse 15. Michelle Kwan.

Quiz 23

MIXED BAG

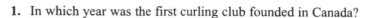

1. In which year was the first curling club founded in Canada?

2. On which horse did H.R.H. Princess Anne win the 1971 Individual European Championships in Three-Day Eventing?

3. In which city are the All-Ireland championship finals in Gaelic football held?

4. Which Briton won the 1997 men's 200m freestyle swimming event at the European Championships?

5. Which Frenchwoman won the alpine combination competition from 1962-'66 at the skiing world championships?

6. Which show jumper was the 1960 B.B.C. Sports Personality of the Year?

7. The annual Iditarod Trail sled dog race is held in which U.S. state?

8. In which year was chess world champion Boris Spassky born?

9. When did the snowboarding world championship begin?

10. Who was the 1920 & '23 world billiards champion?

11. How often are the world tenpin bowling championships held?

12. Who was the 1976 world men's figure skating champion?

13. In which year was the English Rowing Association founded?

14. Which men's squash player was unbeaten between April 1981 and November 1986?

15. In which English city were the canoe marathon world championships first held in 1988?

ANSWERS 1. 1807 2. Doublet 3. Dublin 4. Paul Palmer 5. Marielle Goitschel 6. David Broome 7. Alaska 8. 1937 9. 1993 10. Willie Smith 11. Every four years 12. John Curry 13. 1903 14. Jahangir Khan 15. Nottingham.

THE ULTIMATE SPORTS FACT AND QUIZ BOOK

Quiz 24   MIXED BAG

1. Which country has won the women's world curling championship the most times?

2. When was F.I.N.A., the international governing body of swimming, diving and water polo founded?

3. In which year did Stephen Roche win the Giro d'Italia?

4. What trophy is awarded to the winners of the women's doubles at the table tennis world championships?

5. Which Australian won the 1997/8 world masters darts tournament?

6. In which year were the Taekwondo world championships held?

7. Which country houses the F.E.I., the international governing body of equestrian sports?

8. When were the trampolining world championships first held?

9. How often are the orienteering world championships held?

10. What was the maiden name of show jumper Alison Dawes?

11. Which country were women's volleyball world champions in 1962, '67 & '74?

12. How many people comprise a korfball team?

13. In which West Yorkshire town was rider Harvey Smith born?

14. Which three regattas comprise the F.I.S.A. rowing World Cup, first held in 1997?

15. Which show jumper has won the King George V Gold Cup most times?

ANSWERS 1. Canada 2. 1908 3. 1987 4. The W.J. Pope Trophy 5. Graham Hunt 6. 1973 7. Switzerland 8. 1964 9. Every two years 10. Alison Westwood 11. Japan 12. Eight 13. Bingley 14. Munich, Paris & Lucerne 15. David Broome.

Quiz 25   MIXED BAG

1. Which Russian won the 1996 Giro d'Italia cycle race?

2. What distance did Chris Boardman travel in breaking the 1 hour record in cycling in 1996?

3. By what score did Phil Taylor beat Dennis Priestley in the 1997/8 W.D.C. darts world championship final?

4. Which show jumper has won the Queen Elizabeth II Cup most times?

5. How wide in centimetres is the beam in women's gymnastics?

6. In which South American country were the 1975 swimming world championships held?

7. Which English team won the 1996 European Cup Winners' Cup in women's hockey?

8. Who was the last British man to win the table tennis European Championships?

9. Longe paume was the forerunner of which game?

10. How often is the volleyball World Cup held?

11. How long is the University Boat Race in miles & yards?

12. At which sport did Cecil Smith of Llano County, Texas excel?

13. How many players are in a softball team?

14. What nationality is table tennis champion Anna Sipos?

15. What is the finishing point of the single-handed transatlantic yacht race?

ANSWERS 1. Pavel Tonkov 2. 56.3 km 3. 6-0 4. Liz Edgar 5. 10 centimetres 6. Colombia 7. Hightown 8. John Hilton 9. Real tennis 10. Every four years 11. 4 miles, 374 yards 12. Polo 13. Nine 14. Hungarian 15. Newport, Rhode Island.

QUIZ SCORE SHEET

QUIZ SCORE SHEET

THE ULTIMATE SPORTS FACT AND QUIZ BOOK

THE FACTS

FACTS CONTENTS

THE ULTIMATE SPORTS FACT AND QUIZ BOOK

TENNIS

TENNIS

Brisbane last hosted the Australian championships in 1969.

Albert Costa won the 1998 German Open singles title.

Andrei Medvedev is romantically linked with German tennis star Anke Huber.

Serena Williams pulled out of the 1999 Wimbledon tournament with influenza.

Carlos Moya won the 1998 Monte Carlo Open singles title at Monaco.

Nathalie Tauziat beat Dominique Van Roost in the 1999 Wimbledon ladies singles tournament.

Ion Tiriac was in charge of marketing at the Hannover ATP Tour World Championship in 1998.

Florida-born tennis player Jose de Armas lives in Caracas.

Boris Becker declined the presidency of the German Tennis Federation in 1998.

French tennis player Olivier Delaitre was ranked No. 41 in 1991.

At one stage in 1998 Andre Agassi was ranked 141 in the world.

Natasha Zvereva was born in Minsk.

Petr Korda took the 1998 Australian Open singles title at the age of 30.

TENNIS

Belgian tennis player Sabine Appelmans was born in Aalst in 1972.

The 1998 U.S. Open men's singles final was the first all-Australian affair since 1970.

Olga Barabanschikova was born in Minsk but has lived in Ealing since the age of 12.

Arantxa Sanchez-Vicario won the French Open singles for the third time in 1998.

Yayuk Basuki is ranked Indonesian No. 1.

Lindsay Davenport became the first native-born American to win the U.S. open singles since 1982 when she took the 1998 title.

Dutch tennis player Marion Bollegraf was born in Den Bosch in 1964.

Germany's Marlene Weingartner lost 6-0, 6-0 in the 1999 Wimbledon ladies singles to Monica Seles on June 23rd and 6-0, 6-0 in the Wimbledon ladies doubles on June 24th.

Thomas Endqvist was 1991 I.T.F. junior boys' singles world champion.

Kristina Brandi's father Joe was a former coach to Pete Sampras.

Cara Black was 1997 I.T.F. junior girls' singles world champion.

French tennis player Nathalie Dechy was born in Guadeloupe.

TENNIS

131 countries participated in the 1998 Davis Cup.

There were eight different Grand Slam winners in 1998.

434,807 people watched the 1998 Australian Open.

Alberto Berasategui trained at the Harry Hopman Academy in Florida.

Margaret Court beat Billie Jean King 14-12, 11-9 in the 1970 Wimbledon ladies singles final.

Pete Sampras won $3,931,497 in 1998.

The French tennis championships have been played at the Stade Roland Garros since 1928.

Full seeding at Wimbledon began in 1927.

Perth last hosted the Australian championships in 1921.

Mariaan De Swardt was born in Johannesburg.

Alex Corretja won the 1998 Dubai Tennis Open singles title.

Mahesh Bhupati was ranked 944 in 1992.

The Wimbledon championships were not held between 1940-45.

W. Renshaw beat H.F. Lawford three times in a row in the Wimbledon men's singles final from 1884-86.

The Wimbledon website had a record 145,478 hits per minute during the Krajicek/Ivanisevic semi-final in 1998.

TENNIS

Roy Emerson beat Fred Stolle in the 1964 & 1965 Wimbledon men's singles finals.

Bjorn Borg beat Jimmy Connors in the 1977 & 1978 Wimbledon men's singles finals.

Jelena Dokic lives in New South Wales, Australia.

Albert Costa won the 1999 Estoril Open singles title.

Greg Rusedski won the 1998 E.E.C. singles championship.

Ilie Nastase was ranked No. 1 in the world for 40 weeks.

German tennis star Anke Huber was runner-up in the 1996 Australian Open singles tournament.

Steffi Graf won $412,577 in 1998.

Anna Kournikova was born in 1981.

Tracy Austin was world No. 1 for 22 weeks in total.

Alberto Berasategui won the the 1998 Estoril Open singles championship.

Joannette Kruger is coached by her mother Petro Kruger.

From 1985-91 Boris Becker only failed to appear once in the Wimbledon men's singles final, in 1987.

TENNIS

Swede Jonas Bjorkman was a former national junior champion.

John McEnroe only lost four games in defeating Jimmy Connors in the 1984 Wimbledon men's singles final.

The Hyundai Hopman Cup is held in Perth.

Tim Henman was born on 6th September 1974.

Roy Emerson beat Fred Stolle in the 1964 & 1965 Australian men's singles finals.

TENNIS

Mrs. R. Lambert Chambers beat Miss D.P. Boothby 6-0, 6-0 in the 1911 Wimbledon women's singles final.

Felix Mantilla won the 1998 Samsung Open singles title in Bournemouth.

Greg Rusedski lost 4-6, 7-6, 3-6, 6-1, 6-8 to Jim Courier in the final rubber of Britain's 1999 Davis Cup game with the U.S.

The U.S. Open has been held at Flushing Meadow since 1928.

Florencia Labat was born in Buenos Aires in 1971.

Alex Corretja's mother and father are called Luis and Luisa.

Christchurch, New Zealand, hosted the Australian Championships in 1906.

Cédric Pioline's appearance in the 1999 Nottingham Open was his first final since April 1998.

Yevgeny Kafelnikov was born in Sochi, Russia.

Byron Black won the 1999 Indian Open men's single title.

The 283 tournaments on the I.T.F. women's circuit in 1998 yielded $5,025,000 in prize money.

Mark Philippoussis was leading Pete Sampras 6-4, 1-2 when he retired from their 1999 Wimbledon quarter-final.

TENNIS

Two of the ladies singles semi-finalists at Wimbledon 1999 were unseeded.

The Copa Ericsson is a series of tournaments in South America.

Mats Wilander beat Pat Cash over 5 sets to win the 1988 Australian Open men's singles title.

Miss E.F. Boyd was the Australian ladies singles runner-up from 1922-26.

Serge Bruguera won the 1993 French Open title in five sets against Jim Courier.

Patrick Rafter turned professional in 1991.

Pete Sampras leads 6-0 in his meetings with Tim Henman following their meeting at Wimbledon in 1999.

Scott Draper won the 1998 Stella Artois singles championship.

Greg Rusedski won $1,860,437 in 1998.

Andre Agassi and Boris Becker met in the final of the 1999 Hong Kong Open.

Carlos Moya was ranked 346 in 1994.

Andre Agassi beat Gustavo Kuerten in straight sets in their 1999 Wimbledon quarter-finals encounter.

Byron Black learned to play tennis on his father's avocado plantation.

TENNIS

Mariano Puerta won the 1998 Sicilian Open singles tournament.

Mariano Zabaleta won the 1998 Colombian Open singles title.

Michael Chang was born in Hoboken, New Jersey.

Francisco Clavet turned professional in 1988.

Chinese tennis star Fang Li was born on January 1st, 1973.

Boris Becker's son Noah Gabriel was born in 1994.

Tim Henman was ranked No. 771 in 1992.

Lindsay Davenport beat Jana Novotna in the 1999 Wimbledon quarter-finals.

Mirjana Lucic beat Monica Seles in the 1999 Wimbledon ladies' singles tournament.

Yevgeny Kafelnikov dropped only one set in winning the 1996 French Open singles title.

Greg Rusedski beat Tim Henman 6-2, 6-4 in the A.T.P. Tour Championship qualifier in November 1998. It was the fifth time they'd met.

Cecil Mamiit's mobile phone went off during a point with Sebastien Grosjean in the Citrix Championship in Florida in 1999. Grosjean lost the point.

Andrei Pavel won the 1998 Japan Open singles title.

TENNIS

Jana Novotna twisted her ankle in the French Open in 1999 when she collided with doubles partner Natasha Zvereva.

The father of Jelena Dokic, who knocked Martina Hingis out of the 1999 Wimbledon ladies singles, was arrested at an Edgbaston tournament two weeks before after a series of outbursts from the stands.

Andre Agassi divorced Brooke Shields in 1999.

The I.T.F. Philippe Chatrier Award for outstanding services to the game was presented to Rod Laver at the 1998 world champions' dinner.

Jim Courier was 1992 I.T.F. men's world champion.

Martina Hingis described gay tennis player Amelie Mauresmo as 'half a man' before their 1999 Australian Open final encounter.

Javier Sanchez was 1986 I.T.F. junior boys' singles world champion.

Pascale Paradis was 1983 I.T.F. junior girls' singles world champion.

Steffi Graf beat Kim Clijsters in the 1999 Wimbledon ladies singles tournament.

Hastings, New Zealand, hosted the Australian Championships in 1912.

Tim Henman beat Cédric Pioline in their 1999 Wimbledon quarter-final encounter.

TENNIS

Gustavo Kuerten won the 1998 Mercedes Cup singles final in Stuttgart.

Karol Kucera's family are father Karol, mother Kristina and sister Karin.

Petr Korda won the 1998 Qatar Mobil Open singles title.

The mother of Serena and Venus Williams is called Oracene.

Steffi Graf's win over France's Anne-Gaelle Sidot in the Leipzig Open in 1998 made her the top women's prize-money earner with $20,347,942.

Greg Rusedski was born in Montreal.

Tennis star Pat Rafter was born in Mount Isa, Queensland.

Todd Martin beat Jiri Novak in the 1999 Wimbledon men's singles tournament.

Bjorn Borg was ranked No. 1 in the world for 109 weeks.

Pete Sampras is the son of Greek immigrants.

Guillermo Vilas lost only three games in his 1977 French Open singles final win.

Arantxa Sanchez-Vicario won the 1998 French Open singles despite losing a set 0-6.

The Kooyong Stadium is in Melbourne.

Miss J. Lehane lost the 1960-63 Australian ladies singles finals.

TENNIS

Former U.S. basketball player Julius Erving has claimed to be Alexandra Stevenson's father.

Stefan Edberg ranked No. 1 in the world for 66 weeks.

Marcelo Rios's mother Alicia is a teacher.

Serena Williams's semi-final victory over Martina Hingis in the 1999 Lipton Championships was her 16th successive win.

Brazil's Fernando Meligeni was disqualified from the Estoril Open in 1999 after hitting a spectator with a ball.

Andre Agassi's sister Rita was married to Pancho Gonzales.

Greg Rusedski was ranked 1103 in 1989.

Dominik Hrbaty won the 1998 San Marino International singles title.

Venus Williams won $1,712,246 in 1998.

Evonne Goolagong lost the 1971-73 Australian ladies singles finals.

Magnus Gustafsson won the 1999 Copenhagen Open singles title.

Tim Henman won $1,448,770 in 1998.

Jonas Bjorkman won the 1998 Nottingham Open singles in straight sets over Byron Black.

Katarina Srebotnik won the 1999 Estoril Open women's singles final in straight sets.

GOLF

GOLF

In 1963 Jack Nicklaus became the youngest winner of the U.S. Masters.

Only Gary Player and Bob Goalby beat par in the 1962 U.S. P.G.A. championship.

Vijay Singh won the 1997 South African Open, beating Nick Price by a stroke.

Eight competitors took part in the 1860 British Open.

Australia's Richard Green won the 1997 Dubai Desert Classic, beating Greg Norman and Ian Woosnam in a play-off.

There was a total prize-money fund of £10 for the British Open in 1863.

When Gary Player won the 1965 U.S. Open, he was the 1st overseas winner of the tournament since 1920.

Mark O'Meara netted £300,000 for the 1998 British Open.

The first twelve British Open tournaments were played at Prestwick.

Jack Nicklaus hit 305 in the 1962 British Open, 29 shots behind winner Arnold Palmer.

The U.S. Open was first played in 1895.

New Zealand ladies golfer Lynnette Brooky won the 1998 Austrian Open, winning £12,000.

GOLF

The U.S. Masters was the brainchild of Bobby Jones.

The 1998 South African Open was held at Durban Country Club.

Jack Nicklaus won the 1965 U.S. Masters in 17 under par.

South African Clinton Whitelaw won the 1997 Moroccan Open.

Neil Coles was the leading money earner on the 1964 European Tour winning £7,890.

Billy Mayfair beat Tiger Woods in a play-off to take the 1998 Nissan Open at Pacific Palisades, California.

Art Wall's only win in the majors was the 1959 U.S. Masters.

Kel Nagle won £1,250 for taking the 1960 British Open title.

Amateur Ken Venturi came second in the 1956 U.S. Masters by one shot.

In 1964 Jack Nicklaus headed the money list on the U.S. tour with $113,284.

1967 British Open champion Roberto de Vicenzo had been a runner-up in 1950.

GOLF

Karrie Webb won the 1997 Weetabix Women's British Open winning £82,500.

Gary Player and Seve Ballesteros have each won the world matchplay championship five times.

Bobby Nichols's only major win was the 1964 U.S. P.G.A.

Peter Oosterhuis won the 1973 Volvo P.G.A. Championship.

Northern Ireland golfer Darren Clarke was the highest placed non-American at the 1998 U.S. Masters.

The first official U.S. Amateur championship was in 1895.

Lee Westwood likened having an MRI scan to being in a Smarties tube.

Amateur golfer Graeme Storm's mother caddied for him at the 1999 Amateur Championship at Royal County Down.

The U.S. beat Great Britain and Ireland 10-8 in the 1998 Curtis Cup.

Swede Michael Jonzon won the 1997 Portuguese Open.

The U.S. women's Open was first held in 1946.

Arnold Palmer birdied the last two holes in the 1960 U.S. Masters to take the title by one shot.

A Scot, Donald Ross, created the No. 2 course at Pinehurst which was used for the 1999 U.S. P.G.A. tournament.

GOLF

1964 British Open champion Tony Lema was killed in a private plane crash in 1966.

Fred Bullock led the first three rounds of the 1959 British Open but finished runner-up to Gary Player.

The U.S. beat Great Britain & Ireland 18-6 in the 1997 Walker Cup.

Arnold Palmer's 1958 U.S. Masters win saw the first five-figure winners purse.

Ken Venturi's first major was the 1964 U.S. Open.

Lee Westwood won the 1999 Macau Open.

The U.S. Ladies P.G.A. championship was first held in 1955.

Jack Nicklaus was the fourth man to win all the U.S. Majors.

Maurice Bembridge won the 1974 Volvo P.G.A. Championship.

England's Peter Mitchell won the 1997 Madeira Island Open tournament.

Jean-François Remsey won the 1999 Estoril Open.

Arnold Palmer, Gary Player & Dow Finsterwald engaged in a three-way play-off for the 1962 U.S. Masters.

Arnold Pitts won the Bermuda Open from 1996-98.

The first British Amateur Championship was in 1885.

GOLF

Tiger Woods earned £135,000 for third spot in the 1998 British Open.

Jarmo Sandelin won the 1999 Peugeot Spanish Open.

Fred Couples beat Bruce Lietzke in a play-off for the 1998 Bob Hope Chrysler Classic.

Italian golfer Aldo Casera, who won the 1948 Italian Open, died in 1999.

Sherri Steinhauer won the 1998 Weetabix Women's British Open, winning £100,000.

Dean Robertson won the 1999 Italian Open.

Ian Woosnam won the 1997 Volvo P.G.A. Championship.

Tom Morris Sr. won £6 for winning the 1864 British Open.

Mark James won the 1997 Peugeot Spanish Open.

The two courses at Emirates Golf Club in Dubai need 2 million gallons of water each day during the summer to keep them in condition.

The Internationals beat the United States 20 and a half to 11 and a half in the 1998 President's Cup.

Horton Smith was the first man to win the U.S. Masters twice.

Tom Morris Jr. was the first winner of the British Open's famous claret jug.

GOLF

Steel-shafted putters were used in the U.S. Open for the first time in 1924.

Tiger Woods was U.S. Amateur champion from 1994-6.

Jim Ferrier finished 5th in the 1964 U.S. Masters at the age of 49.

Arnold Palmer was 1954 U.S. Amateur Champion.

The Solheim Cup was first staged in 1990 when the U.S. beat Europe.

Jerome Travers was the second amateur winner of the U.S. Open.

GOLF

In 1962 Jack Nicklaus became the first player since Bobby Jones to hold the U.S. Amateur and U.S. Open titles at the same time.

In 1922 Walter Hagen became the first man to take all three majors.

Cornishman Jim Barnes won the first U.S. P.G.A. in 1916.

England golfer David Carter won the 1998 Murphy's Irish Open, beating Colin Montgomerie in a play-off.

The 1963 U.S. Open saw a three-way play-off between Julius Boros, Jacky Cupit and Arnold Palmer.

Byron Nelson won the French Open aged 43.

Australian Stephen Allen won the 1998 German Open, winning £116,660.

Douglas Edgar, runner-up in the 1920 U.S. P.G.A., died the following year aged 37.

Lee Westwood won $306,000 for winning the Entergy Classic in New Orleans in 1998.

Willie McFarlane beat Bobby Jones in a play-off for the 1925 U.S. Open.

Ray Floyd was 51 years 22 days when he played in the 1993 Ryder Cup.

Jim Barnes won £75 for winning the 1925 British Open.

GOLF

Inventor of the forerunner of the modern golf ball, Coburn Haskell, was a bicycle tyre manufacturer.

Lee Westwood was named European Golfer of the Year in 1998.

Betsy King was 17 under par in winning the 1992 U.S. P.G.A. championship.

Lee Janzen took home $535,000 for winning the U.S. Open in 1998.

Mike Brady lost in a play-off in both the 1911 & 1919 U.S. Open championships.

South Africa beat Spain 3-0 in the 1998 Alfred Dunhill Cup.

Tommy Armour beat Harry Cooper in a play-off for the 1927 U.S. Open.

The amateur women's team trophy played between the U.S. and Great Britain & Northern Ireland was named after Margaret and Harriot Curtis.

Harry Vardon tied 47th in the 1928 British Open.

England won the 1998 World Cup of Golf, held in Auckland, New Zealand.

Leo Diegel beat Walter Hagen in the quarter-final of the 1928 U.S. P.G.A. matchplay - Hagen's first defeat at matchplay in 23 games.

Argentina had three players in the first 11 of the finishers in the 1931 British Open.

GOLF

Swede Mathias Grönberg won the 1998 Smurfit European Open which was held in Dublin.

Royal Lytham and St. Anne's hosted its first British Open in 1926.

American Emilee Klein won the 1996 British Women's Open.

Bobby Jones beat Al Espinosa by 23 shots in a play-off for the 1929 U.S. Open.

In 1932 Gene Sarazen won both British Open and U.S. Open.

Kathy Whitworth earned $1,731,770 between 1959-95, winning 88 tournaments.

Annika Sörenson earned $1,236,789 in 1997.

Bobby Jones was the first man to win British Open and U.S. Open in the same year, in 1926.

George Von Elm hit the lowest score in the 1931 U.S. Open - 69 in Round Two.

Jack Fleck beat Ben Hogan in a play-off for the 1955 U.S. Open.

Don January won the 1967 U.S. P.G.A. title in July.

Tiger Woods's entry in the 1998 Casio World Open was his first Japanese tournament.

Greg Norman caddied for his son in the junior British Open in 1998.

GOLF

José-Maria Olazabal won the 1998 Dubai Desert Classic.

Sophie Gustafson won the 1998 Donegal Irish Open winning £12,900.

Tom Morris Jr.'s body was discovered by his father on Christmas Day, 1874.

Peter Thomson beat Dave Thomas in a 36 hole play-off for the 1958 British Open.

Tiger Woods was 21 years, 104 days old when he won the 1997 U.S. Masters.

GOLF

Davie Strath refused to play-off with Bob Martin in the 1876 British Open so was awarded second place.

Future British Open champion Tom Weiskopf finished 15th in the 1967 U.S. Open.

The Great Britain and Ireland team withdrew from the women's World Amateur Team Championship in Chile in 1998 on advice from the Foreign Office, because of the General Pinochet saga.

Julie Inkster won the 1998 Samsung World Championship.

Australian Stephen Leaney won the 1998 Moroccan Open.

Jack Nicklaus won a princely £2,100 for the 1966 British Open title.

John Ball Jr. was 14 when he took part in the 1878 British Open.

Jamie Anderson, who won the British Open from 1877-79 died in a Poor House in Perth in 1912.

Lora Faircloth won the 1998 Ladies' German Open.

James Foulis took $150 for winning the U.S. Open in 1896.

Lee Westwood was the highest placed Englishman at the 1998 U.S. Masters & U.S. Open.

Tiger Woods headed the 1997 money list on the U.S. tour with $2,066,833.

The 'cut' first appeared in the British Open championship in 1898.

GOLF

Michael Burgess was the highest placed amateur in the 1965 British Open.

Matt Kuchar was the highest placed amateur at the 1998 U.S. Masters & U.S. Open.

Peter Thomson won the 1956 British Open - his third in a row.

Mats Lanner won the 1998 Madeira Island Open, winning £50,000.

The first play-off in the U.S. Open was in 1901.

Nick Faldo was the first man to break over £100,000 earnings on the European Tour with a total of £140,761 in 1983.

The 1905 U.S. Open took place at the Myopia Hunt Club in South Hamilton, Massachusetts.

Dow Finsterwald took $5,500 for winning the 1958 U.S. P.G.A. title.

Brothers Alex, Willie & George Smith played in the 1906 U.S. Open.

Jack Burke Jr. won the 1956 U.S. Masters and U.S. P.G.A.

Golf course designer Donald Ross finished 10th in the 1907 U.S. Open.

Deal hosted the the 1909 British Open.

Amateur Francis Ouimet won the 1913 U.S. Open.

GOLF

Cary Middlecoff's third major win was the 1956 U.S. Open.

Colin Montgomerie has headed the European money list since 1993.

Tom Watson accepted an invitation in May 1999 to become only the 12th honorary member of the Royal and Ancient Golf Club.

The U.S. Open is reputedly Colin Montgomerie's favourite championship of the year.

Jack Nicklaus was the first man to retain the U.S. Masters, in 1966.

English-born Horace Rawlins won the first U.S. Open, in 1895.

Nick Price was the highest-placed foreigner at the 1998 U.S. Open.

Gene Sarazen was 20 years 173 days old when he won the 1922 U.S. P.G.A. title.

Patrick Sjöland won the 1998 Italian Open.

Gordon Sherry was 1995 British Amateur Champion.

Tiger Woods beat Tom Lehman in a play-off for the 1997 Mercedes Championship in California.

Se Ri Pak won the 1998 U.S. Women's Open and U.S. L.P.G.A. titles.

GOLF

Willie Anderson was the first man to win the U.S. Open twice.

Billy Casper won $12,000 for taking the 1959 U.S. Open.

Four players have each won the U.S. Open four times - Jack Nicklaus, Ben Hogan, Bobby Jones & Willie Anderson.

Dave Mann's only major win was the 1965 U.S. P.G.A.

Jimmy Demaret was the first man to win the U.S. Masters three times.

Neil Coles won the 1976 Volvo P.G.A. championship.

Darren Clarke took home £125,000 for winning the 1998 Benson & Hedges International Open.

The Prince's Club, Sandwich, hosted its only British Open in 1932.

David Duval won three out of the last four events of the 1997 U.S. P.G.A. tour.

The 1932 U.S. Open was won by Olin Dutra.

The 1957 British Open was Bobby Locke's last win in the tournament.

Colin Montgomerie hit 14 under par to win the 1998 Volvo P.G.A. Championship.

GOLF

In 1933 Johnny Goodman became the last amateur to win a major.

The first of Bobby Jones's seven majors was the 1923 U.S. Open.

German golfer Sven Strüver won the 1998 Canon European Masters, held at Crans-sur-Sierre, Switzerland.

A fan at the 1999 Phoenix Open was arrested for carrying a gun.

Greg Norman and Colin Montgomerie have both designed courses at Emirates Hill, Dubai.

After two rounds of the 1999 Andersen Consulting Match Play Championship in California only Tiger Woods of the world's Top Ten players survived to reach the last 16.

The 1st Round of the Benson & Hedges Malaysian Open in 1999 was halted because of lightning.

Hsieh Chin-sheng's 64 in the 1st round of the 1998 Hong Kong Open was a course record.

Steve Lowery's house burned down when he was playing the final round of the 1999 Tucson Open.

Golfer Edward Fryatt's father Jim holds the record for the fastest goal in the English football league.

David Park won the European Grand Prix in 1999, only his second senior event on the European Tour.

GOLF

Sergio Garcia's first tournament as a professional was the 1999 Spanish Open.

Bobby Jones came out of retirement to play in the 1934 U.S. Masters.

Denny Shute beat Craig Wood in a play-off for the 1933 British Open.

Ireland won the 1997 World Cup of Golf.

Byron Nelson beat Ben Hogan by one shot to win the 1942 U.S. Masters.

Paul Stankowski beat Jim Furyk in a play-off to win the 1997 United Airlines Hawaiian Open.

None of the four majors were played in 1943.

Nick Faldo won the 1997 Nissan Open at Pacific Palisade, California.

Lloyd Mangrum won a three-way play-off for the 1946 U.S. Open.

Jack Nicklaus has won the U.S. Masters six times.

Sergio Garcia was 1998 British Amateur champion.

Frank Nobilo won the 1997 Greater Greensboro Chrysler Classic, beating Brad Faxon in a play-off.

GOLF

Howard Clark won the 1984 Volvo P.G.A. Championship.

A week after winning the 1997 U.S. Open, Ernie Els won the Buick Classic and $270,000.

Paul Runyan won $1,000 for taking the 1934 U.S. P.G.A.

Herman Keiser won the first post-war U.S. Masters.

John Cook finished 33 under par to take the 1997 Bob Hope Chrysler Classic.

Fred Daly became the first Irish player to win a major when he won the 1947 British Open.

David Duval went to No. 1 in the World Rankings in April 1999 by winning the BellSouth Classic.

Justin Rose's exit from the 1999 Estoril Open was his 17th successive missed cut since he joined the European Tour.

Nick Faldo missed the cut in the 1999 U.S. Masters for the third consecutive time.

Ernie Els got married on New Years Eve, 1998.

The U.S. P.G.A. became a stroke-play competition in 1958.

Sam Snead's first U.S. Masters title was in 1949.

Paul Way won the 1985 Volvo P.G.A. Championship.

GOLF

Chandler Harper's only major win was the 1950 U.S. P.G.A.

Lionel Hebert won $8,000 for his 1957 U.S. P.G.A. win.

Bert Yancey led the first three rounds of the 1967 U.S. Masters but lost by four shots to Gay Brewer.

Frenchman Arnaud Massy was the first overseas winner of the British Open.

Willie Smith, winner of the 1899 U.S. Open was killed during the Mexican revolution in 1915.

GOLF

Mark O'Meara was 1979 U.S. Amateur Champion.

Bobby Nichols, Lee Trevino and Jerry Heard were all struck by lightning during the 1975 Western Open.

Henry Cotton played in the 1957 U.S. Masters at the age of 50.

At the end of 1997, Bernhard Langer was the top all-time money earner on the European tour, with £6,041,241.

Charles Evans Jr. became the third amateur to win the U.S. Open, in 1916.

Brothers Jay and Lionel Hebert won the U.S. P.G.A. in 1960 and 1957 respectively.

The winner of the 1966 U.S. P.G.A., Al Geiberger, was the only player to achieve par in the tournament.

1920 British Open winner George Duncan was 13 behind the leader at the half-way stage.

Dale Hales of South Africa was 18 years 290 days old when he won the 1971 Spanish Open.

In winning the 1922 U.S. P.G.A. Gene Sarazen became the first man to win two majors in a season. He'd won the U.S. Open in July.

Rives McBee equalled the low score 64 in Round Two of the U.S. Open.

GOLF

Charles Evans Jr. led the 1916 U.S. Open tournament throughout winning by two strokes.

Bernhard Langer won the 1997 Conte of Florence Italian Open.

From 1923, when Arthur Havers won, until 1934, when Henry Cotton won, there were no English winners of the British Open.

Scotland's Colin Montgomerie won the 1997 Murphy's Irish Open in Dublin.

The first three finishers in the 1929 British Open had each won a major the previous year.

Byron Nelson had 18 wins on the U.S. P.G.A. tour in 1945.

Germany's Sven Strüver won the 1997 Sun Microsystems Dutch Open.

Jock Hutchinson was runner-up in the two majors held in 1916.

Justin Leonard was 1992 U.S. Amateur Champion.

Sweden's Per-Ulrik Johansson won the 1997 Smurfit European Open.

John McDermott was only 19 years 10 months old when he won the 1911 U.S. Open.

Nick Faldo was 20 years 59 days old when he played in the 1977 Ryder Cup.

GOLF

After winning the British Open, U.S. Open, U.S. Amateur and British Amateur titles in 1930, Bobby Jones retired from the sport to practice law.

Billy Casper played in eight Ryder Cups for the U.S.

Gene Sarazen became the first man to win all four majors by winning the 1935 Masters.

Constantino Rocca won the 1997 Canon European Masters.

Sam Parks Jr., who won the 1935 U.S. Open at Oakmont Country Club was pro at nearby South Hills Country Club.

Lee Westwood won the 1997 Volvo Masters at Montecastillo in Spain.

Amateur Lawson Little was the best placed overseas player in the 1935 British Open.

Ralph Guldahl won the 1937 & 1938 U.S. Open titles.

Tony Manero's 282 in the 1936 U.S. Open was the lowest score in a major up to that point.

The Tournament Players' Championship is open to players who have won official P.G.A. tour events in the previous year.

South Africa won the 1996 World Cup of Golf.

Alf Padgham's only British Open win was in 1936.

GOLF

The Johnny Walker World Championship was first held in 1991 at the Tryall Golf Club in Montego Bay, Jamaica.

71 year-old Sandy Herd played in the 1939 British Open - he'd won it in 1902.

The World Cup was the idea of American industrialist Jay Hopkins.

Lawson Little won the 1940 U.S. Open. He'd previously been U.S. Amateur Champion.

1922 was the first time admission was charged at the U.S. Open.

Craig Wood's first major was the 1941 U.S. Masters.

Dick Mayer's only major win was the 1957 U.S. Open.

Bob Rosburg's only major win was the 1959 U.S. P.G.A.

Bob Charles was the first New Zealander to win a major.

Mike Souchak led the first three rounds of the 1960 U.S. Open, but ended up three behind Arnold Palmer.

Mark O'Meara netted $576,000 for the 1998 U.S. Masters.

José-Maria Olazabal was 1984 British Amateur Champion.

GOLF

Tommy Bolt's 1958 U.S. Open win was his only major.

101 people entered the 1899 British Open.

England's Peter Mitchell won the 1998 Portuguese Open.

The 1905 U.S. Open took place at the Myopia Hunt Club in South Hamilton, Massachusetts.

Dow Finsterwald took $5,500 for winning the 1958 U.S. P.G.A. title.

Brothers Alex, Willie & George Smith played in the 1906 U.S. Open.

Mungo Park won the 1874 British Open and first prize of £8.

Jack Burke, Jr. won the 1956 U.S. Masters and U.S. P.G.A.

The 4th hole of the Old Course at St. Andrews is known as "Ginger Beer".

Catherine Lacoste was only 22 years 5 days old when she won the 1967 U.S. Women's Open.

Vijay Singh was $540,00 better off for winning the 1998 U.S. P.G.A. title.

MOTOR SPORTS

MOTOR SPORTS

Mika Hakkinen's margin of victory over Giancarlo Fisichella in the 1999 Montreal Grand Prix was less than a second.

Jacques Villeneuve dated pop singer Dannii Minogue in 1999.

At the 1999 Le Mans 24 Hour race Peter Dumbreck's Mercedes CLK took flight at 200 m.p.h. but the Scot was not seriously injured.

Alex Criville won his third consecutive Spanish 500 c.c. motor cycle Grand Prix in 1999.

Colin McRae finished fourth in the 1999 Corsica Rally.

Michael Schumacher's win in the 1999 San Marino Grand Prix was his 34th career victory.

Eddie Irvine finished 1.027 in front of Heinz-Harald Frentzen in winning the 1999 Australian Grand Prix.

Porsche have won the Le Mans 24-Hour race most times.

Angel Nieto has won the most 125 c.c. motorcycling world titles - seven in all.

Nigel Mansell achieved pole position 14 times in the 1992 F1 season.

The first Spanish Grand Prix was at Guadarrama in 1913.

Luigi Fagioli was 53 years 22 days old when he won the 1951 French motor racing Grand Prix.

Giacomo Agostini won the 350 c.c. motorcycling world title seven times.

MOTOR SPORTS

Three people died when debris from a wreck hit them during the Vision-Aire 500 Pep Boys Indy Racing League Event in Concord, North Carolina in 1999.

The Granite City Rally is held in Abedeen.

The first Briton to win the 250 c.c. world moto-cross championship was Neil Hudson in 1981.

Mike Thackwell was 19 years 182 days old when he drove in the 1980 Canadian Grand Prix.

Heinz-Harald Frentzen crashed into a wall on lap 66 of the 1999 Montreal Grand Prix at 150 m.p.h.

Mika Hakkinen won the 1999 F1 Brazilian Grand Prix.

The last Formula One Grand Prix in 1999 will be held in October at Suzuka, Japan.

Ricardo Zonta was 1996 F.I.A. Formula 3000 champion.

The 1982 Swiss F1 Grand Prix was held at Dijon in France.

The Mexican motor racing Grand Prix was first held in 1962 and granted World Championship status in 1963.

Jean Alesi's first point in the 1999 F1 season was at the San Marino Grand Prix.

The Zhuhai Grand Prix motor racing circuit was built in 1996.

MOTOR SPORTS

The Suzuka F1 Grand Prix circuit is in an approximate figure-of-eight pattern.

Kenny Roberts Jr. won the Japanese 500 c.c motorcycling Grand Prix in 1999.

Michael Doohan broke his left wrist, right leg and left collar-bone in a fall during qualification for the 1999 Spanish 500 c.c. motorcycle Grand Prix.

The F1 Circuit de Spa-Francorchamps is the longest in use in the world championship.

Tapio Laukkannen won the 1999 Pirelli International Rally.

The Sepang motor racing circuit will host its first F1 Grand Prix in October 1999.

Alex Criville won the Italian 500 c.c. motorcycling Grand Prix in 1999.

The Nurburgring in Germany will host the 1999 Luxembourg Grand Prix.

The Montreal F1 Grand Prix circuit is named after Gilles Villeneuve.

The Autodromo Nationale di Monza was built in 1922.

The Silverstone Grand Prix motor racing circuit is near the village of Silverstone in Northamptonshire.

Damon Hill worked as a motorcycle despatch rided from 1982-85.

Eddie Irvine's 1999 Australian Grand Prix win was his first in 82 attempts.

MOTOR SPORTS

The Virage de Sainte Devote is the first corner of the Monaco Grand Prix.

Alexander Wurz drove into Damon Hill's Jordan in the 1999 Brazilian F1 Grand Prix.

The Hungaroring has hosted the Hungarian F1 Grand Prix since 1986.

Giacomo Agostini won the 500 c.c motorcycling title on eight occasions.

The first recorded motorcycle race took place on 20th September, 1896, between Paris and Nantes.

The 1964 Austrian motor racing Grand Prix was held at Zeltweg.

The 350 c.c. class in the motorcycling world championships was discontinued at the end of the 1982 season.

Jean Alesi was 1989 F.I.A. Formula 3000 Champion.

The first German motor racing Grand Prix was held at Avus in 1926.

The present Le Mans 24-Hour race circuit is 8.48 miles long.

The first long-distance rally was from Peking to Paris between June 10 - August 10, 1907.

The first race for two-wheeled motor cycles was held at Sheen House, Richmond, Surrey in November, 1897.

The Monte Carlo Rally was first held in 1911.

MOTOR SPORTS

Mike Hailwood and Phil Read are the only motorcycle riders to have won world titles in four classes.

The official World Drivers' Championship for rally drivers began in 1979.

Hockenheim motor racing circuit was originally built as a test circuit for Mercedes.

A Formula 1 tyre costs approximately £850.

Damon Hill's fourth place in the 1999 San Marino Grand Prix was his first placing of the season.

Ferrari finished in 3rd and 4th places in the 1999 Barcelona F1 Grand Prix.

MOTOR SPORTS

Ricardo Zonta failed to take part in his home F1 Grand Prix in Brazil in 1999 after injuring his foot in practice.

1958 saw the only Moroccan motor racing Grand Prix.

The first Tourist Trophy race on the Isle of Man was staged in 1907.

Pedro De La Rosa's first point in the 1999 F1 championship was at the Australian Grand Prix.

Monsanto hosted the 1959 Portuguese motor racing Grand Prix.

The Belgian motor racing Grand Prix was first raced in 1925.

In the fourth round of the 1999 World Superbike Championship in Albacete, Colin Edwards and Noriyuki Haga took a win each.

Tommi Makinen was fined $10,000 for his part in a head-on accident whilst practicing for the 1999 Safari Rally.

Heinz-Harald Frentzen's win in the 1999 F1 French Grand Prix was Jordan's second F1 victory.

About 50 competitors in the 1999 Dakar rally were held up and robbed at gunpoint after the end of the 12th Stage.

Rally driver Colin McRae was born in Lanark, Scotland.

McLaren finished in 1st and 2nd places in the 1999 Barcelona F1 Grand Prix.

MOTOR SPORTS

The San Marino F1 Grand Prix is held at the Autodromo Enzo e Dino Ferrari.

Giacomo Agostini won 122 motor cycling Grands Prix.

An oil slick from Johnny Herbert's car caused Alex Zanardi to come off the track in the 1999 San Marino F1 Grand
Prix.

The inaugural Buenos Aires F1 Grand Prix was run in 1947.

Kenny Roberts Jr.'s first 500 c.c. motorcycling Grand Prix win was in Malaysia in April, 1999.

The Canadian motor racing Grand Prix was held at Mont Tremblant in 1968 & 1970.

Colin McRae's 1999 victory in the Safari Rally in Nairobi was his 17th victory at world championship level.

The first Australian motor racing Grand Prix was held at Phillip Island, Victoria.

Rubens Barrichello completed 42 laps of his home F1 Grand Prix in Brazil in 1999 before retiring.

The last motor racing Grand Prix held at Zandvoort was in 1985.

Jim Redman of Rhodesia and Charles Mortimer of the U.K. both won motorcycle Grands Prix in four different classes.

Las Vegas hosted two Formula 1 motor racing Grands Prix in 1981 & 1982.

MOTOR SPORTS

Jarno Trulli picked up his first point of the 1999 F1 season at the Barcelona Grand Prix.

Ferrari's technical director in 1999 at F1 is Ross Brawn.

David Coulthard finished only 4.26 seconds behind Michael Schumacher at the 1999 F1 San Marino Grand Prix.

Only eight of the starters finished in the 1999 Australian F1 Grand Prix.

Carl Fogarty won both races inthe Italian round of the 1999 World Superbike Championship.

By winning the Catalan 500 c.c. Grand Prix in 1999 Alex Criville became the first European in 27 years to win four races in a row.

Michael Schumacher retired after 29 laps of the 1999 Montreal Grand Prix after slamming into a retaining wall.

In the 1955 Le Mans 24-Hours race a Mercedes vaulted a barrier killing 82 spectators and driver Pierre Levegh as it exploded.

Pierluigi Martini, Yannick Dalmas and Joachim Winkelhock won the 1999 Le Mans 24-Hour race completing 366 laps.

Mika Hakkinen led 61 of the 65 laps in the 1999 Barcelona F1 Grand Prix.

McLaren's F1 team manager in 1999 is Ron Dennis.

The R.A.C. motor racing Grand Prix was raced at Brooklands in 1926 & 1927.

MOTOR SPORTS

The first Briton to win the 500 c.c. world moto-cross championship was Jeff Smith in 1964.

The South African Grand Prix was first raced at East London in 1934.

The first French motor racing Grand Prix was held at 1906 at Le Mans.

Jacky Ickx was 1967 European Formula Two Champion.

Olivier Panis was F.I.A. Formula 3000 champion in 1993.

Alex Criville won the 1999 French 500 c.c. motorcycle Grand Prix.

America will host its first F1 Grand Prix since 1991 in the year 2000.

Motorcyclist Claudio Carotti was killed in 1999 in a qualifying race for Italy's national 600 c.c. supersport championship.

Eddie Irvine finished third in the 1999 Montreal F1 Grand Prix.

The A1-Ring which houses the Austrian F1 Grand Prix was originally bulit in 1968.

McLaren's technical director in 1999 is Adrian Newey.

The first moto-cross race was run at Camberley, Surrey, in 1924.

ATHLEITICS

ATHLETICS

John Kibowen's time of 4:48.74 for 2000m made in August 1998 made him the fourth all-time best for the distance.

Roger Black finished third in the 400m at the 1998 British Grand Prix at Sheffield.

Isaac Viciosa won the 1998 5th Avenue Mile Race in New York for the fourth time in succession.

Sonia O'Sullivan won the women's Great North Run in Newcastle in 1998.

Ondoro Osoro won the 1998 Chicago Marathon in 2:06:54. It was his first attempt at the race.

Grigoriy Murzin won the 1998 I.A.U. world 100km in Japan in a time of 6:30:06.

Australian athlete Emma George was a trapeze artist in the Flying Fruit Flies Circus.

In a poll conducted by the European A.A., Jonathan Edwards was voted male athlete of 1998.

In May 1999, the South African federation became the first in the world to offer top athletes monthly salaries.

Iwan Thomas pulled out of the 1999 IAAF World Championships because of an injury to his left foot.

Athlete Donovan Bailey ruptured his Achilles in a basketball game in 1998.

ATHLETICS

German athlete Danny Ecker is son of U.S. basketball player John Ecker.

Australian athlete Lisa-Marie Vizaniari is a kick boxing enthusiast.

Ireland discus thrower Nick Sweeney played rugby union for Irish Schools.

Italian 1500m runner Gennaro Di Napoli was a junior tennis champion.

Meredith Gourdine, who died in 1998, was 1952 Olympic Games long jump silver winner.

Kenyan runners Thomas Nyariki and Jackline Maranga are married.

German athlete Falk Balzer's father Karl-Heinz was a pole-vault champion.

Athlete Nova Peris-Kneebone was an Olympic hockey gold winner in 1996.

The Powderhall Sprint in Edinburgh began in 1870.

Steve Smith won the high jump at a meeting in Gateshead in June 1999 a year after a career-threatening back injury sustained in training.

Linford Christie was born in St. Andrew, Jamaica.

Nigerian runners Osmond and Davidson Ezinwa are twins.

Jackie Joyner Kersee's heptathlon win at the 1998 Goodwill Games was her only heptathlon that year.

ATHLETICS

Australian athlete Alison Inverarity has a degree in architecture from the University of Western Australia.

Cuban athlete Ivan Pedroso is a cousin of hurdler Aliuska Lopez.

Czech Republic pole vaulter Daniela Bartova represented Czechoslovakia at gymnastics at the 1992 Olympic Games.

Maurice Greene ran the 100m in 9.79 in June 1999, shaving 0.05 second off the world record.

Liz McColgan won the world 10,000m title in 1991 less than a year after giving birth to her daughter.

Denise Lewis was second in the 1998 B.B.C. Sports Personality of the Year poll.

Dwain Chambers's time of 10.05 for the 100m at Gateshead in June 1999 was the fastest time by a Briton in this country.

In a poll conducted by the European A.A., Christine Arron was voted female athlete of 1998.

French pole vaulter Jean Galfione's uncle is Olympic fencing champion Jean-Claude Magnan.

Vladimir Dubrovshchik won the first European gold medal for Belarus in athletics.

German athlete Susen Tiedtke's uncle was an Olympic decathlete.

Belgian runner Marleen Renders won the 1995 Antwerp Marathon and the 1998 Berlin Marathon.

ATHLETICS

French hurdler Patricia Girard-Léno is married to kick boxing champion Eddy Léno.

Canadian athlete Leah Pells is a child care counsellor.

Jamaican hudler Gillian Russell is a karate black belt.

German high jumper Alina Astafei is married to volleyball international Alin Stavariu.

Peter Snell was the first sub 1:45 800m runner.

Chilean runner Sebastian Keitel's grandmother won the 1939 South American discus title.

Fiona May, who competes for Italy at long jump, has a degree in economics from Leeds University.

Croatian athlete Branko Zorko had his spleen removed following a traffic accident in 1990.

Nigerian long jumper Chioma Ajunwa played football for Nigeria at the 1991 women's world championships.

Russian athlete Irina Privalova has a degree in journalism from Moscow State University.

Spanish decathlete Francisco Xavier Benet played American Football for a Venezuelan team.

The first three male finishers in the 1998 London Marathon all had names beginning with the letter A.

Said Aouita was the first sub 13-minute 5,000m winner.

ATHLETICS

Craig Virgin was men's world cross-country champion in 1980 & '81.

German discus thrower Anja Möllenbeck is a detective.

Colin Jackson ran in borrowed kit at Dortmund in June 1999 because his luggage was mislaid by the airline.

Ahmed Salah was trampled underfoot at the start of the 1991 Rotterdam Marathon.

Frederick Alderman, who had been the U.S.A.'s oldest surviving Olympic athletics champion, died in 1998.

Hicham El Guerrouj lost only once in 1996, when he fell in the Olympic 1500m Final.

Australian athlete Nick A'Hern owns a hair-dressing salon.

Seven one-carat diamonds were given to athletes setting stadium records at the DN Galan meeting in Stockholm in 1998.

Chinese javelin thrower Li Lei was formerly a volleyball player.

ATHLETICS

In the Finland versus Sweden meet at Helsinki in August, 1998, Finland won both the men's and women's matches.

Swedish high jumper Stefan Holm is 1.81m tall.

Charles Apps, who finished sixth at the 1936 Olympics pole vault event had a successful ice hockey career with the Toronto Maple Leafs.

Wilson Kipketer was Track and Field News male athlete of the year in 1998.

Cuban Olympic athlete Norberto Tellez is a former baseball player.

Ecuadorian athlete Jefferson Perez has had his picture on a postage stamp.

Syrian heptathlete Ghada Shouaa was a former basketball international.

In the Great Britain versus U.S.A. meet in Glasgow in August 1998, U.S. men won by two points, 107-105.

In 1984 Steve Cram stepped on a coke can whilst running, delaying his training programme.

Smith was the most common surname of runners at the 1999 London Marathon.

Marion Jones was Track and Field News female athlete of the year in 1998.

Eloy Quispe, who died in 1998, was a coach to the Bolivian national team.

ATHLETICS

The Boston Marathon began in 1897 as a local Patriot's Day event.

The 8th I.A.A.F. World Cup was held at Johannesburg at 1,748m above sea level.

Finnish walker Valentin Kononen's brother and sisters perform with the Finnish National Ballet.

In July 1985, Sergei Bubka became the first man to pole vault six metres.

At the Commonwealth Games in 1998 Kenyans won all the men's track events from 800m to 10,000m.

Victor Saneyev was world's No. 1 triple jumper from 1968-'76.

Les Golding, British team manager from 1965-'68 died in 1998. He was awarded the O.B.E. in 1988.

Merlene Ottey was Jamaican Sportswoman of the Year 15 times between 1979 and 1997.

Runner Niilo Hartikka of Finland received a special medal for finishing 4th in the 1938 European Championships after being shoved on the finishing straight.

Jim Hines was the first sub 10-second 100m runner.

U.S. cross-country runner Seamus McElligott died in 1998 of smoke inhalation.

Ronaldo da Costa's 2:06:05 in the 1998 Berlin Marathon beat his best by over 3 minutes.

ATHLETICS

Emery Barnes, who was third highest jumper in the world in 1952, played pro football with the Green Bay Packers.

Australian athlete Stephen Moneghetti trained as a civil engineer.

Jonathan Edwards had three fouls in the triple jump at Herculis G.P., Monaco in 1998.

The Németh javelin was ruled illegal by the I.A.A.F..

Ludvik Danek, Czechoslovakian discus thrower, was ranked in the world's top ten for 14 successive years from 1963-'76.

Dr. Clarice Kennedy was 4th at 80m hurdles and 7th in the javelin at the 1938 Commonwealth Games.

Saudi Arabian athlete Saad Shaddad Al-Asmari was a national junior volleyball champion.

Olympic shot champion Wladyslaw Komar appeared in Roman Polanski's film 'Pirates'.

Cuban runner Ana Fidelia Quirot's elder sister was a Cuban basketball international.

Tommie Smith was the first sub-20 second 200m runner.

Raymond Rigby, Australian shot champion, was a male nurse by profession.

Marathon champion Josiah Thugwane was South Africa's first black Olympic athletics champion.

ATHLETICS

Burundi athlete Vénuste Niyongabo lives in Siena, Italy.

Eunice Barber, French heptathlete, was born in Sierra Leone.

Otis Davis was the first sub-45 second 400m runner.

Australian athlete Nick A'Hern's father was an international footballer.

Otto Bengtsson, who was 11th at the javelin at the 1952 Olympics, died in 1998.

There were 25,530 runners in the 1998 Berlin Marathon.

Women's marathon pioneer Beth Bonner was struck by a truck and killed while cycling in 1998.

Steve Ovett ran into some church railings in 1982 whilst training.

New Zealand pole vaulter Denis Petuchinsky was stripped of his 1998 Commonwealth Games silver medal in December 1998 on testing positive for a steroid.

Bert van Vlaanderen was hit by a motorcycle when running the 1999 Paris Marathon.

Spanish walker Jésus Angel Garcia is married to Carmen Acedo, world champion rhythmic gymnast.

BOXING

BOXING

In a June 1999 I.B.F. cruiserweight title fight, holder Arthur William lost to Vassily Jirov.

Mike Tyson was Ring Magazine fighter of the year in 1986 and 1988.

The 1987 world welterweight title fight between Lloyd Honeyghan and Gene Hatcher lasted 45 seconds.

Roberto Duran won world titles at four different weights.

Derek Angol beat Dave Garside for the vacant British cruiserweight title in 1990.

The International Amateur Boxing Association was formed in 1946.

In the 1996 W.B.A. heavyweight fight between Mike Tyson and Bruce Seldon the referee stopped the fight in the first Round.

Ingemar Johansson was Ring Magazine fighter of the year in 1958 and '59.

Robin Reid of Great Britain successfully defended his W.B.C. super-middleweight title against Henry Wharton in May 1997.

The British Boxing Board of Control was formed in 1929.

Thomas Hearns won world titles at six different weights.

Steve Collins vacated his W.B.O. super-middleweight title in September, 1997.

BOXING

Boxer Ike Quartey is Ghanaian.

Len Wickwar fought 463 bouts between 1928-47.

Briton Nigel Wenton lost his W.B.O. light-welterweight bout to Giovanni Parisi in October 1997.

Herbie Hide beat Damon Reed in his April 1998 W.B.O. heavyweight contest when the referee stopped the fight.

George Odwell had 114 knockout wins in his career from 1930-45.

Charles Brewer lost his I.B.F. super-middleweight title in 1998 when defeated by Germany's Sven Ottke.

Naseem Hamed vacated the I.B.F. featherweight title in August 1997.

Richie Woodhall became W.B.C. super-middleweight champion in 1998 when he defeated Thulane Malinga.

Mike Tyson was disqualified in Round Three of his June 1997 fight with Evander Holyfield.

Briton Adrian Dobson retired in Round Six of his December 1997 W.B.O. light-middleweight fight with Ronald Wright.

Ike Williams was Ring Magazine fighter of the year in 1948.

Boxer Felix Trinidad is from Puerto Rico.

BOXING

Arturo Gatti relinquished his I.B.F. super-featherweight title in January 1998.

Oscar De La Hoya took the W.B.C. welterweight title off Pernell Whitaker in 1997.

Naseem Hamed beat Wilfredo Vazquez in Round Seven of their 1998 W.B.O. featherweight fight.

Michael Moorer won on points in his 1997 I.B.F. fight with Vaughn Bean.

The January 1997 light-welterweight bout between Konstya Tszyu and Leonardo Mas ended in a draw.

Steve McCarthy was stripped of his British light-heavyweight title in 1991.

In beating Herbie Hide in June 1999, Vitali Klitschko became the tallest heavyweight boxing champion ever.

Joe Calzaghe beat Chris Eubank in October 1997 to take the vacant W.B.O. super-middleweight title.

Sugar Ray Leonard won titles at five different weights.

Fabrico Tiozzo beat Terry Ray in their May 1998 W.B.A. cruiserweight fight when the referee stopped the fight in the first Round.

The W.B.O. middleweight fight between Lonnie Bradley and Otis Grant in March 1997 ended in a draw.

BOXING

Azumah Nelson retired in 1998 aged 40.

Briton Paul Lloyd lost to I.B.F. bantamweight champion Tim Austin in March 1998.

Boxer Jack Britton fought 350 bouts between 1905-30.

Michael Loewe of Romania took the vacant W.B.O. welterweight title in February 1997.

Ike Quartey was stripped of his W.B.A. welterweight crown in 1998 for not fighting Andrei Pestriaev.

Lennox Lewis took the vacant W.B.C. heavyweight title in February 1997.

William Joppy retained his W.B.A. middleweight title in 1998 by beating Roberto Duran.

Emile Griffith won the world welterweight title in 1961 and world middleweight title in 1966.

Marco Antonio Barrera of Mexico beat Briton Richie Wenton for the vacant W.B.O. super-featherweight title in October 1998.

Boxer Gerry Penalosa represents the Philippines.

Joe Louis spent 11 years 252 days as world heavyweight champion.

Ezzard Charles was Ring Magazine fighter of the year in 1949 and '50.

BOXING

Rocky Marciano was Ring Magazine fighter of the year in 1952, '54 and '55.

In a May 1999 I.B.F. welterweight bout against Hugo Pineda, Felix Trinidad retained his title.

Eugenia Williams scored the March 1999 world heavyweight fight between Lennox Lewis and Evander Holyfield 115-113 to Holyfield.

Henry Akinwande was disqualified in Round Five of his July 1997 fight with Lennox Lewis.

Joe Frazier was Ring Magazine fighter of the year in 1970 and '71.

Flyweight boxer Carlos Salazar represents Argentina.

BOXING

Briton Carl Thompson beat Ralf Rocchigiani in October 1997 to take the W.B.O. cruiserweight title.

The February 1998 W.B.A. light-middleweight fight between Laurent Boudouani and Guillermo Jones resulted in a draw.

Boxer Billy Bird fought 318 boughts between 1920-48.

Herbie Hide's W.B.O. heavyweight title fight with Tony Tucker in June 1997 took place in Norwich.

Evander Holyfield became W.B.C./W.B.A./I.B.F. heavyweight champion in October 1990.

The attendance for the world heavyweight title fight between Jack Dempsey and Gene Tunney in Philadelphia in 1926 was 120,757.

The W.B.A. light-heavyweight fight between Louis Del Valle and Eddy Smulders in September 1997 took place in Aachen.

Sugar Ray Robinson had 110 knockout wins in his career from 1940-65.

Barney Ross was a world lightweight, junior welterweight and welterweight champion.

Michael Loewe relinquished his W.B.O. welterweight title in February 1998.

Boxer Wayne McCullough is managed by his wife Cheryl.

Boxer Jose Bonilla represents Venezuela.

Fernando Vargas retained his I.B.F. light-middleweight title in March 1999 by beating Briton Howard Clark.

BOXING

The two W.B.O. fights in 1997 between super-featherweights Julien Lorcy and Arnulfo Castillo both ended in draws.

Roy Jones was disqualified in his March 1997 W.B.C. light-heavyweight title fight with Montell Griffin.

The 1914 world middleweight bout between Al McCoy and George Chip lasted 45 seconds.

Briton Ensley Bingham lost his November 1996 W.B.O. light-middleweight title fight with Ronald Wright.

Julio César Chavez headlined Don King's 'Grand Slam of Boxing'.

Wilfred Benitez was 17 years 176 days old when he first won the world light-heavyweight title.

Dariusz Michalczewski defended his W.B.O. light-heavyweight title in 1997 by beating Briton Nicky Piper.

Byron Mitchell beat Frankie Liles in June 1999 to take the W.B.A. super-middleweight title.

Boxer George Marsden fought 311 bouts between 1928-46.

Oscar De La Hoya relinquished his W.B.C. super-lightweight title in 1997.

Sandy Saddler had 103 knockout wins in his career from 1944-56.

Carl Thompson lost his W.B.O. cruiserweight title in March 1999 to Johnny Nelson.

Choo In-joo retained his W.B.C. super-flyweight title in June 1999 by knocking out Pone Saengmorakot.

BOXING

Jimmy Wilde had 98 knockout wins in his career from 1911-23.

Joe Louis fought in 27 world title fights.

Vic Toweel knocked down Danny O'Sullivan 14 times during their 1950 world bantamweight title fight.

Harry Simon beat Kevin Lueshing in May 1999 to retain his W.B.O. light-middleweight title.

Miguel Angel Gonzalez and Julio César Chavez drew their March 1998 W.B.C. super-lightweight title fight.

Wilfredo Vazquez was stripped of his W.B.A. featherweight title for not fighting Antonio Cermeno.

Grant beat Washington in an I.B.F. cruiserweight bout in 1997.

Boxer Hugo Soto represents Argentina.

Carl Thompson beat Chris Eubank in April 1998 and again in July 1998.

Light-flyweight boxer Juan Cordoba is Argentinian.

In their two meetings in December 1996 and April 1997, Ralf Rocchigiani outpointed Stefan Angehrn on both occasions.

In a world light-heavyweight unification bout in June 1999, Roy Jones beat Reggie Johnson on points.

Keith Holmes beat Hassine Cherif in April 1999 to regain his W.B.C. middleweight title.

Boxer Jane Couch beat Sandra Geiger in 1996 for the world welterweight title. Geiger ended up in hospital with a broken nose, fractured hand and cracked ribs.

BOXING

Bombadier Billy Wells was the first heavyweight to win outright ownership of the Lonsdale Belt.

Holder Erik Morales retained his W.B.C. super-bantamweight title in May 1999 by knocking out Juan Carlos Ramirez.

Sharmba Mitchell retained his W.B.A. super-lightweight title in April 1999 on points over Reggie Green.

In 1681 the Duke of Albemarle organized a match between one of his footmen and a butcher.

At 270 lbs, Primo Carnera is the heaviest world champion ever.

José Luis Lopez was stripped of his W.B.O. welterweight title after failing a drugs test.

Lennox Lewis beat Gary Mason in 1990 to take the British and European heavyweight title.

In 1995 Wayne McCullough became the first non-Japanese boxer to win in Japan in six years when he took the W.B.C. bantamweight title.

Trevor Berbick was sentenced to four years in jail in 1992 for rape.

All bouts above middleweight use 10oz gloves.

When Luis Resto's gloves were checked after a fight against Billy Collins in 1983 at Madison Square Gardens it was discovered that the padding had been removed which resulted in a jail sentence for trainer Panama Lewis.

Briton Terry Dunstan was beaten by Imamu Mayfield in their March 1998 I.B.F. cruiserweight title fight.

SNOOKER

SNOOKER

Silvino Francisco lost 12-9 to Kirk Stevens in the final of the 1985 Dulux British Open.

Mike Hallett turned professional in 1979. His first major tournament victory was in 1988, beating Stephen Hendry 8-5 in the Fosters Professional Tournament.

A maximum break at the 1999 Benson & Hedges Masters would have netted the potter an £80,000 car.

John Spencer used a two-piece cue to win the 1977 World Championship.

Ken Doherty's first professional appearance in the 1990 Rothmans Grand Prix resulted in a 5-2 defeat in the 1st Round by Jason Smith.

Tony Drago's first professional appearance in the 1985 Goya Matchroom Trophy resulted in a 5-2 1st Round defeat by Roger Bales.

Snooker player François Ellis is from South Africa.

After Steve Davis beat Doug Mountjoy in the 1981 World Championship final, the players met again in the quarter-final of Langs Scottish Masters where Davis won 5-0.

Steve Davis won his six World Championships using a cue he was given at the age of 14.

Neal Foulds's first professional tournament meeting with Steve Davis resulted in an 8-10 defeat in the 1st Round of the Embassy World Championship.

SNOOKER

Peter and Silvino Francisco met in the 5th Round of the 1987 Mercantile Credit Classic. Silvino won 5-1.

Stephen Hendry first won the Scottish Championship in 1987 at the age of 18.

In 1980 Terry Griffiths won the Benson & Hedges Masters and Benson and Hedges Irish Masters.

Jimmy White came back from 3-0 down to John Parrott in the 1999 Liverpool Victoria Charity Challenge to win 5-4 on the final black.

Matthew Stevens's first major final was the 1998 U.K. Championship.

Ronnie O'Sullivan equalled Darren Morgan's three-year old tournament record of a 143 total clearance in the 1999 Welsh Open.

Stephen Hendry first won the Embassy World Championship in 1990 at the age of 21.

Alex Higgins won the World Championship on his debut in the competition in 1972.

Steve James's first major professional tournament victory was the 1990 Mercantile Credit Classic.

Joe Johnson's first professional engagement was a 9-3 defeat by Bill Werbeniuk in the 1979 Coral U.K. Championship.

In 1989, Tony Knowles was whitewashed 5-0 in successive tournaments, the Anglian British Open and Benson & Hedges Masters.

SNOOKER

Tony Meo was knocked out by John Parrott in the 1st Round of the 1986 and 1987 Embassy World Championships.

Wayne Jones turned professional in 1984.

Warren King won the 1986 & 1987 Australian Championships.

John Rea won the 1989 Scottish Championship, beating Murdo Macleod 9-7.

A French infantry captain named Mingaud invented the leather tip of a cue in 1807.

Alec Brown invented a miniature ebony cue the size of a fountain pen for tricky shots but it was outlawed because of its size in 1938.

SNOOKER

Tony Drago came from 4-2 down to beat Stephen Hendry 5-4 in the semi-final of the 1998 Irish Open.

Maureen McCarthy scored two points in her game against Mike Dunn at the Benson & Hedges snooker championship in 1998.

Graham Miles lost 22-12 in the 1974 World Championship final to Ray Reardon.

Ray Reardon's 27-16 win over Alex Higgins in the 1976 Embassy World Championship was the biggest margin of victory in his wins in the world finals.

Dean Reynolds's 1988 win in the English Championship was his first major victory.

Alain Robidoux of Canada was born in 1960.

Willie Thorne's first major win was the 1985 Mercantile Credit Classic.

Darren Morgan played five qualifying rounds in the 1989 Embassy World Championship before losing to John Virgo 10-4 in the 1st Round.

Gary Wilkinson turned professional in 1987.

Canadian Kirk Stevens was whitewashed in successive tournaments in 1981 in the Jameson International and Northern Ireland Classic.

Jim Wych reached the quarter-final of the Embassy World Championship in 1980 at his first attempt.

SNOOKER

In his first appearance in the final stage of the Embassy World Championship in 1984, Mario Morra of Canada lost 10-3 to compatriot Cliff Thorburn.

Snooker player Robin Hull missed the final black and a 147 clearance in his win against Tom Finstad in the 1999 World Professional Championship qualifier.

Steve Davis's 147 in the 1982 Lada Classic was the first live televised total clearance.

Anthony Hamilton's win over Stephen Hendry in the 1999 British Open was the first time in nine attempts he'd beaten him.

The Lion Brown New Zealand Masters was first staged in 1988.

Coral sponsored the U.K. Open from 1979-85.

David Taylor first played in the World Championship in 1970.

Kelly Fisher won the 1998 women's world championship.

John Virgo's only major win was the 1979 U.K. Championship.

Pearl Assurance took over sponsorship of the British Open in 1990.

Doug Mountjoy won the 1982 Welsh Championship beating Terry Griffiths 9-8.

The first Irish winner of the Benson and Hedges Irish Masters was Alex Higgins in 1989.

SNOOKER

Stacey Hillyard was the first woman to make a century in competition, in the Bournemouth League in 1985.

Ann-Marie Farren was the 1987 women's world champion.

Steve Newbury's first major championship final was the 1987 Matchroom Welsh Championships.

Allison Fisher was the 1986 women's world champion.

John Spencer made a 147 clearance in the 1979 Holsten Tournament.

The B.B.C.'s first snooker outside broadcast was in 1950.

Ronnie O'Sullivan won the first two frames against James Wattana in their 1999 Welsh Open quarter-final with clearances of 144 and 147.

Snooker player Jim Bear is Canadian.

Eddie Charlton was a world professional championship semi-finalist on eight occasions.

Steve Davis beat Patsy Fagan in the 1979 World Championship qualifying round and again in 1980 in the 1st Round proper.

Karen Corr was the 1990 women's world champion.

Dennis Taylor's first appearance in the World Championship was a 1st round defeat in 1973 by Cliff Thorburn.

Alex Higgins was suspended for the whole of the 1990-91 season.

SNOOKER

Rex Williams turned professional in 1951.

Jimmy White's first appearance in the 1st Round of the Embassy World Championship was 1981, when he lost 10-8 to Steve Davis.

James Wattana was born in 1970.

Former world champion Cliff Thorburn lost 10-5 to Nick Dyson in the qualifying round of the 1991 Embassy World Championship.

Eddie Sinclair won the 1982 Scottish Championship.

Former world champion John Spencer lost in the qualifying rounds of the Embassy World Championship from 1987-91.

Northern Ireland snooker player Jason Prince turned professional in 1990.

Snooker player Dene O'Kane was born in 1963.

Murdo Macleod beat Eddie Sinclair 11-9 in the 1983 Scottish Championship.

John Parrott whitewashed Perrie Mans 10-0 in qualifying for the 1984 Embassy World Championship.

Tony Jones's first whitewash as a professional was suffered at the hands of Neal Foulds in the 1984 Rothmans Grand Prix.

RUGBY

RUGBY

Italy will enter the Five Nations tournament in 2000, making it the Six Nations.

Leigh Centurions suffered six sendings off in the 1998 season.

13-a-side in rugby league was introduced in 1906.

The 132 regular matches in the 1998 J.J.B. Super League saw an attendance of 910,912.

James Lowes of Bradford Bulls was 1997 Man of Steel award winner.

Bath rugby union winger Adedayo Adebayo is one of 17 children.

Bedford rugby union fly-half Anthony Yapp's sister Jo plays scrum-half for England women.

Paul Newlove's transfer fee from Featherstone Rovers to Bradford Northern in 1993 was fixed by tribunal at £245,000.

Harlequins' player Robert Liley played in France for Cahors.

Rugby League player Ike Owens was transferred in 1948/49 from Leeds to Castleford for £2,750.

Leicester rugby union player David Lougheed joined them from the Balmy Beach club in Toronto.

RUGBY

Wakefield Trinity suffered six sendings off in the 1998 league season.

1908 saw the first Australian rugby league tour of England.

London Irish hooker Richard Kirke is a former corrosion consultant.

Three South African international players made appearances for British rugby league clubs in 1998.

Brothers Graeme and Stephen Bachop played rugby union for New Zealand against South Africa in 1994.

Wigan's Andy Platt was 1993 Man of Steel Award winner.

The official rugby league Hall of Fame was introduced in 1988.

The attendance of the 165 games played in rugby league's 1st Division in 1998 was 259,442.

Manchester Sale rugby union player Dylan O'Grady is a former nightclub bouncer.

Rotherham rugby union player David Scully works as a firefighter.

Rugby league player Trevor Skerrett was transferred from Wakefield Trinity to Hull in 1980/81.

Pool A in the 1997/98 Heineken European Cup featured Toulouse, Milan, Leicester and Leinster.

RUGBY

The first radio broadcast of the rugby league Challenge Cup Final was in 1927.

Moseley rugby union player William Drake-Lee is son of former England prop William Drake-Lee.

Leeds Rhinos signed Iestyn Harris from Warrington in 1997 for £350,000.

Australian rugby league coach Tony Currie played for Leeds.

Mark Aston of Sheffield Eagles won the 1998 Lance Todd Trophy in rugby league.

Gavin Miller of Hull Kingston Rovers was 1986 Man of Steel Award winner.

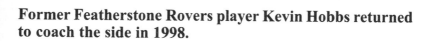

Former Featherstone Rovers player Kevin Hobbs returned to coach the side in 1998.

1910 saw the first British tour of Australia and New Zealand.

Rugby league player Gary Connolly moved from St. Helens to Wigan in 1993 for £250,000.

Bedford rugby union player Simon Crabb was voted New Zealand's most promising player in 1993.

RUGBY

Garry Schofield scored 31 tries for Great Britain in rugby league from 1984-94.

Ireland won the Rugby Union Youth World Cup in April 1998.

Newcastle rugby union player Garath Archer is son of former Gosforth wing Stuart Archer.

The first rugby league game in France was an exhibition game between England and Australia in Paris in 1933.

Paul Newlove was 18 years 72 days old when he made his Great Britain rugby league Test debut in 1989.

Harlequins' full-back James Staples played football for Greenwich Borough with West Ham star Ian Wright.

Martin Offiah scored 26 tries for Great Britain rugby league team from 1988-94.

In 1948 King George VI was the first reigning monarch to attend a rugby league game.

Rugby league player Alan Hunte moved from St. Helens to Hull Sharks in 1997 for £250,000.

Vai'aga Tuigamala's brother Toa'lua plays rugby union for Orrell.

Rotherham rugby union player Gregory Austin was born in the same village as Sir Don Bradman, Australian cricketer.

RUGBY

Andy Gregory led Salford to consecutive First Division championships in 1995 & '96.

Wigan Warriors crowd of 6,005 against Sheffield Eagles in June was their lowest crowd since Super League started.

Orrell's Stockport-born rugby union player Paul Manley played for the Ngtapa club in New Zealand.

The timekeeper and hooter system of signalling the end of a match in rugby league was launched in 1972.

Rugby league player Graham Steadman moved from Featherstone Rovers to Castleford in 1989 for £170,000.

Alex Murphy scored 16 tries for the Great Britain rugby league team from 1958-71.

Ulster finished bottom of the 1997/98 Heineken European Cup, Pool B.

The try value in rugby league was increased to four points in 1983.

Rugby league player Lee Crooks was involved in two £150,000 transfers – from Hull to Leeds in 1987 and Leeds to Castleford in 1990.

Lewis Jones of Leeds kicked 66 goals for Great Britain rugby league team from 1954-57.

Jeff Grayshon was 36 years 8 months old when he played for Great Britain rugby league team against New Zealand in 1985.

RUGBY

Moseley rugby union player Anthony Healy played for Marmande in France.

Neil Jenkins made his debut with Pontypridd in 1990.

Paul Ringer, former Welsh rugby union player, was jailed in 1999 for fraud.

London Welsh rugby union player James Storey is son of B.B.C. athletics commentator Stuart Storey.

Wigan Warriors versus Hull Sharks was the opening game in J.J.B. Super League 1999.

In the 1998 Anzac Test on April 24th New Zealand beat Australia 22-16.

Wigan's Eric Ashton was awarded the M.B.E. in 1966.

In the final of the Papua New Guinea rugby league 50th anniversary tournament in 1998, the host nation beat Tonga 54-12.

Bath rugby union player David Lyle was born in San Diego, U.S.A.

York rugby league coach Dean Robinson played for Wakefield Trinity.

Gloucester rugby union player Simon Devereux received a prison sentence in 1995 for assault.

RUGBY

Newcastle Knights finished second in the 1998 Australian National Rugby League table.

Harlequins' scrum-half Huw Harries is a qualified pharmacist.

Welsh rugby league player Jonathan Davies scored 24 points for his country against Papua New Guinea in 1991 at Swansea.

Wakefield rugby union player Paul White is by profession a dentist.

Worcester rugby union player Dean Ball is a former carpenter.

Paul Loughlin of St. Helens scored 31 goals for Great Britain from 1988-92.

Hunslet's Geoff Gunney was awarded the M.B.E. in 1970.

Huddersfield Giants signed Garry Schofield from Leeds in February 1996 for £135,000.

Peter Ramsden of Huddersfield was 19 years old when he received the Lance Todd Trophy in 1953.

Melbourne Storm finished third in the 1998 Australian National Rugby League table.

Scotland's rugby league team lost both their games in the 1999 Tri-Nations championship with France and Ireland.

Newcastle rugby union player Neil Frankland is a chemist by profession.

RUGBY

Waterloo rugby union player Martin O'Keefe has represented Merseyside at badminton.

In Australia, North Sydney's rugby league team is North Sydney Bears.

Premiership Two club Worcester had two points deducted in 1998 for fielding an unregistered player, Tom Robinson.

Pontypridd's heaviest defeat in their 123 year history was losing 71-14 to Stade Français in the 1998/99 European Cup quarter final.

Rugby league player Clive Sullivan was awarded the M.B.E. in 1974.

Brisbane Broncos' average home crowd in 1998 was 20,252.

Joe Lydon kicked 26 goals for Great Britain rugby league team from 1983-92.

St. Helens player Bobbie Goulding scored 32 points for Great Britain against Fiji in 1996.

Borders finished bottom of Pool C in the 1997/98 Heineken European Cup.

West Hartlepool finished runners-up to Bedford in the Allied Dunbar 2 League in 1998.

Bath rugby union player Andrew Long has played cricket for Dorset.

RUGBY

Rugby league player Chris Hesketh was awarded the M.B.E. in 1976.

Gary Hetherington is chief executive at Leeds rugby league club. His wife Kath is chairwoman of Gateshead.

On his Five Nations debut in 1986 against England, Frenchman Thomas Castaignède won the game with a last minute drop goal.

Bedford rugby union player Robert Ashworth was educated at Bradford Grammar School.

The sin bin was introduced in rugby league in 1983.

Allan Agar of Featherstone Rovers was 1983 Man of Steel.

Cheltenham-born Gloucester lock Robert Fidler is son of former England lock John Fidler.

The average attendance in rugby league's second division in 1998 was 865.

Newcastle rugby union player Nicholas Popplewell was an Irish schools hockey international.

1998 J.J.B. Super League young player of the year was Lee Gilmour of Wigan Warriors.

Worcester rugby union scrum-half Ben Harvey is a nephew of actress Jan Harvey.

RUGBY

Canterbury's rugby league team in Australia's National League is Canterbury Bulldogs.

Waterloo flanker Stephane Lanie joined the club from Grenoble.

Gael Tallec was the only French international to appear for a British rugby league club in 1998.

Scotland beat Ireland 30-13 in the 1999 Five Nations Tournament.

Robbie Paul of Bradford Bulls won the 1996 Lance Todd Trophy in rugby league.

Leading goal scorer in the 1998 Australian national rugby league was Ivan Cleary of Sydney City.

French rugby union player Xavier Garbajosa plays for Toulouse.

Rugby league player Roger Millward was awarded the M.B.E. in January 1983.

England's win in December 1998 against South Africa was their first against any of the leading southern hemisphere teams since the 1995 World Cup.

Leicester flanker Neil Back's personalized number plate is B4CKY.

Wales beat South Africa in a rugby union international in June 1999 less than a year after losing 96-13 to them in Pretoria.

RUGBY

Japan beat Chinese Taipei in a 1998 World Cup qualifier 134-6.

Thurrock, in Courage League's London Division One, beat London Irish 16-10 in the 1991/92 Pilkington Cup.

Brian O'Meara was ruled out of Ireland's four match 1999 summer tour to Australia because of a broken thumb.

Villa Rockets contended for a Super League franchise in rugby league in summer 1999.

The capacity of Wigan's new J.J.B. stadium is 25,000.

Sheffield Eagles forward Darren Turner was banned for six games in Febraury 1999 for making obscene gestures to Salford fans.

London Irish's takeover of Richmond and London Scottish was approved by the R.F.U. in June 1999.

John Leslie, Scotland rugby union player, was born in Lower Hutt, New Zealand.

Springboks' press liaison officer Alex Brown was Charlene's (Kylie Minogue's) first boyfriend in soap Neighbours.

Mike Catt was born in Port Elizabeth, South Africa.

When Scotland beat Spain 85-3 in 1998, it was the first time in 111 years they'd scored five tries in an international.

RUGBY

Fiji won the 1999 Hong Kong Sevens.

Rugby league coach John Kear took charge of Paris St. Germain for part of 1996.

Briton Harvey Howard played for Western Suburbs Magpies in the 1998 Australian rugby league season.

China beat Singapore in the 1999 Hong Kong Sevens to register their first win in the tournament.

Iestyn Harris of Leeds Rhinos was 1998 J.J.B. Man of Steel Award winner.

Thirty Super League games in 1998 saw an attendance of 10,000 or more.

Rugby league player Jeff Grayshon was awarded the M.B.E. in 1992.

James Lowes of Bradford Bulls was 1997 Super League player of the year.

Carlisle's Mick Morgan was 1982 Man of Steel winner.

RUGBY

Nigel Wright transferred from Wakefield Trinity to Wigan in 1993 for £140,000.

Leeds rugby league side scored three tries in six minutes against Wakefield in May 1999.

The 1998 women's World Cup was staged in the Stadion Des Eendracht, Amsterdam.

Two Fijian international players made appearances for British rugby league clubs in 1998.

Australian coach Stuart Raper played for Oldham.

Dean Bell of Wigan won the 1993 Lance Todd trophy in rugby league.

Castleford rugby league player Malcolm Reilly was awarded the O.B.E. in 1991.

Bradford Bulls had five players sent off in the league in 1998.

Bath rugby union player Richard de Villiers's grandfather played for Natal.

Rugby league player Geoff Clarkson was involved in 12 transfers in his 17-year career from 1966-84.

Cheltenham-born Gloucester rugby union player Laurie Beck played water polo for Southwest Juniors.

Castleford coach Stuart Raper is older brother of Castleford player Aaron Raper.

RUGBY

1998 J.J.B. Super League player's player of the year was Iestyn Harris.

Hull Sharks coach in 1999 is Peter Walsh.

Keighley Cougars signed Daryl Powell from Sheffield Eagles in April 1995 for £135,000.

England beat France 21-10 in the 1999 Five Nations.

Geoff Pimblett scored nine goals in England's 1978 rugby league match versus Wales at St. Helens.

Warrington coach in 1999 is Darryl van de Velde.

Australian rugby union player Adam Leach signed for Harlequins after advertising his services on the Internet.

Rugby league player Garry Schofield was awarded the O.B.E. in 1994.

Robbie Paul of Bradford Bulls was 1996 Super League player of the year in 1996.

Harlequins won Pool D of the 1997/98 Heineken European Cup.

Ulster captain David Humphreys scored the winning try against Stade Français in their 1998/99 European Cup semi-final.

Wigan rugby league club's mascot is Pieman.

RUGBY

Murrayfield is to host the 2000 Silk Cut Challenge Cup Final.

Sale rugby union player Steve Hanley's father is director of rugby at Aspatria.

Llanelli signed former rugby league player Scott Quinnell from Richmond in 1998.

Croatia led New Zealand 12-10 in the 1999 Hong Kong Sevens with two minutes to go before finally succumbing to the Kiwis 17-12.

Salford Reds' rugby club mascot is the aptly-named Daredevil Duck.

The match between Spartans and Cinderford on December 19, 1998 was abandoned after 35 minutes following a dual sending off.

Rugby union player Tony Underwood was born in Ipoh, Malaysia.

Bradford Bulls' players (and brothers) Henry Paul and Robbie Paul released a single, 'Ain't No Stopping Us Now', in February 1999.

Paul Grayson scored all of Waterloo's points in their 1992/93 Pilkington Cup victory against Bath.

Wakefield rugby union player Terence Garnett is a judo black belt.

HORSE RACING

HORSE RACING

The Juddmonte International Stakes is the principal race of the three-day August meeting at York.

Only Royale won the 1993 & '94 Yorkshire Oaks.

Kool Kat Katie won the 1997 E.P. Taylor Stakes at Woodbine race track.

1912 Grand National-winning jockey Ernie Piggott was Lester Piggott's grandfather.

The 1000 Guineas was sponsored by General Accident from 1984-92.

Fleet was the appropriately named winner of the 1967 1000 Guineas.

Owner of 1963 Grand National-winning horse Ayala was hairdresser Mr. Pierre 'Teasy-Weasy' Raymond.

Skip Away won 4 out of 11 starts in 1997 winning $4,089,000.

The owner of the 1938 Grand National-winning horse Battleship was married to the famous Hollywood film star Randolph Scott.

Jonjo O'Neill was National Hunt champion jockey for the first time in 1977/8.

Stan Mellor rode 1035 winners in his National Hunt career.

Mr. What won the 1958 Grand National by 30 lengths.

HORSE RACING

1961 Grand National-winning jockey Bobby Beasley was grandson of 1891 winner Henry Beasley.

Terry Biddlecombe rode 908 winners in his National Hunt career.

Australia's Melbourne Cup is sponsored by Fosters.

1939 Grand National-winning horse Workman had finished third in 1938.

My Babu won the 1948 2000 Guineas. Our Babu won it in 1955.

John Osborne's 2000 Guineas winners included Pretender in 1869 & Prince Charlie in 1872.

1924 Grand National winner Master Robert was an 11 year-old former plough horse.

The Grand National was first televised in 1960.

Michael Oliver trained 1986 Grand National winner West Tip.

The winner of the 1998 Kentucky Derby won $738,800.

Owner of 1960 Grand National winner Merryman II, Miss Winifred Wallace, was the first unmarried woman to own the winning horse.

An automatic starting barrier was first used in the 1925 Grand National.

HORSE RACING

The Queen Elizabeth II Stakes at Ascot is run over exactly 1 mile.

Catchas Catchcan won the 1998 Yorkshire Oaks.

1946 Cheltenham Gold Cup winner Prince Regent was favourite for the 1946 Grand National.

Halling won the 1995 & '96 Eclipse Stakes.

The 1980 Sussex Stakes was won by Posse.

Champion won the 1800 Epsom Derby.

Jockey Major Jack Wilson who rode the 1925 Grand National winner Double Chance also played cricket for Yorkshire.

1926 Grand National-winning jockey Billy Watkinson was born in Tasmania.

Enzeli was the first Irish-trained Ascot Gold Cup winner since Levmoss in 1969.

1927 Grand National-winning horse Sprig had been fourth in the previous two Nationals.

Pyrrhus the First won the 1846 Epsom Derby.

Jockey of 1946 Grand National-winning horse Lovely Cottage, Captain Bobby Petre, died in 1996 aged 84.

HORSE RACING

1989 Grand National winner Little Polvier won the 1987 Scottish Grand National.

1947 Grand National-winning jockey Eddie Dempsey only set foot in England two days before the race.

Winner of the 1875 Epsom Derby was Galopin.

Fred Archer rode five Epsom Derby winners.

1964 Grand National winner Team Spirit and 1967 winner Foinavon shared the same sire, Vulgan.

Mr. Frisk, ridden by amateur jockey Mr. Marcus Armytage ran the 1990 Grand National in 8:47.8, beating Red Rum's record by 14.1 seconds.

1948 Grand National-winning jockey Arthur Thompson was captured by the Germans in World War II but stole a bicycle from a guard and rode it to the British lines.

Gentlemen won 4 out of 6 starts in 1997, winning $2,125,300.

1984 Grand National-winning jockey Neale Doughty taught himself to ride on pit ponies in Wales.

The owner of 1992 Grand National winner Party Politics, Mrs. Thompson, picked up a winning cheque of £99,943.

Jerry Bailey won 272 out of 1043 races in 1997.

HORSE RACING

The Middle Park Stakes at Newmarket is for 2-year-olds.

1926 Grand National-winning jockey Billy Watkinson died three weeks after his victory following a fall at the Bogside track.

Sir Michael Stoute took over training the Queen's horses in 1999.

Sheila's Cottage, 1948 Grand National winner, is buried at the bottom of jockey Arthur Thompson's garden in Wexford.

1949 Grand National-winning jockey Leo McMorrow was killed in a motoring accident.

Chief Bearhart won the 1997 Canadian International Stakes and Breeders' Cup Turf.

Top weight in the 1986 Grand National, Essex, was from Czechoslovakia.

Frank Wootton was champion flat race jockey from 1909-12.

The horse which finished second in the 1998 Kentucky Derby won $170,000.

Owner Michael Worcester who won the 1997 Cheltenham Gold Cup with Mr. Mulligan made his fortune selling ice cream cones.

The Coronation Stakes at Royal Ascot is for 3-year-old fillies.

HORSE RACING

The Eclipse Stakes, usually run at Sandown Park, was run at Kempton Park in 1973.

Mary Hinge, Jo Blob and Betty Swallocks were all horses trained by Julie Cecil.

The first three horses home in the 1950 Grand National were all trained in Yorkshire.

1948 Grand National-winner Sheila's Cottage was the first mare to win the event since 1906.

The winner of the Preakness Stakes in 1998 won $650,000.

Riderless horse Popham Down ran across the front of the 23rd fence in the 1967 Grand National causing the chaos which resulted in Foinavon's win.

Grand National starter Mr. Leslie Firth pressed the lever in 1951 with half the runners facing the wrong way which resulted in 12 fallers at the first fence as the jockeys attempted to make up lost ground.

1955 Grand National-winning jockey Pat Taaffe won again in 1970.

Vincent O'Brien trained Grand National winners from 1955-57 - the only man to achieve this feat in three successive years with three different horses.

Fred Rimmell trained 1956 Grand National winner ESB. His father Tom had trained 1932 winner Forbra.

HORSE RACING

Owner of 1962 Grand National winner Kilmore was film producer Nat Cohen.

The first radio broadcast of the Grand National was in 1927.

Three racegoers were hit by lightning at the abandoned Warwick meeting on June 2, 1999.

HORSE RACING

Jump racing ceased at Windsor on Thursday, 3rd December, 1998.

The capacity of Newbury racecourse is 60,000.

Only four horses completed the 1980 Grand National.

Charlie Elliott and Steve Donoghue were joint champion flat race jockeys in 1923.

Zagreb won the 1996 Irish Derby.

Lester Reiff was champion flat-race jockey in 1900.

French Derby winner Montjeu won the Irish Derby in 1999 by five lengths.

1969 Grand National-winning jockey Eddie Harty represented the Republic of Ireland in the 1960 Olympics at Three-Day Eventing.

Owner of 1972 Grand National winner Well To Do Captain Forster inherited the horse from its previous owner Mrs. Sumner in 1971 after her death from cancer.

Trainer Mary Reveley trained 1995 & '97 Cesarewitch winners Old Red & Turnpole.

John Thorne, the jockey of Spartan Missile which was runner-up to Aldaniti in the 1981 Grand National, died the following year while riding in a point-to-point.

HORSE RACING

Steve Cauthen was first champion flat race jockey in 1984.

The Aga Khan tried to sell 1999 Ascot Gold Cup winning horse Enzeli as a jumper in 1998.

Mrs. Geraldine Rees in 1982 became the first woman to complete a Grand National.

The St. James's Palace Stakes at Royal Ascot is for 3-year-olds.

The Oaks is named after the Epsom home of the 12th Earl of Derby.

1969 Grand National-winning jockey John Cook broke his leg the following season and was unable to continue his racing career.

Balisada won the 1999 Coronation Stakes at Royal Ascot at 16-1.

Grittar in 1982 became the first favourite since Merryman II in 1960 to win the Grand National.

Pat Taaffe won the Cheltenham Gold Cup four times.

Saeed bin Suroor was leading flat-race trainer in 1996.

Tom Dreaper trained the winner of the Cheltenham Gold Cup on five occasions.

Insurance won the 1932 & '33 Champion Hurdle at Cheltenham.

HORSE RACING

Esha Ness 'won' the 1993 Grand National which was voided after two false starts.

The 1973 Whitbread Gold Cup was run at Newcastle.

1994 Grand National winner Minniehoma was owned by comedian Freddie Starr.

The 1976 Mackeson Gold Cup was run at Haydock Park.

Fiddler's Pike, fifth in the 1994 Grand National, was ridden by 51 year-old Mrs. Rosemary Henderson.

Sendawar, winner of St. James's Palace Stakes at Ascot in 1999 was the Aga Khan's first Group One winner in England for ten years.

Racing commentator Lord Oaksey came 2nd in the 1963 Grand National on Carrickbeg, riding under the name of Mr. John Lawrence.

Only 27 ran in the 1996 Grand National.

Richard and Michael Hills were the first twins to ride in the same Epsom Derby.

Night Nurse died in 1998 at the age of 28.

Leo Temple missed his first ride at Bangor-on-Dee on November 27, 1998 by going to Bangor by mistake.

Event of the Year won the 1998 Jim Beam Stakes at Turfway Park race track.

HORSE RACING

1973 Grand National winner Red Rum received 23 lbs from runner-up Crisp.

The Shergar Cup, between teams of horses from Europe and the Middle East was first held at Goodwood in 1999.

Charlotte Brew was the first woman to ride in the Grand National.

Red Candle won the 1973 Hennessey Gold Cup, beating Red Rum into second place.

Red Rum's owner was Noel le Mare.

Mrs. Florence Nagle was the first woman to be granted a licence to train racehorses in Britain.

In the Groove won the 1991 Coronation Cup at Epsom.

Flame of Tara won the 1983 Coronation Stakes at Ascot.

Graham Bradley's first winner was Talon at Sedgefield on March 11, 1980.

Fred Winter was the last Grand National-winning jockey to train the winner of the race.

The total drop at Becher's Brook at Aintree is 6ft 9 inches.

2nd, 3rd and 4th in the 1975 Grand National were alliterative horses – Red Rum, Spanish Steps and Money Market.

HORSE RACING

There were 32 runners in the 1922 Grand National.

1928 Grand National-winning jockey William Parker Dutton trained 1956 Cheltenham Gold Cup winner Limber Hill.

Donald McCain Jr., son of the trainer of Red Rum, rode in the 1996 Grand National on Sure Metal finishing last.

The 1997 Grand National took place on Monday 7th April.

One of the syndicate members who owned 1998 Grand National winner Earth Summit was Ricky George, whose goal for Hereford knocked Newcastle out of the 1972 F.A. Cup.

L'Escargot won the 1970 & '71 Cheltenham Gold Cup.

Britain's oldest racecourse, at Chester, staged its first meeting in 1540.

There were 66 runners in the 1929 Grand National.

Music Hall won the 1920 Scottish Grand National.

Jockey Tommy Cullinan won the 1930 Cheltenham Gold Cup and Grand National.

1921 Grand National winner Shaun Spadah fell at the first in the 1922 race.

Three former Grand National winners were in the field for the 1933 race – Forbra, Shaun Goilin and Gregalach.

HORSE RACING

The entry fee for the 1923 Grand National was £100.

Golden Miller won the 1934 Grand National and Cheltenham Gold Cup.

1923 Grand National winning jockey Captain Geoffrey Bennet died in 1924 after being kicked after a fall.

In retaining the Grand National in 1936, Reynoldstown became the first horse to do so since 1870.

Sire and dam of 1938 Grand National-winning horse Battleship were Man O'War and Quarantaine.

The winner of the 1998 Belmont Stakes won $600,000.

Rag Trade finished last in the 1975 Grand National and was first in the 1976 Grand National.

Geri won the 1997 Woodbine Mile at Woodbine race track.

Robert Robson trained 12 winners of the Oaks.

Cut Above won the 1981 St. Leger.

In The Wings won the 1990 Coronation Cup at Epsom.

Steel Pulse won the 1972 Irish Derby.

As well as winning the 1973, '74 & '77 Grand Nationals, Red Rum was runner-up in 1975 & '76.

HORSE RACING

Countess Diana won the 1997 Alcibiades Stakes at Keeneland race track.

Former British Lions rugby player John Douglas owned 1979 Grand National winner Rubstic.

Amateur jockey Marcus Armtage was a journalist with the Racing Post.

Quick As Lightning was the appropriately named winner of the 1980 1000 Guineas.

Assert won the 1982 Irish Derby.

Film star Gregory Peck owned Owen's Sedge, which ran in the 1963 Grand National.

Fred Winter saddled the 1965 & '66 Grand National winners in his first two seasons as a trainer.

Pay the Butler won the 1988 Japan Cup.

Mr. Snugfit was 2nd in the 1985 Grand National and 4th in the 1986 Grand National.

Only three horses finished the 1951 Grand National.

1952 Grand National winner Teal was destroyed after injuring himself in the 1953 Cheltenham Gold Cup.

HORSE RACING

The Champion Stakes at Newmarket became the Dubai Champion Stakes in 1982.

Paddy Prendergast was leading flat-race trainer from 1963-5.

Keith Piggott rode American Sister to victory in the 1939 Champion Hurdle at Cheltenham.

All Irish Classics are run at the the Curragh.

1922 Grand National winner Music Hall was bred in County Kildare.

Red Rum won the 1974 Scottish Grand National as well as the Aintree Grand National.

Sergeant Murphy was the first Grand National winner to be owned by an American.

Tim Molony rode the winner of the Champion Hurdle four years in a row from 1951-54.

Ardross won the 1981 & '82 Ascot Gold Cup.

Only two horses finished the 1928 Grand National.

Of the 42 horses in the 1928 Grand National, only ten were left in the race after the eighth fence after a pile up at the Canal Turn.

CRICKET

CRICKET

Allan Lamb topped Northamptonshire's batting averages in the 1995 county championship.

Umpire Nigel Plews was born in Nottingham.

The father of Scotland's opening batsman Mike Smith was at Cambridge at the same time as West Indies cricket team psychologist Rudi Webster.

Shaiza Khan faced the first ball for M.C.C. Women against a Surrey U21 Select XI on May 11, 1999.

Warwickshire dismissed Nottinghamshire for 76 in their second innings on June 17th 1999.

A win in the County Championship earns 12 points.

The ball which Shoaib Akhtar bowled to remove the New Zealand captain's leg stump in the 1999 World Cup semi-final travelled at 92 m.p.h.

CRICKET

Pakistan wicketkeeper Moin Khan broke the small finger of his left hand before the 1999 World Cup.

Of Warwickshire's first 17 scheduled days of county cricket in 1999, five were washouts.

England captain Nasser Hussain's sister Benazir dances with the Royal Ballet Company.

80-year-old Australian Trevor Guy, who manhandled John Snow at the 1971 Sydney Test, pleaded for forgiveness in early 1999.

Saeed Anwar hit a career best of 188 for Pakistan in the 1999 three nation Asian Championship.

Ghulam Ahmed, Indian Test bowler and former captain of the team, died in 1998.

Makhaya Ntini became the first black African to represent South Africa in 1998.

Blue balls were used by ladies in Edwardian times in case they became over-excited at the prospect of red ones.

In 1989 Brian Lara became the youngest captain of Trinidad and Tobago.

Mark Taylor, Australian cricketer, was born in Wagga-Wagga.

Nick Knight was caught out for a duck in England's final warm-up game before the 1999 World Cup against Hampshire.

The World Cup warm-up match between Kenya and Glamorgan was rained off.

CRICKET

Muttiah Muralitaharan's first day as a Lancashire player was delayed as the game against Gloucestershire was postponed.

Nasser Hussain once ruined the engine in Graham Gooch's car by putting in the wrong fuel.

Australia qualified for the 1999 World Cup final following their semi-final tie against South Africa by virtue of a higher Super Six qualifying position.

Geoff Boycott made 22 Test centuries for England.

The stand of 194 by Saeed Anwar and Wajahatullah Wasti in the 1999 World Cup semi-final for Pakistan versus New Zealand was a World Cup 1st wicket record.

Umer Rashid took career best figures of 4 for 41 for Sussex against Yorkshire in June 1999.

Javangal Srinath took 8 for 86 for India against Pakistan in the 1999 three nation Asian Championship.

Jason Gillespie made his Test debut for Australia versus West Indies in the 2nd Test in 1996/7.

Former Essex bowler Neil Williams's middle name is Fitzgerald.

England beat ACB Chairman's XI in a warm up for the 1998/99 Ashes series by one run.

Glamorgan bowler Steven Watkin's middle name is Llewellyn.

A tie in the County Championship earns six points.

CRICKET

Glenn McGrath was born in Narromine, New South Wales.

The legal weight of a ball of between 5.5-5.75 oz was specified in 1874.

Glamorgan were the only county to oppose the introduction of a two-division championship from 2000.

Alex Tudor's first two wickets in Test cricket were Australia's Waugh brothers.

Terry Jenner is the spin-bowling coach credited with contributing to Shane Warne's success.

Courtney Walsh's second wicket in the 1st Test for West Indies against South Africa in December 1998 made him his country's leading Test wicket-taker.

Heath Streak became Zimbabwe's first bowler to take 100 Test wickets in 1998.

The first over in England's game versus Queensland in November 1998 took 25 minutes after an injury to Hayden and a trip to a local sawmill by a groundsman to acquire some sawdust to prevent slippage on the field by bowlers.

Rookie England player Chris Read was born in Paignton, Devon.

Anil Kumble took 6 for 70 for India in the 1st innings of the First Test against Pakistan in January 1999. This was the first time the teams had met on Indian soil for 12 years.

Darren Lehmann's maiden one-day century for Australia in November 1998 was against Pakistan.

CRICKET

Nottinghamshire didn't win in the county championship in 1967 but didn't finish bottom.

Somerset's 554 against New Zealand in June 1999 was their highest score against a touring side.

West Indies 3-0 defeat by Pakistan in 1997 was their first Test series whitewash since 1928.

England beat India 5-0 in a 1959 Test series.

Surrey's name in the 1999 C.G.U. National League is Surrey Lions.

Shaun Pollock of South Africa became the fastest player to achieve 1,000 runs and 100 wickets in Limited Over Internationals when South Africa beat New Zealand in March 1999.

Don Bradman averaged 201.5 in the 1931/2 series for Australia against South Africa.

An unexpected swarm of bees halted play for a time during the Bangalore Test match between India and Pakistan in 1979/80.

A.F. Giles and T.A. Munton hit 141 for Warwickshire against Worcestershire in 1996 in a tenth wicket partnership.

India captain Nari Contractor had his skull fractured by Charlie Griffith against the West Indies in a Test and didn't play international cricket again.

All five Tests in the 1960/61 series between India and Pakistan were drawn.

CRICKET

Dominic Cork took 8 for 53 before lunch for Derbyshire against Essex on his 20th birthday.

England bowled Sri Lanka out for 99 in their 1999 one-day game at the W.A.C.A. ground.

Australia's first Test victory in England was in 1882.

Charles Bannerman hit 165 for Australia in the official first Test against England in 1877.

England won the Brisbane Test against Australia in December 1928 by 675 runs.

The Sydney Test between Australia and England in 1932 was the first of the 'Bodyline' series.

Cricketer Ian Healy's father was a bank manager.

Steve Waugh's century for Australia against West Indies in the Third Test in March 1999 was his 19th in Test cricket.

The first Test match between Australia and New Zealand was in 1946.

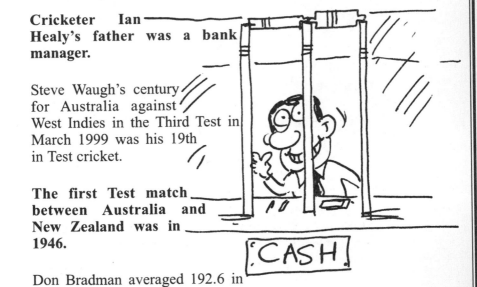

Don Bradman averaged 192.6 in his four Tests at Headingley.

CRICKET

The 'timeless' Test of 1939 between South Africa and England was played at Kingsmead, Durban.

L.G. Rowe made 214 and 100 n.o. on his Test debut for the West Indies against New Zealand in 1971/2.

N.D. Hirwani took 16 wickets for India against West Indies in a 1987/88 Test.

J.E. Barrett was the first Australian to carry his bat through a completed innings in a Test against England.

Wally Hammond scored 51 and took 5 wickets in his first Test against South Africa in 1927/28.

Jim Laker took 7 for 103 on his Test debut against West Indies.

P.J. Petherick of New Zealand took a hat-trick against Pakistan on his Test debut in 1976.

B.R. Taylor took 5 for 86 and scored 105 for New Zealand against India on his Test debut in 1964/65.

A.C. Hudson of South Africa was the first player to score a century and a duck on his debut having scored 163 and 0 in his innings against West Indies.

Graham Gooch's debut against Australia in 1975 saw him score ducks in both innings.

The brothers E.M. Grace, G.F. Grace and W.G. Grace all played against Australia in an 1880 Test for England.

The Strang, Rennie and Flower brothers all played for Zimbabwe against New Zealand in 1997/8.

CRICKET

Mark and Steve Waugh were the first twins to play Test cricket.

India were dismissed for 58 & 82 in a single day by England in the 1952 Manchester Test.

Chris Broad made six Test centuries for England.

England used 30 different players in their 5-match Test series against Australia in 1921.

27 wickets fell on one day in the 1888 Lord's Test between England and Australia.

Eddie Hemmings topped Sussex's bowling averages in the 1993 season.

England Test captain F.R. Brown was born in Peru.

F.J. Titmus also played football for Watford.

Zimbabwe Test captain A. Flower was born in South Africa.

Viv Richards made 1710 Test runs in the year 1976 in eleven Test matches.

Two South African test cricketers have been knighted - Murray Blissett and William Henry Milton.

Kapil Dev took 75 Test wickets in the year 1983 and 74 Test wickets in the year 1979.

A. Sandham was the first batsman to score 300 in a Test innings, in 1929/30.

CRICKET

K.C. Wessels has played for and against Australia.

The first time an extra day was added to a Test match was at Christchurch in 1946/47 between New Zealand and England.

The first Test match streak was seen in 1975.

Don Bradman scored 1671 at Melbourne in Test matches.

Dennis Lillee took 82 wickets at Melbourne in Test matches.

Cricketer John Inverarity's daughter is an Australian high jump champion.

G.R. Viswanath scored a duck and a century for India in the 1969/70 Test against Australia at Kanpur.

Sunil Gavaskar was bowled first ball by Malcolm Marshall in India's 1983/4 Test versus West Indies at Calcutta.

Allan Border featured in 62 Test century partnerships.

Eleventh man Mushtaq Ahmed hit 59 for Pakistan versus South Africa at Rawlpindi in 1997/98.

Bill Lawry of Australia received a head wound from a ball by P.M. Pollock of South Africa in the 1966/7 Test at Durban. He had ten stitches then returned to top score for the side in the innings.

Ian Botham reached his century against India at Headingley in 1979 by hitting a six.

Sunil Gavaskar scored his 10,000th run in Test cricket at Ahmedabad.

CRICKET

Colin Milburn scored a duck on his first Test innings.

Chris Broad hit 114 for England against New Zealand in the 1988 1st Test between the teams.

Kapil Dev's 89 against England in 1982 at Lord's included 70 runs from boundaries.

1570 runs were scored in the 1988 county championship meeting between Essex and Kent.

Len Hutton batted for 797 minutes for England against Australia at the Oval in 1938.

Northants beat Warwickshire in their 1988 county championship game at Northampton after following-on.

Gordon Greenidge scored in 22 century opening stands for the West Indies.

Former Derbyshire cricketer Ole Mortensen was born in Vejle, Denmark.

C.E.L. Ambrose took 7 for 1 in 32 balls for the West Indies versus Australia at Perth in 1992/3.

Brian Lara reached his century for the West Indies against India at St. Johns in 1996/7 by hitting a six.

Former Hampshire cricketer Cardigan Connor's middle name is Adolphus.

S.M. Patil of India was knocked unconscious by a ball on his Test debut in 1980/81.

CRICKET

Brothers Graham and Christopher Cowdrey both played for Kent in the 1980's.

England's Peter Lever took a hat-trick to end the Third Test against Pakistan at Leeds in 1971.

Wasim Akram scored 12 sixes in his 257 n.o. for Pakistan versus Sri Lanka in 1996/7.

Former Kent cricketer David Sabine was born in Papakura, New Zealand.

In his innings of 43 against Australia at Bridgetown in 1954/55, Garfield Sobers hit ten fours and three singles.

Former Lancashire batsman Gehan Mendis's middle name is Dixon.

A mouse stopped play in the 1962 Edgbaston Test between England and Pakistan.

Essex bowler Ronnie Irani represented the North of England at basketball.

West Indies batsman J.S. Solomon was out 'hit wicket' when his cap fell off onto the bails in the 2nd Test against Australia in 1960/61.

Former Leicestershire bowler Winston Benjamin represented the Leeward Islands from 1985-88.

Former Warwickshire cricketer Alvin Kallicharan's middle name is Isaac.

CRICKET

Of his 310 n.o. against New Zealand at Headingley in 1965, John Edrich scored 238 in boundaries.

Hedley Verity took 14 wickets in a day for England against Australia at Lord's in 1934.

Peter Such made his England Test debut against Australia in 1993.

Graeme Hick took a wicket with his third ball in Test cricket in 1991.

Former Nottinghamshire cricketer Christopher Scott's middle name is Wilmot.

Mark Taylor scored centuries in the first two Tests for Australia against England in 1993.

Wally Hammond hit 10 sixes in his 336 n.o. for England against New Zealand in 1932/33.

Nottinghamshire beat Kent in their 1993 county championship match after following-on.

C.B. Fry played cricket and football for England.

Staffordshire beat Cheshire in the 1993 Minor Counties championship final.

Mike Denness made four Test centuries for England.

C.A. Connor took 9 for 38 for Hampshire against Gloucestershire in their 1996 county championship game.

Darren Gough took a hat-trick for Yorkshire against Kent in the 1995 county championship.

CRICKET

Ian Botham was born in Heswall, Cheshire.

Philip Bainbridge topped Durham's batting and bowling averages in the 1993 county championship.

Ian Healy made his Australian Test debut against Pakistan in 1988.

I.M. Chappell and G.S. Chappell were the first brothers to score centuries in the same innings of a Test, at the Oval in 1972.

F.D. Stephenson was the first man to 100 wickets in the 1988 county championship.

Australia's first three batsmen in the 1993 Test at Lord's against England scored centuries.

Former Hampshire cricketer Rajesh Maru was born in Nairobi in 1962.

In the second Test between India and New Zealand in 1976/77 India scored 524 but no-one scored a century.

Kapil Dev hit four consecutive sixes off the bowling of Eddie Hemmings in India's 1990 Test at Lord's.

Bill Athey topped Sussex's batting averages in the 1993 county championship.

S.J. Cook of South Africa was bowled first ball on his debut by India's Kapil Dev at Durban in 1992/93.

R.B. Simpson batted for 762 minutes for Australia against England at Manchester in 1964.

CRICKET

Umpire Barrie Leadbeater was born in Leeds.

Javed Miandad of Pakistan featured in 50 Test century partnerships.

There were an aggregate of 1642 runs in the 1995 county championship match between Nottinghamshire and Kent.

C. Hill was dismissed for 99, 98 & 97 in three consecutive innings for Australia against England in 1901/2.

N.E. Briers and A.R.K. Pierson hit 122 in a 10th wicket stand for Leicestershire against Worcestershire in 1995.

England's D.S. Steele took a wicket with his fourth ball in Test cricket at Lord's in 1975.

Dominic Cork made his England Test debut against West Indies in 1995, taking 7-43 in the second innings.

Daryll Cullinan topped Derbyshire's batting averages in the 1995 county championship.

Mike Brearley scored a duck in his first Test innings.

Australian Test captain T.P. Horan was born in Ireland.

M.J.G. Greatbatch made his debut for New Zealand against England in the 1988 2nd Test.

Anil Kumble topped Northamptonshire's bowling averages in the 1995 county championship.

L.O. Fleetwood-Smith of Australia bowled 522 balls in an innings against England at the Oval in 1938 and took one wicket.

CRICKET

Jason Gallian made 7 and 0 in his 1995 England Test debut against West Indies.

Colin Cowdrey was the first cricketer to play 100 Tests.

Hampshire bowler Dimitri Mascarenhas's first name is Adrian.

T.J. Matthews of Australia took a hat-trick in each innings against South Africa in a 1912 Test.

James Bovill headed Hampshire's bowling averages in the 1995 county championship.

Bowler Eddie Hemmings's middle name is Ernest.

Steve Waugh averaged 362 for Australia in the 1995/6 Test series versus Sri Lanka.

Mike Selvey took a wicket with his sixth ball in Test cricket in 1976.

Mark Ilott topped Essex's bowling averages in 1993.

Warwickshire won the 1995 county championship by 32 points.

South African cricketer O. Henry made his first Test appearance in 1992/3 against India at the age of 40 years, 295 days.

Hugh Morris hit 166 n.o. and 104 n.o. for Glamorgan against Nottinghamshire in the 1995 county championship.

Derbyshire won the 1993 Benson and Hedges Cup Final by six runs.

CRICKET

Leslie Ames also played football for Gillingham.

Leicestershire hit 638 against Worcestershire in the 1996 county championship.

Carl Hooper topped Kent's batting averages in the 1993 county championship.

R.C. Irani took M. Azharuddin's wicket with his fifth ball in Test cricket in 1996.

India's Kapil Dev won the first Test against England at Lord's in 1986 by hitting a six.

Tom Moody took 13-159 for Worcestershire in their 1996 county championship game against Gloucestershire.

Viv Richards and Jeffrey Dujon made centuries in the 1988 2nd Test for West Indies against Pakistan.

Lancashire beat Northamptonshire in the 1996 Benson & Hedges Cup Final.

Andrew Symonds topped Gloucestershire's batting averages in the 1995 county championship.

M.J.K. Smith scored a duck in his first Test innings.

K.F. Barrington reached Test centuries by hitting a six on four occasions.

Devon beat Norfolk in the 1996 Minor Counties championship final.

Eleventh man Rodney Hogg hit 52 for Australia against West Indies in Georgetown in 1984/5.

CRICKET

Ricky Ponting made his Test debut for Australia in 1995 against Sri Lanka.

Mike Gatting topped Middlesex's batting averages in the 1993 county championship.

England scored only 37 runs in the pre-lunch session against Australia at Adelaide in 1932/33.

West Indies Test captain G.A. Headley was born in Panama.

Ted Dexter made 9 Test centuries for England.

Warwickshire hit 645 against Sussex in the 1996 county championship.

West Indies bowler Malcolm Marshall's middle name is Denzil.

Allan Lamb made a century on his debut as Test captain for England in 1989/90 against West Indies.

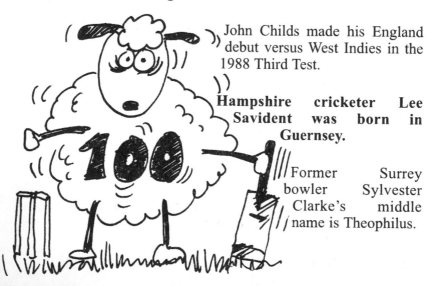

John Childs made his England debut versus West Indies in the 1988 Third Test.

Hampshire cricketer Lee Savident was born in Guernsey.

Former Surrey bowler Sylvester Clarke's middle name is Theophilus.

CRICKET

Winston Benjamin topped Leicestershire's bowling averages in the 1993 county championship.

Derek Pringle took a wicket with his sixth ball in Test cricket in 1982.

Sussex hit 591 against Essex in their 1993 county championship game.

Pakistan's Mohammad Wasim scored a duck and a century against New Zealand in a 1996/7 Lahore Test.

A.W. Nourse of South Africa was the oldest player to score a maiden Test century. He achieved the feat at the age of 43 years and 294 days.

Carl Hooper made 178 n.o. for West Indies versus Pakistan in his first innings of the 3rd Test in 1993.

M.J.K. Smith scored a duck on his first Test innings.

Kim Barnett carried his bat through the innings for Derbyshire twice in the 1993 county championship.

Sunil Gavaskar shared in 22 century opening stands for India.

Adrian Dale and Viv Richards made a 4th wicket stand of 425 for Glamorgan versus Middlesex in the 1993 county championship.

A.A. Mallett took M.C. Cowdrey's wicket with his fifth ball in Test cricket at the Oval in 1968.

Warwickshire beat Sussex in the 1993 Nat West Trophy final.

CRICKET

Ian Botham took 5 for 1 against Australia in 28 balls at Edgbaston in 1981.

Sachin Tendulkar scored seven Test centuries before his 21st birthday.

Umpire Trevor Jesty was born in Gosport.

Andy Caddick took 9-32 for Somerset against Lancashire at Taunton in an innings of their 1993 county championship match.

Mark Ilott topped Essex's bowling averages in the 1995 county championship.

Of his 32 overs bowled in an innings for India against England at Madras in 1963/4, R.G. Nadkarni bowled 27 maidens.

Russell Cake scored 101 in the first innings for Cambridge University against Oxford University in the 150th University Match in 1995.

M.J. Turnbull played cricket for England and rugby and hockey for Wales.

Umpire Chris Balderstone was born in Huddersfield.

W.G. Grace captained England at the age of 50 years and 320 days.

Worcestershire scored 670 against Somerset in the 1995 county championship.

Australian Test cricketer Len Pascoe's original surname was Durtanovich.

CRICKET

Roger Twose made his debut for New Zealand against India in the 1995 second Test, contributing a catch.

A.G. Ganteaume of West Indies scored 112 in his only Test innings in 1947/8.

Shaun Pollock made his Test debut for South Africa against England in the 1995 1st Test, taking 3-98.

Essex hit 616 against Kent at Chelmsford in the 1988 county championship.

Andy Moles topped Warwickshire's batting averages in the 1993 county championship.

Former Glamorgan cricketer Rodney Ontong was born in Johannesburg in 1955.

Nasser Hussain topped Essex's batting averages in the 1995 county championship.

Northants scored 59 in an innings against Surrey in the 1995 county championship.

Hansie Cronje topped Leicestershire's batting averages in the 1993 county championship.

Mark Ramprakash's middle name is Ravin.

Graham Gooch made 133 in England's second innings against Australia in the 1st Test at Old Trafford in 1993 before being given out for handling the ball.

1606 runs were scored in the 1996 county championship game between Somerset and Derbyshire.

CRICKET

In 1964/5 W.M. Lawry and R.B. Simpson of Australia became the first opening pair to score double-centuries in the same Test innings.

Michael Bevan was the first batsman to 1000 first-class runs in the 1996 season.

Former Middlesex bowler Norman Cowans was born in Enfield St. Mary, Jamaica.

Stuart Law made his Test debut for Australia against Sri Lanka in 1995.

G.O.B. Allen was 45 years 245 days old when he captained England against the West Indies in 1947/8 at Kingston.

West Indies bowler Wayne Daniel's middle name is Wendell.

Ian Botham became England's youngest Test captain this century in 1980 in the game against West Indies at Nottingham.

Captains Mike Gatting and Imran Khan both hit centuries in a 1987 Test match at the Oval for England and Pakistan respectively.

The 1000th Test hundred was scored in the 643rd Test match by I.M. Chappell in 1968/9.

Peter Hartley took a hat-trick for Yorkshire against Derbyshire in the 1995 county championship.

Basil D'Oliveira made 5 Test centuries for England.

M.C.J. Ball took 14-169 for Gloucestershire against Somerset in the 1993 county championship.

CRICKET

Captains Kapil Dev of India and Allan Border of Australia both hit centuries in a 1986/7 Test at Madras.

Tony Lewis scored a duck on his first Test innings. It was also his first as captain.

Anil Kumble was the first man to take 100 wickets in the 1995 county championship.

C.C. Lewis & B.N. French's seventh wicket partnership of 301 for Nottinghamshire against Durham in the 1993 county championship was a county record.

Sunil Gavaskar scored 124 & 220 for India in their match against West Indies at Port-of-Spain.

Richard Hadlee dismissed Tony Dodemaide to become joint leading wicket taker in Test cricket.

England's Herbert Sutcliffe was bowled first ball in the 1932/3 Christchurch Test against New Zealand.

Graeme Hick made two double centuries for Worcestershire in the 1988 county championship.

John Emburey took a wicket with his 4th ball in Test cricket in 1978.

W.M. Woodfull's innings of 161 for Australia versus South Africa at Melbourne in 1931/2 included only five fours.

Graham Gooch topped Essex's batting averages in the 1993 county championship.

Stuart Carlisle made his Test debut for Zimbabwe against Pakistan in 1995.

CRICKET

Former Nottinghamshire cricketer Michael Field-Buss was born in Malta.

N. Gordon of South Africa bowled 738 balls in a Durban Test against England in 1938/9 and took 1 wicket.

Ian Healy was run out in both innings of Australia's Test against West Indies in Georgetown in 1990/1.

Martin Bicknell took 1-155 on his England Test debut in 1993.

Geoff Boycott featured in 47 Test century partnerships.

Vinod Kambli hit centuries for India against Pakistan in the 2nd and 3rd Tests of their 1993 series.

H.J. Tayfield bowled 16 consecutive maiden overs for South Africa against England at Durban in 1956/7.

Glenn McGrath made his Test debut for Australia against New Zealand in November 1993.

Former Somerset cricketer Greg Palmer is son of umpire K.E. Palmer.

Martin Crowe scored 30 and 299 for New Zealand against Sri Lanka at Wellington.

Allan Border & Steve Waugh both made centuries in the 1993 3rd Test for Australia against New Zealand.

Cricketer C.B. Fry held the world long jump record.

Nottinghamshire hit 629 against Durham in their 1993 county championship game.

CRICKET

Geoff Boycott batted on each day of England's Trent Bridge Test against Australia in 1977.

Peter Martin made his Test debut for England against West Indies in June 1995.

Dominic Cork topped Derbyshire's 1995 bowling averages in the county championship.

P.D. Bowler was the first man to score hundreds on debuts for two counties - Leicestershire and Derbyshire.

In the six match Test series between Australia and England in 1970/1 none of Australia's l.b.w. appeals were upheld.

Dermot Reeve topped Warwickshire's bowling averages in the 1993 season.

P.W. Sherwell made nine stumpings for South Africa in the 1910/11 series against Australia.

Aravinda de Silva topped Kent's batting averages in the 1995 county championship.

Brothers Darren and Martin Bicknell have played for Surrey since 1987 & 1986 respectively.

Richie Richardson scored a duck in his first Test innings.

Six players made their Test debut for Zimbabwe in the 1993 1st Test against Pakistan.

England cricketer J.W.H.T. Douglas won the 1908 Olympic middleweight boxing gold.

CRICKET

Tim Robinson topped Nottinghamshire's batting averages in the 1995 county championship.

Clive Lloyd featured in 41 Test century partnerships for West Indies.

Phil Newport topped Worcestershire's bowling averages in the 1993 county championship.

Australia's Steve Waugh's middle name is Rodger.

S. Chanderpaul averaged 130 for West Indies in the 1994/5 Test match series against New Zealand.

Hampshire batsman William Kendall's middle name is Sawley.

India's R.G. Nadkarni bowled 21 consecutive maiden overs in the first innings against England at Madras in 1963/64.

Umpire Kevin Lyons was born in Cardiff.

Four of England's players against New Zealand at Lord's in 1986 kept wicket.

Surrey beat Gloucestershire after following on in the 1995 county championship season.

Substitute fielder Gursharan Singh took four catches for India in the 1983/4 Ahmedabad Test against West Indies.

A.J. Hollioake and J.E. Benjamin hit a 10th wicket partnership of 100 for Surrey against Warwickshire in 1995.

CRICKET

Tim Curtis and Robin Smith made their England Test debuts in the 1988 4th Test against West Indies.

England lost the 1993 six match Test series against Australia 4-1.

Nick Knight made his England debut in the 1995 4th Test against the West Indies, scoring 17 & 13.

Wilf Slack made 163 n.o. and 105 n.o. for Middlesex against Glamorgan in 1988.

Matthew Maynard topped Glamorgan's batting averages in the 1993 county championship.

The official width of a cricket bat is 4 inches.

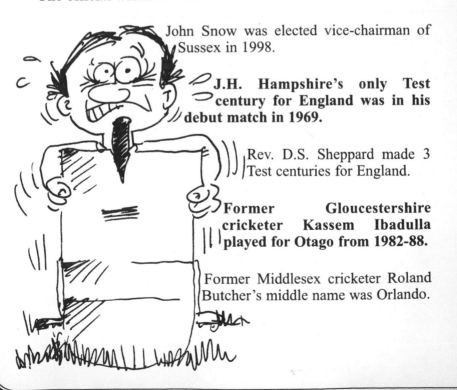

John Snow was elected vice-chairman of Sussex in 1998.

J.H. Hampshire's only Test century for England was in his debut match in 1969.

Rev. D.S. Sheppard made 3 Test centuries for England.

Former Gloucestershire cricketer Kassem Ibadulla played for Otago from 1982-88.

Former Middlesex cricketer Roland Butcher's middle name was Orlando.

CRICKET

Ian Botham took 13 wickets and scored 114 for England against India at Bombay in 1979/80.

Graham Gooch scored 456 in England's match against India at Lord's in 1990.

Aravinda De Silva made his Test debut for Sri Lanka against England in 1993.

Sunil Gavaskar batted for 708 minutes for India against England at Bangalore in 1981/2.

Desmond Haynes made 143 n.o. for West Indies against Pakistan in his 2nd innings in the 1st Test in 1993.

Graham Gooch was the first man to hit 2000 first-class runs in the 1993 season.

Jack Hobbs shared in 24 century opening partnerships for England.

11th man John Snow hit 59 n.o. for England against West Indies at the Oval in 1966.

Christopher Cairns topped Nottinghamshire's bowling averages in the 1993 county championship.

R.B. Desai of India had his jaw fractured by a ball from R.C. Motz of New Zealand in the 1967/8 Test at Dunedin.

Phillip Cottey topped Glamorgan's batting averages in the 1995 county championship.

Intikhab Alam took a wicket with his first ball in Test cricket.

CRICKET

Len Hutton scored a duck in his first Test innings.

J.P. Hewitt took a wicket for Middlesex with his first ball in first-class cricket in the 1996 county championship.

Retired umpire Harold 'Dickie' Bird was born in Barnsley.

Lance Gibbs bowled 37 maidens in his 53.3 overs in an innings for West Indies against India at Bridgetown in 1961/2.

Allan Donald topped Warwickshire's bowling averages in the 1995 county championship.

Former Glamorgan cricketer Stephen Barwick's middle name is Royston.

Lance Klusener made his South Africa Test debut against India in the 1996 2nd Test, taking 8-64 in the 2nd innings.

Wasim Akram topped Lancashire's bowling averages in the 1995 county championship.

D.W. Hookes hit five fours in a row off Tony Greig's bowling in Australia's 1976/7 Melbourne Test against England.

Essex scored 662 against Hampshire in the 1995 county championship.

Greg Chappell scored 380 in Australia's match against New Zealand at Wellington in 1973/4.

Paul Strang made his Test debut for Zimbabwe in the 1995 2nd Test against Pakistan.

H. Ironmonger of Australia only conceded 28.32 runs per 100 balls in his 14 match Test career.

CRICKET

A.J. Hollioake made 123 on his first class debut for Surrey against Derbyshire in 1993.

Adam Parore hit 100 n.o. for New Zealand against West Indies in the 1995 1st Test.

P.F. Warner's only Test century for England was in his debut Test against South Africa in 1898/99.

Vincent Wells topped the bowling averages for Leicestershire in the 1995 county championship.

Both Viv Richards and Richie Richardson played football for Antigua.

Jacques Kallis made his debut for South Africa against England in the 1995/6 3rd Test.

Denis Compton won an F.A. Cup winners medal with Arsenal.

Ian Botham's son Liam played county cricket for Hampshire.

Bert Ironmonger appeared for Australia in an Ashes Test at the age of 50 years, 327 days.

Steve Waugh averaged 107.25 for Australia in the 1994/5 Test series against West Indies.

Former Gloucestershire cricketer Kamran Sheeraz's middle name is Pasha.

Alec Stewart and Nick Knight both made centuries for England against Pakistan in the 1996 2nd Test.

CRICKET

Nottingham cricketer Noel Gie's middle name is Addison.

Graham Rose took 13-88 for Somerset against Notts in their 1996 county championship fixture.

Former Hampshire cricketer Richard Dibden's middle name is Rockley.

Nayan Mongia hit 152 & 0 for India in the 1996 Test against Australia.

Wasim Akram scored 257 n.o. for Pakistan versus Zimbabwe in the 1996 1st Test.

Tom Moody topped Worcestershire's batting averages in the 1995 county championship.

Ian Healy scored 161 n.o. for Australia in their 1st innings in the 1st Test versus West Indies in 1996/7.

Robert Croft made his England Test debut against Pakistan in 1996.

Imran Khan scored 117 and took 11 wickets for Pakistan versus India in 1982/3 at Faisalabad.

Andrew Symonds hit 161 n.o. on his first-class debut in 1995 for Gloucestershire.

Northants scored 781 versus Notts in the 1995 county championship.

Oxford won the 1995 University Match versus Cambridge by 9 wickets.

Ben Hollioake's middle name is Caine.

CRICKET

Mark Ramprakash was the first man to 2000 first-class runs in the 1995 season.

Robin Smith topped Hampshire's batting averages in the 1995 county championship.

Dominic Cork took a hat-trick for England against West Indies in the 1995 4th Test.

Phil Tufnell took 13-123 for Middlesex versus Lancashire in their 1996 county championship game.

Michael Watkinson headed the England batting averages in their 1995 six-match Test series versus West Indies.

Chris Broad hit 139 for England in the 1988 Bicentenary Test against Australia.

Warwickshire's Dominic Ostler's middle name is Piers.

Nottinghamshire made only 44 against Warwickshire in an innings of their 1988 county championship game.

Norman Cowans topped Middlesex's bowling averages in the 1993 county championship.

Dean Headley took 3 hat-tricks for Kent in the 1996 county championship.

Saqlain Mushtaq made his Test debut for Pakistan against Sri Lanka in 1995.

Mark Ilott took a hat-trick for Essex against Northants in the 1995 county championship.

CRICKET

Robin Jackman took Gordon Greenidge's wicket with his fifth ball in Test cricket in 1980/81.

Aravinda De Silva hit two double centuries for Kent in the 1995 county championship.

Alan Knott scored a duck in his first Test innings.

Bowler David Lawrence's middle name is Valentine.

A.C. Hudson of South Africa scored a duck and a century in the 1991/2 Bridgetown Test against West Indies.

Kim Barnett went to Leek High School.

Sunil Gavaskar was bowled first ball by Geoff Arnold in India's Test against England at Edgbaston in 1974.

Former Derbyshire cricketer Martin Jean-Jacques was born in Dominica.

Eddie Hemmings took a wicket with his fourth ball in Test cricket in 1982 against Pakistan.

Former Surrey cricketer James Boiling was born in Delhi, India.

Sarfraz Nawaz took 7 for 1 in 26 balls against Australia at Melbourne in 1978/9.

CRICKET

Kim Barnett topped Derbyshire's batting averages in the 1993 county championship.

M.J. Greatbatch made three catches as substitute for New Zealand against England in the 1987/8 Christchurch Test.

Durham's P.D. Collingwood took a wicket with his first ball in first-class cricket in 1996.

Stuart Milburn topped Yorkshire's bowling averages in the 1995 county championship.

Dickie Bird umpired 66 Test matches from 1973-96.

Moin Khan hit 117 n.o. for Pakistan versus Sri Lanka in the 1995 3rd Test 2nd innings.

Mike Atherton averaged 108.33 in the 1996/7 Test series against New Zealand.

New Zealand wicket keeper L.K. Germon made his Test debut as captain in the 1995 1st Test versus India.

Andy Caddick topped Somerset's bowling averages in the 1993 county championship.

A.N. Hornby played cricket and rugby for England.

Steven Watkin topped Glamorgan's bowling averages in the 1995 county championship.

Len Hutton was 300 n.o. at close of play at the end of the second day against Australia at the Oval in 1938.

Umpire Graham Burgess was born in Glastonbury.

CRICKET

Robert Bailey & Matthew Maynard made their England Test debut against West Indies in the 1988 5th Test.

Brothers Alan and Colin Wells played together at Sussex in the 1980's.

Bob Woolmer made 3 Test centuries for England.

Andrew Flower and Andrew Whittall made centuries and Grant Flower made a double century for Zimbabwe in the 1995 1st Test against Pakistan.

David Graveney took 14-165 in Gloucestershire's 1988 fixture against Worcestershire.

Miran Bux was Pakistan's oldest Test player. He was 47 years and 302 days old when he left the field on the last day against India in 1954/55.

D.B. Vengsarkar made a century on his debut as captain for India versus West Indies in 1987/8.

Vincent Wells hit two double centuries for Leicestershire in the 1996 county championship.

Surrey scored 652 against Durham in the 1995 county championship.

There was only play on the second day of the 1st Test in 1993 between Sri Lanka and India.

Brian Lara, Jimmy Adams and Junior Murray each hit centuries for West Indies against New Zealand in the 1995 2nd Test.

Saeed Anwar scored a duck in his first Test innings.

CRICKET

Paul Adams made his Test debut for South Africa against England in the 1995/6 4th Test.

Former Derbyshire cricketer Gul Khan's middle name is Abbass.

T.A. Merrick and Wasim Akram took hat-tricks in the 1988 season for Warwickshire and Lancashire respectively.

Christopher Adams topped Derbyshire's batting averages in the 1996 county championship.

A.C. Storie took five catches in an innings for Warwickshire against Leicestershire in 1988.

Former Durham player Colin Campbell's middle name is Lockey.

Former Nottinghamshire cricketer Franklyn Stephenson's middle name is Dacosta.

Mark Ramprakash topped Middlesex's batting averages in the 1995 county championship.

Brendan Julian made his Australia Test debut against England in 1993.

Essex bowler Ashley Cowan's middle name is Preston.

David Boon and Steve Waugh made centuries and Allan Border a double century in Australia's innings and 148 run victory in the 4th Test against England in 1993.

Lancashire hit 686 against Essex in the 1996 county championship.

CRICKET

Michael Slater, David Boon and Mark Waugh all hit centuries in the 1993 2nd Test for Australia against New Zealand.

Leicestershire hit 681 against Yorkshire in the 1996 county championship.

Durham's 67 against Middlesex at Lord's was the lowest in the 1996 county championship.

Martyn Moxon topped Yorkshire's batting averages in the 1993 county championship.

Australia scored 3641 runs in ten innings against England in the 1993 six match Test series.

G.H.S. Trott made 0 & 143 on his debut as captain for Australia against England in 1896.

J.D. Carr took six catches for Middlesex against Warwickshire in an innings in their 1995 county championship game.

Mark Ramprakash scored three double centuries for Middlesex in the 1995 county championship.

Alec Stewart topped Surrey's batting averages in the 1993 county championship.

Brian Close scored a duck in his first Test innings.

Hugh Morris was the first man to 1000 first-class runs in 1993.

Frank Worrell batted for 682 minutes for West Indies against England at Bridgetown in 1959/60.

CRICKET

Robin Smith topped Hampshire's batting averages in the 1993 county championship.

Ian Chappell of Australia shared in 18 century partnerships for the second wicket in Tests.

James Daley topped Durham's batting averages in the 1995 county championship.

Eleventh man Wasim Bari hit 60 n.o. for Pakistan against West Indies at Bridgetown in 1976/77.

Jason Lewry topped Sussex's bowling averages in the 1995 county championship.

England scored only 19 runs before lunch against Australia on one day of the Brisbane Test in 1958/59.

Umpire Barrie Meyer was born in Bournemouth.

South Africa were dismissed by England in 50 minutes in an innings at Edgbaston in 1924.

Northamptonshire players hit four centuries in an innings versus Nottinghamshire in the 1995 county championship.

R.K. Illingworth took a wicket with his first ball in Test cricket in 1991.

Mark Ilott took 9-19 for Essex against Northamptonshire in the 1995 county championship.

L.F. Kline of Australia took a hat-trick to end the 1957/58 second Test against South Africa at Cape Town.

CRICKET

Mike Atherton and Graeme Hick hit centuries for England against West Indies in the 1st innings of the 1995 Fifth Test.

Ian Botham also played football for Scunthorpe United.

Jeremy Hallett topped Somerset's batting averages in the 1995 county championship.

David Boon was 184 n.o. in his second innings for Australia against England in the 1988 Bicentenary Test.

Glamorgan made only 47 at Swansea against Lancashire in an innings of their 1988 county championship fixture.

Former Gloucestershire cricketer Jeremy Lloyds was born in Penang, Malaysia.

Dean Headley topped Kent's bowling averages in the 1995 county championship.

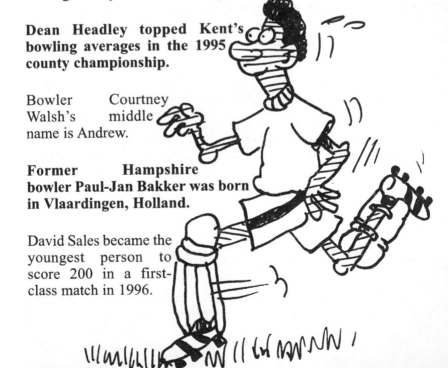

Bowler Courtney Walsh's middle name is Andrew.

Former Hampshire bowler Paul-Jan Bakker was born in Vlaardingen, Holland.

David Sales became the youngest person to score 200 in a first-class match in 1996.

CRICKET

N.J. Astle, G.I. Allott, R.G. Kennedy & G.R. Loveridge all made their Test debut for New Zealand versus Zimbabwe in 1996.

Former Middlesex cricketer Alexander Barnett was born in Malaga.

Jimmy Adams made 208 for West Indies against New Zealand in the 1996 2nd Test 1st innings.

Warwickshire bowler Gladstone Small's middle name is Cleophas.

Imran Khan studied at Keble College, Oxford.

Graeme Hick's middle name is Ashley.

Minal Patel, Ronnie Irani and Alan Mullally all made their England debut in the 1st Test against India in 1996.

M.C. Ilott, M.N. Lathwell, M.J. McCague & G. P. Thorpe all made their England Test debut in the 1993 3rd Test against Australia.

Former Warwickshire cricketer Piran Holloway was born in Helston, Cornwall.

Somerset beat Derbyshire after following on in the 1995 county championship.

Leicestershire bowler Chris Lewis's middle name is Clairmonte.

Dennis Amiss made 11 Test centuries for England.

CRICKET

John Crawley topped Lancashire's batting averages in the 1995 county championship.

The 1993 county championship match between Worcestershire and Nottinghamshire was tied.

The lowest innings totals in the 1993 county championship were Nottinghamshire's 68 versus Surrey at the Oval and Middlesex's 68 against Worcestershire at Worcester.

Courtney Walsh topped Gloucestershire's bowling averages in the 1993 county championship.

Nick Knight topped Warwickshire's batting averages in the 1995 county championship.

Darren Gough took M.J. Greatbatch's wicket with his fifth ball in Test cricket in 1994.

Umpire Kenneth Palmer was born in Winchester.

C.S. Cowdrey took Kapil Dev's wicket with his fourth ball in Test cricket in a 1984/5 Test.

David Byas was the first man to 1000 runs in the 1995 first-class season.

England's G.A. Lohmann took 8 for 7 in 49 balls against South Africa at Johannesburg in 1895/6.

Brian Lara and Carl Hooper hit centuries for West Indies versus England in their 1995 sixth Test 1st innings.

R.E. Foster captained England at cricket and football.

CRICKET

Rahul Dravid & Sourav Ganguly both made their Test debut for India against England in the 1996 2nd Test.

Arthur Shrewsbury was the first batsman to score 1000 runs in Tests.

Alan Igglesden topped Kent's bowling averages in the 1993 county championship.

Wasim Akram topped Lancashire's bowling averages in the 1993 county championship.

1808 runs were scored in the 1993 county championship match between Sussex and Essex.

West Indies won the first three of five Tests in their 1988/9 series in Australia.

Former Surrey batsman Grahame Clinton's middle name is Selvey.

John Wood topped Durham's bowling averages in the 1995 county championship.

Former Glamorgan cricketer Colin Metson was born in Goffs Oak, Hertfordshire.

Worcestershire made 628-7 against Somerset at Taunton in 1988.

Jonathan Lewis topped Gloucestershire's bowling averages in the 1995 county championship.

Eleventh man R.O. Collinge of New Zealand hit 68 n.o. against Pakistan at Auckland in 1972/3.

CRICKET

New Zealand scored only 69 off 90 six-ball overs against Pakistan at Dacca in 1955/6.

Umpire John Harris was born in Taunton.

Jim Laker took a wicket with his fourth ball in Test cricket against West Indies in 1947/8.

David Sales's 210 n.o. for Northants in 1996 was the record championship score for a first-class debut.

Northants scored 46 in an innings against Essex in the 1995 county championship.

Former Derbyshire cricketer Rajeshwar Sharma was born in Nairobi.

14 of J. Brigg's 15 wickets for England against South Africa at Cape Town in 1888/9 were bowled.

Derbyshire's Karl Krikken was given out for handling the ball in their 1996 match against the Indian touring side.

N.R. Gaywood scored 138 for Devon versus Lincolnshire in the 1995 Minor Counties championship.

Former Hampshire cricketer Christopher Smith's nickname was 'Kippy'.

D.L. Bairstow also played football for Bradford City.

Former Lancashire batsman Gehan Mendis was born in Colombo.

Henry Olonga made his Test debut for Zimbabwe in 1995.

CRICKET

Martin Crowe scored 143 in his 2nd innings for New Zealand against England in the 1988 3rd Test.

Hansie Cronje scored 101 in his 2nd innings for South Africa against New Zealand in their 1995 Test.

Essex were bowled out for 57 in the 1996 NatWest Trophy Final.

C.E.L. Ambrose made his debut for West Indies versus Pakistan in the 1988 1st Test.

Former Leicestershire cricketer Justin Benson was born in Dublin.

Steve Waugh hit 200 for Australia against West Indies in the 1995 4th Test.

Graeme Hick was the first batsman to 1000 first-class runs in 1988.

A.J. Traicos holds the record as Zimbabwe's oldest Test player.

Former Hants bowler Stephen Jeffries was born in Cape Town in 1959.

J. Southerton was 49 years 119 days old when he made his debut for England against Australia in 1876/7.

Bowler Curtly Ambrose's middle names are Elconn Lynwall.

Andy Caddick made his England Test debut against Australia in 1993.

South Africa won the 1995/96 Test series against England 1-0.

THE ULTIMATE SPORTS FACT AND QUIZ BOOK

FOOTBALL

FOOTBALL

Brian McClair scored Manchester United's only goal in their 1992 League Cup Final win.

There were an average of 2.21 goals per game in the 1990 World Cup Finals.

Paul McGrath was 1993 P.F.A. Player of the Year.

A twice-retaken penalty kick for Notts County at Portsmouth in 1973 was missed by all three takers – Don Masson, Brian Stubbs and Kevin Randall.

Scotland's first ever World Cup point was gained from their 1-1 draw with Yugoslavia in the 1958 Finals.

John Wark scored in both legs of Ipswich's 1981 U.E.F.A. Cup Final win over AZ 67 Alkmaar.

In his 46 league games for Portsmouth in 1992/3 Guy Whittingham scored 42 goals.

The 1901 F.A. Cup Final replay took place at Bolton.

In his four years with Manchester United from 1990-'94, defender Neil Whitworth played once.

Ally McCoist scored Rangers's consolation goal in the 1997/8 Scottish F.A. Cup Final.

Only eight players have scored a total of ten or more goals in World Cup Finals tournaments.

Martin Buchan was Burnley manager in 1985/6.

FOOTBALL

Nigel Jemson scored the only goal for Nottingham Forest in their 1990 League Cup Final win.

Argentina were winners of the Under-20 world championships in 1995 & '97.

Sunderland were last crowned league champions in 1935/6.

Kuwait beat Macao 10-1 in a 1994 World Cup qualifier.

Newcastle signed Alain Goma from Paris St. Germain in summer 1999 for £4.75m.

Alan Shearer was England's top scorer in the 1998 World Cup Finals with two goals.

Arsenal defender Nigel Winterburn was at Oxford United in the 1983/4 season, but did not play any league games.

Burnley's top league scorer in the 1990/1 season was Ron Futcher.

Marco Negri was top goalscorer in the Scottish Premier Division in 1997/8 with 32 league goals.

Bury play at Gigg Lane.

Just Fontaine scored a hat-trick in France's 7-3 win against Paraguay in the 1958 World Cup.

Fifteen teams entered the first F.A. Cup competition.

FOOTBALL

Northern Ireland forward Kevin Wilson played all 46 league games for Chelsea in 1988/9, scoring 13 goals.

Charlie Nicholas scored both of Arsenal's goals in their 1987 League Cup Final win.

Malta's first football friendly was their game in February 1957 versus Austria at the Empire Stadium, Gzira.

In their 14 games in the World Cup Finals, South Korea have a negative goal ratio of 11:43.

Wolves signed Watford player Darren Bazeley on a free transfer in summer 1999.

Goalkeeper Dave Beasant played twice for England.

Chris Pike was Cardiff City's top league goalscorer in 1990/1 with 14 goals.

Hellas Veronas were 1985 Serie A champions in Italy.

Jürgen Klinsmann scored three goals in the 1998 World Cup Finals.

Over 3 million people attended the games at the 1994 World Cup Finals.

Nearly 19 million people in Britain watched the European Champions League Cup Final on television in 1999.

The 1998/9 league fixture between Manchester United and West Ham United was delayed by a power failure.

FOOTBALL

West Ham's 17-year old boy wonder Joe Cole made his first-team debut in the 1999 F.A. Cup match against Swansea.

The present F.A. Cup trophy was made in 1911 by Fattorini and Sons of Bradford.

In his first four seasons with Manchester City, defender Clive Wilson played in four games, without scoring.

Lee Sharpe's first game for Sampdoria on loan from Leeds United was against Bologna.

Darren Huckerby scored hat-tricks in successive weeks in 1999 against Macclesfield and Nottingham Forest.

Steve McManaman scored both goals in the 2-1 League Cup Final win over Bolton.

Rigobert Song became the youngest player to be sent off in the World Cup Finals in 1994.

Dundee spent their January 1999 break from the Scottish Premier League in Whitley Bay.

Charlton Athletic defender Eddie Youds was born in Liverpool.

Of their 23 World Cup Finals games, Scotland have won four.

Brazil have scored 173 goals in the World Cup Finals.

Burnley scored 102 goals in league Division 1 in 1960-'61.

Woking of the Isthmian League beat West Bromwich Albion 4-2 in the 1991 F.A. Cup.

FOOTBALL

Dwight Yorke's mother lives in Robert Street, Canaan, Tobago.

Of their 80 games in the World Cup Finals, Brazil have won 53.

Oleg Blokhin was 1975 European Footballer of the Year.

Aston Villa's Jimmy Brown was 15 years 349 days old when he played against Bolton in 1969.

4th Division Wrexham beat 1st Division Arsenal 2-1 in the 1992 F.A. Cup.

Blackpool won the Anglo-Italian Cup in 1971.

Nigel Clough scored twice in Nottingham Forest's 1989 League Cup Final win.

Gabriel Batistuta scored a hat-trick for Fiorentina against Cagliari in their January 1999 4-2 win.

Tony Philliskirk was Bolton's top league scorer in 1990/1 with 19 goals.

Spaniard Roberto Martinez signed for Wigan Athletic in July 1995 from Balaguer.

Arsenal won the 1970 U.E.F.A. Cup.

Brighton & Hove Albion bought Aston Villa's John Gregory for £275,000 in July 1979.

Barnet play at Underhill Stadium.

FOOTBALL

Alan Dicks was manager of Bristol City from 1967-'80.

Paolo Rossi was 1982 European Footballer of the Year.

Derek Fazackerley was 37 years 182 days old when he played for Bury in 1989.

Of their 66 games in World Cup Finals, Italy have won 38.

David Platt was Aston Villa's top league scorer in 1990/1 with 19 goals.

Howard Kendall managed Blackburn from 1979-'81.

Cardiff City were formerly known as Riverside F.C.

The Malta Football Association was founded in 1900.

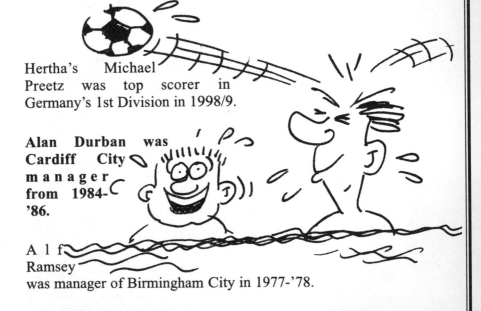

Hertha's Michael Preetz was top scorer in Germany's 1st Division in 1998/9.

Alan Durban was Cardiff City manager from 1984-'86.

A l f Ramsey was manager of Birmingham City in 1977-'78.

FOOTBALL

Dion Dublin was Cambridge United's top league goalscorer in 1990/1 with 17 goals.

Sam Bartram made 579 league appearances for Charlton from 1934-'56.

Ten teams have lost all their World Cup Finals games.

Chelsea bought Dennis Wise from Wimbledon in 1990 for £1.8m.

Alan Oakes was manager of Chester City from 1976-'82.

Beaumont Asquith was 37 years, 3 months old when he played for Barnsley against Coventry in 1927.

Vancouver Whitecaps paid £275,000 to Carlisle United for Peter Beardsley in April 1981.

Coventry City were known as Singers F.C. from 1883-'98.

Luther Blissett was A.F.C. Bournemouth's top league goalscorer in 1990/1.

Malcolm Allison succeeded Bert Head as Crystal Palace boss in 1972.

Gary Blissett was Brentford's top league goalscorer in 1990/1.

Bradford City manager Paul Jewell scored their only F.A. Cup goal in 1990/1, against Shrewsbury.

Liverpool bought Dean Saunders from Derby for £2.9m in 1991.

FOOTBALL

Grimsby Town are known as The Mariners.

Arsenal bought Bobby Gould from Coventry in February 1968 for £90,000.

Argentina have scored 100 goals in the World Cup Finals.

Bill Dodgin managed Brentford from 1953-'57 and his son, also called Bill, managed them from 1976-'80.

Exeter City's top league goalscorer in 1997/8 was Darren Rowbotham.

Bordeaux won the 1998/9 French title thanks to a last minute goal by substitute Pascal Feindouno against Paris St. Germain at Parc des Princes.

Wimbledon won the F.A. Cup in 1987/8.

Socrates was 1983 South American Player of the Year.

Blackpool play at Bloomfield Road.

Paul Gascoigne's booking for Middlesbrough against Spurs in February 1999 was his 11th in 22 league games.

Ted Drake scored 42 goals for Arsenal in the season 1934/5.

John McGovern was Bolton Wanderers' manager from 1982-'5.

Liverpool bought Ian Rush from Chester City in 1980 for £300,000.

FOOTBALL

Malta joined F.I.F.A. in 1959.

A.F.C. Bournemouth were formed as Boscombe St. Johns in 1899.

Eddie Firmani was Charlton Athletic manager from 1967-70.

Craig Russell was Sunderland's top league goalscorer in 1995/6.

Pelé was discovered by Valdemar De Brito, a member of Brazil's 1934 World Cup team.

West Bromwich Albion play at the Hawthorns.

Barcelona bought Gary Lineker from Everton in 1986 for £2.8m.

Of their 57 games in the World Cup Finals, Argentina have won 29.

Everton's record attendance was 78,299 against Liverpool in 1948.

Wrexham's top goalscorer in 1995/6 was Karl Connolly.

Brian Clough briefly managed Brighton & Hove Albion in 1973/74.

Of his ten league goals for West Ham in 1995/96, Julian Dicks scored five from penalties.

Matthias Sammer was 1996 European Footballer of the Year.

FOOTBALL

Margaret Thatcher is Honorary Vice-President of Blackburn Rovers.

Swansea City's record attendance was a 1968 F.A. Cup game versus Arsenal. It attracted 32,796 people.

Stoke City play at the Britannia Stadium.

Victor Ikpeba scored Nigeria's only goal in their 1998 World Cup win over Bulgaria.

Cesar Sampaio scored the first goal of the 1998 World Cup Finals.

Brian Labone made 451 league appearances for Everton from 1959-72.

Porto's 1998/9 Portuguese league title was their fifth in a row.

Dwight Yorke is a Trinidad & Tobago international.

Everton keeper Neville Southall sat down on the pitch at Leeds at half-time against a goalpost during their 1991 league fixture. He'd done it before against Wimbledon.

Ray Kennedy played 17 games for England whilst at Liverpool.

Kenny Dalglish was a Rangers fan as a child.

Norway beat San Marino 10-0 in a 1994 World Cup qualifier.

Chesterfield's home ground is the Recreation Ground.

FOOTBALL

Goalkeeper Pat Jennings scored for Spurs against Manchester United in 1967.

Brunei lost 8-0 to Hong Kong in a World Cup qualifier on 23 February, 1985 then 8-0 to China in another qualifier three days later.

Rudi Kreitlein refereed the 1966 World Cup game between England and Argentina.

Gianluca Vialli scored two extra-time goals in the 1989/90 European Cup Winners' Cup Final for Sampdoria.

Kim Book was the Northampton goalkeeper in their 8-2 defeat by Manchester United in the 1970 F.A. Cup.

Rangers had three players sent off in their 1995/6 European Champions Cup campaign.

Teddy Sheringham was the first Millwall player to score 100 goals in competitive games.

Former Leeds United forward Tony Yeboah was born on 6.6.66.

Tottenham Hotspur bought Willem Korsten from Vitesse Arnhem in summer 1999.

The Football League was the brainchild of Aston Villa's William McGregor.

Ossie Ardiles has coached Guadalajara in Mexico and Shimizu S-Pulse in Japan since being ousted by Tottenham.

The 1977 League Cup Final was replayed twice.

FOOTBALL

F.I.F.A. referee Ken Aston thought up the idea of red and yellow cards.

Sampdoria's only Serie A title was in 1991.

Patrick Kluivert scored Ajax's winning goal in the 1994/5 European Champions Cup final.

Adrian Ilie scored Romania's only goal in their 1998 World Cup victory over Colombia.

Cyril Knowles played four times for England in 1967/8.

Marc Rieper scored Denmark's only goal in their 1998 World Cup win over Saudi Arabia.

Former Leeds United forward Tommy Wright was born in Dunfermline in 1966.

The 1910 F.A. Cup Final replay took place at Everton.

Gianfranco Zola scored Italy's goal against England in their February 1997 World Cup qualifier.

Emmanuel Petit scored the last goal of the 1998 World Cup Finals.

West Germany beat Cyprus 12-0 in a 1970 World Cup qualifier.

Craig Ramage was Watford's top league goalscorer in 1995/6.

The First Division/Premier League champions have retained the title on 20 occasions.

FOOTBALL

The 1990/1 European Champions Cup Final between Red Star Belgrade and Marseille finished goalless.

John Sheridan scored Sheffield Wednesday's only goal in their 1991 League Cup Final win.

Ipswich goalkeeper Richard Wright has represented England at Schools, Youth and Under-21 level.

Slobodan Komljenovic scored Yugoslavia's only goal in their 1998 World Cup win against the U.S.A.

Newcastle United were last league champions in 1926/7.

Everton bought Tony Cottee from West Ham United in 1988 for £2.2m.

David Platt was P.F.A. Player of the Year in 1990.

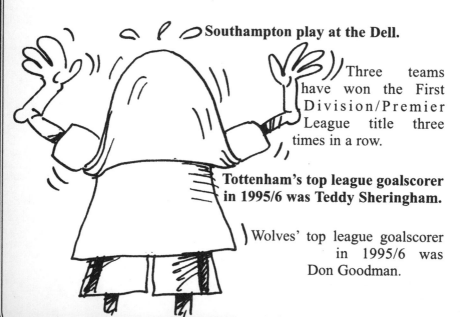

Southampton play at the Dell.

Three teams have won the First Division/Premier League title three times in a row.

Tottenham's top league goalscorer in 1995/6 was Teddy Sheringham.

Wolves' top league goalscorer in 1995/6 was Don Goodman.

FOOTBALL

Bradford City's 1911 F.A. Cup Final replay win against Newcastle United was at Old Trafford.

Brazil were winners of the Under-20 world championship in 1983 and '85.

Footballer Harry Makepeace won the league championship with Everton and the cricket county championship with Lancashire.

February 1996 saw David Ginola voted Head of the Year by the British Hairdressing Foundation.

Ghana won the 1991 and '95 Under-17 World Championships.

The original F.A. Cup was stolen in 1895 and never recovered.

Lev Yashin was 1963 European Footballer of the Year.

The Italian League was founded in 1898 when three games were played.

The U.S. women's football team beat Nigeria 7-1 in the 1999 World Cup.

Clive Allen was 1987 P.F.A. Player of the Year.

Chris Sutton signed for Chelsea in July 1999 for £10m.

The 1886 F.A. Cup Final replay took place at Derby.

Scotland lost 1-0 to Denmark at Ibrox in a March 1998 friendly.

FOOTBALL

France beat Northern Ireland 4-0 in a 1958 World Cup quarter-final.

Bochum and Nurnberg were relegated from the German first Division in 1998/9. They had been promoted to the division the previous season.

Helmut Schön, former coach of West Germany, died in 1996.

Football coach Louis van Gaal played for Antwerp, Telstar and Sparta Rotterdam.

Liam Brady was the first Celtic manager not to have played for the club.

Nigeria won the 1985 and '93 Under-17 World Championships.

Maccabee S.C. of Los Angeles won the 1977 and '78 U.S. Open Cup.

Burnley have been champions of the four divisions other than the Premiership.

Barnet were beaten 7-4 by Crewe in their first Football League game in 1991/2.

Tomas Brolin appeared on a stamp celebrating Sweden's hosting of the 1992 European Championships.

Three of the games in Group B of the 1998 World Cup finished 1-1.

The Football Association of Ireland was fined £20,000 by U.E.F.A. after the Irish government refused visas to the Yugoslavia team in June, 1999.

FOOTBALL

Scotland's October 1999 Euro 2000 qualifier is to be played at Ibrox Park.

Fulham's Paul Peschisolido was born in Scarborough, Ontario, Canada.

Northern Ireland beat Switzerland 1-0 in a friendly at Belfast in April 1998.

Martin Palermo missed three penalties for Argentina versus Colombia in their 1999 Copa America game.

The 1999 European Champions Cup Final featured two non-Italian teams for the first time since 1991.

Peter Osgood scored in the original 1971 European Cup Winners' Cup Final and subsequent replay.

China beat Norway 5-0 in their 1999 Women's World Cup semi-final clash.

Benfica's 18-0 aggregate win over Stade Dudelange in the 1965 European Champions Cup was the biggest in its history.

Dino Baggio scored in each leg of Juventus's 1993 U.E.F.A. Cup Final win over Borussia Dortmund.

In their 45 World Cup Finals games England have scored 62 goals.

Czechoslovakia scored first in the 1962 World Cup Final against Brazil.

FOOTBALL

Newcastle United won the 1969 U.E.F.A. Cup.

Barcelona won the 1991/2 European Champions Cup after beating Sampdoria in the final.

Dino Baggio scored in each leg of Parma's 1995 U.E.F.A. Cup Final win over Juventus.

Former Liverpool and England defender Mark Wright scored ten league goals whilst at Derby County.

Tottenham Hotspur bought Steffen Freund from Borussia Dortmund in 1998 for £730,000.

Stan Collymore played three times for England whilst at Nottingham Forest.

John McGrath, former Newcastle United centre-half, died on Christmas Day, 1998.

Stix, Baer and Fuller F.C. of St. Louis won the U.S. Open Cup in 1933 and '34.

Dion Dublin scored five goals in his first two games for Aston Villa in 1998.

Christopher Wreh, Arsenal's Liberian forward, began his league career with Monaco.

Canadian Alex Bunbury played two league games for West Ham United in 1992.

Mechelen won the 1988 European Cup Winners' Cup.

Nigel Clough became player-manager of Burton Albion in 1998.

FOOTBALL

England and Aston Villa defender Gareth Southgate was born in Watford.

Nigel Spackman's first league club was Bournemouth.

Denilson scored his first goal for Real Betis in February 1999 since his £22m move from São Paulo.

Wolverhampton Wanderers have been champions of all four divisions, excepting the Premier League, and Division Three (North).

In the three seasons between 1995-98, Nottingham Forest's Andrea Silenzi made 12 league appearances without once scoring.

In his 43 league appearances for Leeds United from 1994-96, Nigel Worthington scored one goal.

When Paris St. Germain won the 1986 French league title, they became the first team from the capital to win the league since 1936.

FOOTBALL

Canada's first international game was away to the United States in 1885. Their first home game was in 1957.

Nigel Spink spent 20 seasons with Aston Villa before transferring to West Bromwich Albion in 1995/6.

Gerry Francis played 12 times for England whilst at Q.P.R.

Neville Southall's first league club was Bury.

Chelsea's 21-match unbeaten run in the Premier League in 1998/9 ended at Arsenal on 31st January 1999.

Greek team Larissa won the 1988 league title.

Dallas Burn won the 1997 U.S. Open Cup.

Arsenal's Nwankwo Kanu was born in Owerri, Nigeria.

Ray Wilkins was the first England player to be sent off in the World Cup Finals.

Andy Sinton's first league club was Cambridge United.

Former England goalkeeper Chris Woods played no league games for Sunderland in the 1996/7 season.

Viv Anderson played 30 games for England.

After 23 games of the 1998/99 Premiership season Everton averaged 0.57 goals a game.

FOOTBALL

Icelander Johannes Edvaldsson won two league titles with Celtic in the 1970's.

In his 1,005 football league appearances between 1965-98, goalkeeper Peter Shilton scored once.

Tottenham player Tim Sherwood's first league club was Watford.

Before the start of the 1999 women's World Cup U.S.A. striker Mia Hamm had won 174 caps.

John Barnes's first attempted signing as Celtic's head coach was Bulgarian midfielder Stilian Petrov.

A skydiver crashed onto the Trinity Road stand at Aston Villa during the December 1998 fixture against Arsenal.

Andy Cole was the first million-pound player at Newcastle. He cost £1.75m.

Arsenal's Patrick Vieira was born in Dakar, Senegal.

David O'Leary and Brian Talbot shared a room before the 1979 F.A. Cup Final. They met as managers when Leeds played Rushden & Diamonds in the 1998/99 F.A. Cup.

In the Top 20 European club rankings published on 1st January, 1999, Manchester United were 19th on 73.03 points. Bayern Munich were 1st on 100.94 points.

Harry Redknapp's wife is the sister-in-law of Frank Lampard.

FOOTBALL

India's football team withdrew from the 1950 World Cup qualifiers when their players were refused permission to play barefoot.

23 million people watched the England versus Argentina World Cup game in 1998.

England's friendly against Belgium in October 1999 will be played at Sunderland's Stadium of Light.

Leeds bought Charlton defender Danny Mills in June 1999 for £4m.

Barnsley beat West Bromwich 1-0 in the 1912 F.A. Cup Final after a 0-0 draw.

Alex Ferguson was Scotland's assistant manager to Jock Stein when he died during a World Cup qualifier in 1985.

Before the start of the 1999 women's World Cup, U.S.A. player Kristine Lilly had won 178 caps.

Werder Bremen beat Monaco 2-0 in the 1991/2 European Cup Winners' Cup Final.

In his full England international appearances Dennis Wise has scored once.

Alan Shearer scored 3 goals in 5 games in his first season with Southampton.

Lazio headed Serie A in February 1999 for the first time since 1974/5.

FOOTBALL

Bradford City player Lee Sharpe's first league club was Torquay United.

In his four seasons with Newcastle United from 1993-96, Scott Sellars scored 5 goals.

Mark Hateley played 32 times for England.

The full name of the Fairs Cup was the International Industries Fairs Inter-Cities Cup.

England beat Morocco 1-0 in a friendly in Casablanca in May 1998.

Steve Bould signed for Sunderland in summer 1999 from Arsenal.

Nikos Dabizas was the first Greek to play in an F.A. Cup Final.

Nottingham Forest bought Hans Segers from P.S.V. Eindhoven in the 1984/5 season.

Former Aberdeen defender David Winnie was Iceland's first foreign Footballer of the Year.

David Seaman's first league appearances were for Peterborough United.

Veteran keeper Les Sealey's first league club was Coventry City.

In his 1985 season at Hvidovre, former Manchester United goalkeeper Peter Schmeichel scored six league goals.

FOOTBALL

Malta's national stadium at Ta'Qali served as a military airport during World War II.

Group 2 games in the 1966 World Cup were played at Villa Park and Hillsborough.

Kennet Andersson scored a hat-trick for Bologna against Sampdoria in March 1998.

Goalkeeper Steve Ogrizovic scored for Coventry against Sheffield Wednesday in 1986.

Leonidas scored four goals for Brazil in their 6-5 win over Poland in the 1938 World Cup Finals.

The 1987/8 European Champions Cup Final finished goalless.

There were an average of 5.38 goals per game in the 1954 World Cup Finals.

Mick Jones scored Leeds United's winner in their 1-0 aggregate win over Ferencvaros in the 1968 Fairs Cup.

Chilean Ivan Zamorano scored a hat-trick for Internazionale versus Venezia in a 6-2 win at the San Siro in January 1999.

Tottenham were last league champions in 1960/1.

Leslie Knighton was Arsenal manager from 1919-25.

The attendance at the 1968 League Cup Final was 97,887.

FOOTBALL

Grimsby goalkeeper Walter Scott saved three penalties in a 1909 game against Burnley.

Ralph Coates scored Tottenham's only goal in their 1973 League Cup Final win.

Sunderland sold 36,000 season tickets for the 1999/2000 season.

Norway club Rosenborg banned female journalists from their changing rooms in 1999.

Torquay banned pre-match kickabout shots on goal fearing legal action from fans hit by misses.

After F.A. Cup final replays in successive years from 1910-12, the next wasn't until 1970.

Rangers beat Leeds in the Second Round of the 1992/3 European Champions Cup.

Argentina's Abel Balbo scored a hat-trick in Parma's 6-3 win at Piacenza in January 1999.

Mexico beat St. Vincent 11-0 in a 1994 World Cup qualifier.

Macao lost 10-0 to Japan twice in qualifiers for the 1998 World Cup.

Werder Bremen won the 1992 European Cup Winners' Cup.

The last second division team to win the F.A. Cup were West Ham United in 1980.

Liechtenstein lost 11-1 at home to Macedonia in a 1998 World Cup qualifier.

FOOTBALL

Brian Lewis, a member of the Colchester team that knocked Leeds out of the F.A. Cup in the 1970's, died in December 1998.

Football team Rushden & Diamonds resulted from a merger in 1992 between Rushden Town and Irthlingborough Diamonds.

Hernan Crespo scored a hat-trick in Parma's February 1999 win at Juventus.

When York City met Stoke City in the 1998/9 F.A. Cup manager Alan Little faced brother Brian across the benches.

Benfica striker Karel Poborsky was born in Jindrichuv-Hradec in the Czech Republic.

The general secretary of F.I.F.A., Michael Zen-Ruffinen, is a former international referee.

Manchester United's mascot Fred the Red had his nose broken during the squad's celebration of the 1996 Premiership.

Valerenga defender Fredrik Kjolner, who scored against Chelsea in the 1998/9 European Cup Winners' Cup is a prison guard when not playing football.

FOOTBALL

West Ham sponsor the New South Wales state league side Blacktown.

Paolo DiCanio was banned for 11 games following his push on Paul Alcock.

Harry Redknapp made 149 appearances for West Ham as a player.

Birmingham-raised Stewart Baxter led Halmstads of Sweden and Tromso of Norway to league titles.

Florin Raducioiu, West Ham's former foreign import, didn't play in a League Cup tie against Stockport as he was shopping at Harvey Nichols.

Leeds United banned the Sheffield Wednesday band from playing at Elland Road in November 1998.

Carlos Dittborn, President of the Chilean F.A. died a short while before the 1962 World Cup started in his country.

Gabriel Batistuta scored a hat-trick for Argentina against Jamaica in the 1998 World Cup.

Three games in Group H of the 1998 World Cup finished 1-0.

Aston Villa's Lee Hendrie is the nephew of former Barnsley boss John Hendrie.

West Auckland beat Juventus for the Sir Thomas Lipton Trophy in 1911.

Rot-Weiss Essen were German league champions in 1955.

FOOTBALL

Former England midfielder David White scored nine league goals in his spell with Leeds United from 1993-96.

Spain beat Austria 9-0 in a Euro 2000 Group Six qualifier in March 1999.

Arsenal beat Everton 3-1 in the 1999 Women's League Cup Final.

Justin Edinburgh was sent off in the 1994 Worthington Cup Final.

The three teams relegated to Division 1 in the 1997/8 season, Bolton, Barnsley and Crystal Palace, were the three that had been promoted the previous year.

Manchester United exited the 1995/6 U.E.F.A. Cup on away goals to Rotor Volvograd.

Brentford play at Griffin Park.

Alan Shearer has not won at Southampton since leaving the club in 1992.

Bristol City payed £62,000 to West Bromwich Albion for Bobby Gould in December 1972.

Henrik Larsson scored four goals in Celtic's 7-1 win at Motherwell in February, 1999.

The U.S. women's football team beat Brazil 2-0 in their 1999 World Cup semi-final.

Coventry City forward Noel Whelan scored seven league goals for Leeds in his spell there from 1992-6.

FOOTBALL

Goalkeeper Steve Sherwood scored for Watford against Coventry in 1984.

Dion Dublin, Michael Owen & Chris Sutton each scored 18 league goals in the Premiership in 1997/8.

Parma won the 1992/3 European Cup Winners' Cup beating Royal Antwerp 3-1.

Maltese club Floriana F.C. were formed in 1894.

Comedian Jasper Carrott opened Birmingham's £4.5m Railway End at St. Andrews in February 1999.

Real Zaragoza beat Chelsea and Arsenal in the 1994/5 European Cup Winners' Cup.

Australia lost 6-1 and 3-1 to North Korea in 1966 World Cup qualifiers.

The 1999/2000 European Champions League will consist of 32 clubs.

Newcastle United's Duncan Ferguson spent six weeks in Barlinnie jail for assaulting Raith Rovers player John McStay whilst at Rangers.

FOOTBALL

Prior to 1900 Millwall's name was 'The Dockers'.

In his three seasons at Chelsea, Muzzy Izzet didn't play a single game.

Milan beat Barcelona 4-0 in the 1993/4 European Champions Cup Final.

John Osborne, West Bromwich Albion's goalkeeper in the 1968 F.A. Cup Final, died in November 1998.

Ronaldo and Cesar Sampaio each scored twice for Brazil in their 1998 World Cup game against Chile.

Kevin Phillips of Sunderland and Pierre Van Hooijdonk of Nottingham Forest each scored 29 league goals in Division One in 1997/8.

Leeds United's original 1971 away leg to Juventus in the U.E.F.A. Cup was abandoned because of a waterlogged pitch.

English coach Stewart Baxter led AIK Stockholm to the Swedish league title in November 1998.

Bologna's last Serie A title was in 1964.

Napoli took the 1988/9 U.E.F.A. Cup.

Christian Vieri scored Italy's only goal in their 1998 World Cup victory over Norway.

Andrei Kanchelskis was sent off in the 1994 League Cup Final.

FOOTBALL

Bradford City chairman Geoffrey Richmond made his future by buying and selling the Ronson lighter business.

Peter Schmeichel was Player of the Tournament in the 1992 European Championship.

The Azteca, Etrusco, Questra and Tricolore were all types of football used for World Cup Final tournaments.

Tony Parkes had his first spell as Blackburn Rovers caretaker manager following Bobby Saxton's departure in December 1986.

Chelsea's John Terry made his European debut at Valerenga in the 1998/9 European Cup Winners' Cup.

St. Johnstone lost the 1998/9 Scottish League Cup Final 2-1 to Rangers three weeks after having lost to the same team 7-0.

Gustavo Poyet's first game for Chelsea was the 1997 Charity Shield game.

West Ham's Paulo Futre exited Highbury before a game with Arsenal because he wasn't allowed to wear the No. 10 shirt.

Group 1 games in the 1966 World Cup were played at Wembley and White City.

The last match Brian Laudrup played for Chelsea was in the European Cup Winners Cup against F.C. Copenhagen. He scored and was later sold to them.

Wrexham's club cat, Gladys, was sponsored by Petsmart in 1998.

FOOTBALL

Tore Andre Flo scored twice for Chelsea against Blackburn at Ewood Park in a league match in 1998 after coming on as sub with 12 minutes to go.

Spanish footballer Ramon Moya was booked in 1998 for kissing a linesman.

Singapore hosted a RoboCup in 1998 involving teams of robot footballers.

Football scout Harry McShane is father of actor Ian McShane.

The transfer deadline is on 5 p.m. on the final Thursday in March.

Jermaine Pennant became the second youngest player to appear in the F.A. Cup when he played for Notts County in 1998/9 against Sheffield United.

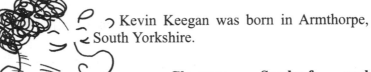

Kevin Keegan was born in Armthorpe, South Yorkshire.

Clarence Seedorf and Fernando Hierro of Real Madrid fell out with each other in a 1999 draw with Dynamo Kiev over who should take a free kick.

Numbers on the backs of F.A. Cup Final shirts were first in evidence in 1933.

Greek American A.A. of New York won the U.S. Open Cup from 1967-69.

FOOTBALL

Gordon Banks kept a clean sheet in 35 of his 73 England games.

Before being released by Wimbledon, Joe Kinnear had been the second longest serving Premiership manager after Alex Ferguson.

Barry Town player Eifon Williams scored a hat-trick on March 20 1999, then was transferred to Torquay United for whom he scored a hat-trick on March 27th.

Ronnie O'Brien signed for Juventus after being released by Middlesbrough in 1999.

Eric Gerets is to replace Bobby Robson as coach at P.S.V. Eindhoven in the 1999/2000 season.

Sunderland were crowned First Division champions in 1999 ater winning 3-1 at Barnsley.

George Graham had a trial for Newcastle United when he was 16.

Chris Ramsay, former Brighton & Hove Albion player, became the first black England manager when he was put in charge of the Under-20 squad in March 1999.

Juventus's Nuovo Stadio Delle Alpi was built for the Italia '90 World Cup Finals.

Chelsea's visit to Charlton Athletic at the Valley in April 1999 was their first since 1983.

Udinese striker Marcio Amoroso was top scorer in Italy's Serie A in 1998/9.

FOOTBALL

Liverpool's original home leg against Borussia Mönchengladbach in the 1973 U.E.F.A. Cup Final was abandoned because of a waterlogged pitch.

Elvir Bolic scored Fenerbahce's goal which saw Manchester United's first home defeat in European competition in 1966.

Frank Rikjaard scored the winner for Milan in their 1989/0 European Champions Cup win versus Benfica.

P.F.A. Player of the Year in 1998 was Dennis Bergkamp.

Borussia Mönchengladbach were relegated from the German First Division in 1998/9.

Davor Suker was top goalscorer in the 1998 World Cup Finals.

Juventus's new coach Carlo Ancelotti's first home game in 1999 saw a 2-0 win over Vicenza.

Finnish centre-back Sami Hyppia signed for Liverpool from Willem II in summer 1999.

France beat Paraguay by a golden goal in their 1998 World Cup game.

John Sillett was manager of Hereford United from 1974-78.

David Nish played five games for England whilst a Derby County player.

Zimbabwe players refused to travel to Zaire for a World Cup qualifier in 1996 because they feared getting the Ebola virus.

FOOTBALL

Coventry City midfield player Paul Telfer was born in Edinburgh.

Lilian Thuram scored both of France's goals in their 1998 World Cup semi final against Croatia.

Cardiff City's mascot is Barclay the Bluebird.

Wimbledon goalkeeper Neil Sullivan played one game for Crystal Palace whilst on loan in 1991/2.

Chelsea midfielder Didier Deschamps won a record 83rd cap for France against Ukraine in 1999.

Burnley won the Anglo-Scottish Cup in 1978/9.

Patrick Kluivert scored in the quarter-finals and semi-finals of the 1998 World Cup for the Netherlands.

Edinburgh-born Gordon Strachan's league career began with Dundee in the 1974/5 season.

The attendance at the 1967 League Cup Final was 97,952.

Aston Villa's Steve Stone was born in Gateshead.

Fourth Division Rochdale played Second Division Norwich City in the 1962 League Cup Final.

Blackburn Rovers's record attendance was 61,783 against Bolton in an F.A. Cup tie in 1929.

Steve Claridge scored Leicester's winner in their 1997 League Cup Final against Middlesbrough.

FOOTBALL

Maltese club Hamrun Spartans F.C. was founded in 1907.

Alan Shearer was 1997 P.F.A. Player of the Year.

Ernest Willimowski scored four goals for Poland in their 1938 World Cup game against Brazil but still ended on the losing side.

Oxford United were Third Division champions in 1983/4.

1754 goals have been scored in the 580 games in the World Cup Finals.

Cagliari were 1970 Serie A Champions in Italy.

Portugal were winners of the Under-20 World Championships in 1989 and '91.

Trinidad beat Antigua 11-1 in a 1974 World Cup qualifier.

Brooklyn Hispano S.C. of New York won the 1943 and '44 U.S. Open Cup.

Greece boycotted the 1964 European Championships as they didn't want to play Albania.

Gilles Grimandi's sending off against Leeds in December 1998 was Arsenal's fifth sending off of the 1998/9 season.

Rivaldo scored two of Brazil's quarter-final goals against Denmark in the 1998 World Cup.

Juan Alberto Schiaffino scored 4 goals for Uruguay in their 1950 World Cup victory against Bolivia.

FOOTBALL

When Chelsea led the Premier League in December 1998 it was their first time at the top since November 11, 1989.

Goalkeeper Ray Cashley scored for Bristol City against Hull in 1973.

Argentina beat England 4-3 on penalties in their 1998 World Cup game.

The F.A. Cup Final was replayed in successive years from 1981-83.

Hull City were Third Division champions in 1965/6.

John McGovern was 16 years and 205 days old when he played for Hartlepool United in a May 1966 league game.

Barry Hayles of Bristol Rovers was top scorer in the Nationwide League Division Two in 1997/8.

France beat West Germany 6-3 to take third place in the 1958 World Cup.

Ukrainian Nationals of Philadelphia won the 1960 and '61 U.S. Open Cup.

Leeds signed Norwegian defender Eirik Bakke from Sojindal in summer 1999.

Wrexham were Third Division champions in 1977/8.

In the 1958 World Cup Finals England only selected 20 players instead of the permitted 22.

FOOTBALL

Brazil beat England 3-1 in a 1962 World Cup quarter-final.

Maldives lost 12-0 to Syria twice in qualifiers for the 1998 World Cup.

Francis Lee played 27 times for England whilst at Manchester City.

Goalkeeper Andy Goram scored for Hibs against Morton in 1988.

Juventus beat Borussia Dortmund 6-1 on aggregate in the 1992/3 U.E.F.A. Cup.

In his three seasons with Celtic from 1994-7 Pierre van Hooijdonk scored 44 goals.

Sheffield Wednesday were last crowned football league champions in 1929/30.

Aston Villa's record attendance was 76,588 against Derby County in a 1946 F.A. Cup tie.

Brazil, Bulgaria, Hungary and Portugal were in Group 3 of the 1966 World Cup.

Pat Stanton was 1970 Scottish P.F.A. Player of the Year.

Geoff Horsfield of Halifax Town was top scorer in the 1997/8 G.M. Vauxhall Conference.

Terry Cooper scored the only goal of the 1968 League Cup Final for Leeds United.

FOOTBALL

Ronaldo scored Barcelona's only goal in their 1997 European Cup Winners' Cup Final win over Paris St. Germain.

Tottenham's Swiss international Ramon Vega's first league club was Grasshoppers.

Former England player John Salako was born in Nigeria.

Maltese club Sliema Wanderers F.C. were founded in 1909.

Ian Rush scored seven league goals in his 1987/8 spell with Juventus.

Kevin Keegan scored in the home and away legs for Liverpool in their 1976 U.E.F.A. Cup Final against Bruges.

Paul Durkin refereed the 1997/8 F.A. Cup Final.

Manchester City missed three penalties in a 1912 game against Newcastle.

In his five seasons with Rangers defender Chris Vinnicombe scored one league goal in 23 games.

South African international Eric Tinkler's playing career began in 1993/4 with Vitoria Setubal.

Salvatore Schillaci was top scorer in the 1990 World Cup Finals.

N.Y. Pancyprian-Freedoms of New York won the U.S. Open Cup in 1982 and '93.

Chile beat Yugoslavia 1-0 to take third position in the 1962 World Cup Finals.

FOOTBALL

Oldrich Nejedly was top scorer in the 1934 World Cup Finals.

Gary Jones of Notts County was top goalscorer in Nationwide League Division Three in 1997/8.

Australia beat the Solomon Islands 13-0 in a 1998 World Cup qualifier.

Martin Chivers scored both goals for Tottenham in their 1971 League Cup Final win.

John Radford played two games for England whilst at Arsenal.

Chelsea were last crowned league champions in 1954/5.

In his four seasons with Wolves from 1993-7 Geoff Thomas scored eight league goals.

Newcastle signed Elena Marcelino from Real Mallorca in summer 1999 for £5m.

Davor Suker scored Croatia's only goal in their 1998 World Cup game with Romania.

Mark Hughes scored both goals in Manchester United's 1991 European Cup Winners' Cup win over Barcelona.

Northern Ireland played France in the quarter-finals of the 1958 World Cup in Sweden.

Anders Limpar scored a hat-trick for Arsenal against Coventry in their last game of 1990/1.

FOOTBALL

Trevor Brooking played 47 times for England.

Goalkeeper Alan Paterson scored for Glentoran against Linfield in 1989.

Australian Joe Marston appeared in the 1954 F.A. Cup Final for Preston.

Michael Owen was born on the 14th December, 1979.

Guillermo Stabile was top scorer in the 1930 World Cup Finals.

England defender Rio Ferdinand is the cousin of Les Ferdinand.

Schalke 04 won the 1997 U.E.F.A. Cup.

Vic Crowe was Aston Villa manager from 1970-74.

F.C. Porto won the 1986/7 European Champions Cup after being 1-0 down.

Nigel Clough played 14 times for England.

Jody Morris is the first Chelsea player since Alan Hudson to have been born within a mile of Stamford Bridge.

FOOTBALL

Phönix Karlsruhe were 1909 German league champions.

Slovan Bratislava won the 1969 European Cup Winners' Cup.

Billy McNeill was 1965 Scottish P.F.A. Player of the Year.

Maltese club Naxxar Lions F.C. were founded in 1920.

The 1912 F.A. Cup Final replay took place at Bramall Lane.

Australia are the only country to have played World Cup qualifiers on every continent.

Ajax won the 1986/7 European Cup Winners' Cup Final beating Lokomotiv Leipzig.

Liverpool won the League Cup from 1981-84.

Ralph Coates played four times for England.

Milan won the Scudetto in 1998/9 by one point over Lazio.

Simon Donnelly and Phil O'Donnell signed for Sheffield Wednesday from Celtic in summer 1999.

Salernitana, Sampdoria, Vicenza and Empoli were relegated from Serie A in Italy in 1998/9.

Ajax won the 1991/2 U.E.F.A. Cup.

Hector Pineda scored Argentina's goal in their 1-0 win over Croatia in the 1998 World Cup.

THE THINGS THEY SAID

THE THINGS THEY SAID

"I'd flatten anyone who ever suggested I threw a game" - Dennis Lillee after having £10 at 500-1 against England beating Australia at Headingley in 1981.

"Bald" - Ireland hooker Keith Wood on being asked to describe his character.

"It's a bit like going to heaven without having to die first." - Tony Banks on being made Minister for Sport.

"I think it is natural for footballers to like golf." - Philippe Albert.

"The first thing that ran across my mind was to bite him back."- Evander Holyfield after the Tyson chewing.

"I wouldn't want to fight a war with the Belgians on our side." - Dave Bassett on Nico Claesen.

"He is the moaningest Minnie I've ever known." - John Bond on Kenny Dalglish.

"People are more polite here than in Holland. They give you more space." - Chelsea goalkeeper Ed De Goey.

"I believe he could play until he is 80 - but I think he is right to give up at the end of the season." - George Boateng on Peter Schmeichel.

"Me." - George Graham on being asked what was the most important thing he had brought to Spurs.

"I'm a winner. I just didn't win today." - Greg Norman in 1998.

"It was a good result and, I stress, a good result." - Lawrence Dallaglio after England beat South Africa in 1998.

"Some of the dummies he threw even sent me the wrong way - and I was sitting in the dug out." - Harry Redknapp on David Ginola.

THE THINGS THEY SAID

"We called him the cat because he gave us kittens." - Danny Blanchflower on goalkeeper Norman Uprichard.

"He grunts most of the time when he's moving." - Tim Henman on tennis player Mariano Zabaleta who beat him in the 1999 German Open.

"I hoped you'd still be in hospital." - Tim Henman joking to Jim Courier at the 1999 Davis Cup.

"... brilliant but lackadaisical footballing skills which make me look like a cross between Chris Waddle and Niall Quinn." - cricketer Alex Tudor on his footballing prowess.

"I am a clean rider, my conscience is clear." - Marco Pantani after expulsion from the 1999 Tour of Italy.

"I can't believe I won on this circuit. I've never won here before in my life." - motorcyclist Carl Fogarty on Misano.

"He's big, he's white, and he can hit." - Frank Bruno on man-mountain Vitali Klitschko.

"I think I have been brought in to add steel and discipline - to kick a few backsides." - Phil Thompson on rejoining Liverpool

"I agree the lad's pace can be deceptive. He's much slower than you think." - Bill Shankly on Roy Evans.

"Thank God we weren't playing the whole of Samoa." - Gareth Davies after Wales lost to Western Samoa in 1991.

"I saw a lot of green and I wanted to see a lot of brown." - trainer Bob Baffert on the program of venues for the proposed world series racing championship in March 2000.

THE THINGS THEY SAID

"She is a very, very strong girl. A couple of times I thought I was playing a guy." - Lindsay Davenport on Amelie Mauresmo.

"It was a real Lionel." - Justin Rose after missing the cut in the 1999 Moroccan Open.

"Does that mean changing a Chinaman?" - Brian McMillan, former South Africa cricketer on being reprimanded for advising a team mate to bowl a 'coolie creeper' to Ashraf Mall, a South African batsman of Indian descent in 1999.

"Buy two new shoulders." - rugby's Keith Wood's response on being asked what he'd do if he won the lottery.

"We do not have a crisis." - Martina Hingis on her exit from Wimbledon in 1999.

"I personally believe that we need a complete change, a complete shake-up." - Viv Richards on the West Indies team for the 1999 World Cup.

"We have no hang-ups about playing the Australians." - England rugby union coach Clive Woodward in 1999.

"Coping with the language shouldn't be a problem. I can't speak English." - Paul Gascoigne on moving to Lazio.

"I just know there are more golden years ahead." - Shane Warne at the 1999 World Cup.

"I don't want to be the next Carl Lewis." - athlete Maurice Greene.

"He is so unlucky that I was not at all surprised that he was injured - Gianluca Vialli on Pierluigi Casiraghi's injury at West Ham in November 1998.

"We had loads of missing players today. I didn't know the names of half of our substitutes." - Derby boss Jim Smith after their 2-1 win at Liverpool in November 1998.

THE THINGS THEY SAID

"There was certainly the suspicion that some influential people at the F.A. wanted a clean sweep at the top." - Graham Kelly, former F.A. Chief Executive.

"There was a plate full of sandwiches in the dressing room afterwards and I advised the players to eat as much as they could because the cupboard is bare." - Steve Coppell on the troubles at Crystal Palace.

"Dutch goalkeepers are protected to a ridiculous extent. The only time they are in danger of physical contact is when they go into a red light district." - Brian Clough.

"Dennis is like a pianist who works on his skill." - Arsène Wenger on Mr. Bergkamp.

"It was Liverpool 2 Liverpool 2, because we gave them both of their goals." - Gerard Houllier on their February 1999 draw with West Ham United.

"We've had our first bad month for two years and suddenly the world's at an end, I'm no good at my job and everybody else is crap." - Harry Redknapp on the fickle fans of West Ham United.

"I believe after the week we have had against Manchester United, Chelsea and Arsenal that there are four teams who have the potential to be champions - including us." - Villa boss John Gregory in December 1998.

"He sent my wife a lovely bunch of flowers and he sent me a quid for a pint tonight." - Brian Kidd on Alex Ferguson.

"It was a truly, truly unique performance. We will never forget it." - Gordon Strachan on Steve Dunn's refereeing in Coventry's game against Wimbledon in December 1998.

"A tart, a fairy, a little girl." - Harry Redknapp on Florin Raducioiu.

THE THINGS THEY SAID

"I'm a great believer in living in the present." - George Graham

"I didn't sing to the players, however. I think that might have demotivated them" - Watt Nicol, Kevin Keegan's 'Mr. Motivator'.

"It was the first time I've scored from a free-kick in the first team. I've always practised them but I don't do it alongside Beckham because he'd make me look stupid." - Manchester United winger Terry Cooke whilst on loan.

"We murdered them and they know it. We flippin' hammered them." - England cricket coach David Lloyd on drawing with the mighty Zimbabwe in 1997.

"By the time we get over there we will be chomping at the bit so much we will be eating people." - Alex Ferguson on their away tie at Juventus in 1999.

"The European Cup was harder to win then than it is now." - Bob Paisley's widow Jessie in 1999.

"I feel we've now got to win every game and I feel we also need a few snookers." - Ron Atkinson at Forest in 1999.

"With so many players either on international duty or gaining treatment we only had about three guys at training and had a quick game of one-and-a-half a side." - Celtic 'keeper Jonathan Gould.

"I behaved in an unacceptable manner. I don't even remember properly what I did but I hope and pray I can be forgiven." - Ian Wright following a 5-1 defeat at West Ham in 1999.

"Pete is the greatest tennis player on earth to have ever picked up a racket." - Medvedev on Sampras.

"I have never missed a tournament through illness or injury." - golfer Colin Montgomerie.

THE THINGS THEY SAID

"Here comes the Messiah." - Jason Leonard greeting Rob Andrew following the latter's call-up to the England rugby union squad in 1997.

"My wife hits harder than him" - Wigan rugby league player on Brisbane Bronco's player Gordon Tallis.

"I don't think I'm in 100% condition to be part of the national team." - Leonardo of Brazil on leaving the Copa America squad in 1999.

"Of course my name is not on the leaderboard - I am the wrong nationality." - golfer Colin Montgomerie at the 1999 U.S. Masters.

"They asked me to help and I was happy to do so." - Ray Wilkins on taking over from jailed Graham Rix at Chelsea in 1999.

"... the city is now the sporting capital of England" - Sports minister Tony Banks on mighty Leicester.

"I did not come here on holiday or to enjoy myself. I came here to play and become a legend in London with Chelsea." - Gianluca Vialli on signing for the Blues.

"They've made great progress without two pennies to rub together." - Joe Royle on Macclesfield Town.

"I'm working round the clock to save the club and it has been murder. I'm past the Kenny Dalglish stage. I've gone potty." - Terry Venables at Spurs.

"I am Bartman, not Batman'" - H. Bartlett McGuire, tennis administrator and legal advisor.

"They are calling us veterans but we are a long way from finished yet." - 26 year old Arantxa Sanchez-Vicario after winning the 1998 French Open singles title.

THE THINGS THEY SAID

"A waste of time." - Alex Ferguson on friendly internationals.

"They couldn't find many holes." - Ruud Gullit on Manchester United after their 0-0 draw with Newcastle United in the 1998/9 season.

"I'd rather go back to Canberra and cart bricks for my dad." - Ned Zelic, Australian footballer on the prospect of returning to Q.P.R.

"I'd get withdrawal symptoms if I hadn't had a curry for a while but these days I feel the same about roast chicken and all the trimmings." - Nasser Hussain.

"It wasn't much of a kiss because I still had my lion's head on." - Hercules, sacked mascot at Aston Villa after hugging Miss Aston Villa in 1998.

"I've never pushed to win here." - Arantxa Sanchez-Vicario on her 1999 Wimbledon singles exit.

"I feel almost sorry for South Africa." - Steve Waugh on Australia's defeat of South Africa in the 1999 World Cup.

"I am excited about this England side." - rugby coach Clive Woodward.

THE THINGS THEY SAID

"You can't race in England and not want to race in England." - The Aga Khan.

"Maybe if we win the final it will be a good time for me to bow out." - Pakistan cricketer Wasim Akram in 1999.

"After five years on the road I desperately need some rest." - South Africa cricket coach Bob Woolmer.

"I could be playing until I'm 40." - Jeremy Guscott in February 1999.

"Given the right car, and the right backing nothing is impossible." - Nigel Mansell on a comeback possibility, in 1997.

"I'm a Cablinasian." - Tiger Woods on his ethic background.

"Brive has been a terrific break for me." - Scotland and Brive rugby player Gregor Townsend.

"I've scored 25,556 runs and I want to reach 30,000 before I retire." - former Derbyshire captain Kim Barnett on joining Gloucs in 1999.

"I would not want to take Mika... off the road in order that Michael can win a world championship." - racing driver Eddie Irvine in 1998.

"If they miss, I hit." - West Indies bowler Keith Arthurton after taking 4 for 31 versus Pakistan in the 1998 Wills International Cup.

"They're trying to pick holes in him but I can't pick a hole." - jockey Norman Williamson on horse Teeton Mill.

"Lewis is a jumper. My man's a leaper." - Mike Powell's coach Randy Huntington following the breaking of the world long jump record in 1991.

THE THINGS THEY SAID

"I signed a very good contract when I came home. I've doubled it since and I hope to quadruple it soon. If the bosses don't make any effort, I may think about leaving." - Chelsea man Frank Leboeuf in February 1999.

"The trip to America to catch a Super Bowl game and an ice hockey game was intended to give me a lift." - Paul Merson on going a.w.o.l. from Aston Villa.

"He was diving left, right and centre." - Joe Kinnear on David Ginola in January 1999.

"Stan had the lot and threw it all away. Nobody has ever got inside his head and maybe never will."- manager Frank Clark on Stan Collymore.

"That was not an Alan Ball team." - Alan Ball on his team Portsmouth after their 5-1 home defeat by Leeds United in the 1998/9 F.A. Cup.

"Hull is very nice. The weather is very like home." - Hull City's Spanish import Antonio Doncel-Varcarcel.

"The Jerk of the World." - golfer Fred Funk on Colin Montgomerie in 1997.

"The only way we could win this game is if we put out 15 players." - Malcolm Shotton, Oxford boss on their 1999 F.A. Cup game with Chelsea.

"To say they are playing bad cricket is being nice to them. It's unbearable." - Clive Lloyd on the West Indies in 1997.

"They are capable of beating Lazio but then again I wouldn't be surprised if Lazio beat them." - Egil Olsen, Valerenga boss on Chelsea's prospects in the European Cup Winners' Cup.

THE THINGS THEY SAID

"I was trying to find out who we were playing" - Australian Test cricket captain Warwick Armstrong on reading a paper in the outfield at the Oval in 1921 against England.

"Everything is going down the drain. There is no respect, no manners." - Malcolm Marshall following the sacking of Rohan Kanhai from the West Indies Cricket Board in 1992.

"If you're a fighter and you just have a big heart, you wind up in the cemetery. But if you got heart and skill, then you got what it takes to be champion of the world and François Botha has both." - boxing trainer Panama Lewis.

"I'm lucky. Stick with me and some of it will rub off on you." - Jacques Villeneuve to Craig Pollock.

"Today it was as if they had different heads." - Italy rugby union player Diego Dominguez on the Welsh rugby union team.

"Don't you get knighted if you score a hat-trick at Wembley?" - Kevin Keegan after Paul Scholes's hat-trick against Poland in March 1999.

"I like the Scots. They are like the Finns because they have a good sense of humour and are not two-faced." - footballer Mixu Paatelainen.

"In pre-season training all we did was run over a hill, it was like a scene from 'Zulu'"- Steve Claridge on Barry Fry's training methods.

"One thing you can say is that this is a match between two confident sets of players, albeit from different planets." - Kevin Keegan on the Manchester United versus Fulham Cup tie in 1999.

"Let's hope he's not on for longer than 14 minutes." - Kevin Keegan on the prospect of playing against Ole Gunnar Solsjaer following his late contribution to the 8-1 drubbing of Nottingham Forest.

THE THINGS THEY SAID

"Par today is 68, there's no breeze, the greens are holding and it should be a piece of cake. I wouldn't be surprised if Ernie Els shoots 65." - Nick Faldo at the 1999 South African Open.

"Anna knows everything and what she doesn't know she thinks she knows." - Nick Bollettieri, former coach of tennis star Anna Kournikova."

"When I was batting it was stiff, but I thought it would get better. Unfortunately it got worse." - Sri Lanka Test cricket captain Arjuna Ranatunga on a calf muscle injury.

"Juninho doesn't want to close any doors." - Bryan Robson on his former Middlesbrough player's possible return to the club.

"I'm your pal! I'm your pal! Listen to me." - trainer Brendan Ingle to Naseem Hamed during the latter's title fight against Kevin Kelley in 1997.

"Good enough for the homeless but not for an international striker" - Pierre Van Hooijdonk on his rejection of a £7,000 a week pay increase offer at Celtic.

"Plan B. That's all I've got to say. See you in Qatar" - the enigmatic Nick Faldo.

"Sport is like the theatre. People like to see good-looking people who are dressed properly." - tennis star Anna Kournikova.

"Give me the winning ball." - John Bromwich to a ball boy at 5-3, 40-15 up in the final set against Bob Falkenburg in the 1948 Wimbledon men's singles final. Falkenburg went on to win.

"Strikers win matches, defenders win championships." - Villa boss John Gregory in November, 1998.

THE THINGS THEY SAID

"Anyone who went to the toilet and came back would not have believed it." - Martin O'Neill on Leicester's 4-2 home defeat by Chelsea in November, 1998.

"He's a headless chicken at times." - David O'Leary on Lee Bowyer.

"A strange and terrible place." - Mrs. Andrea Emerson on her husband's choice of domicile, Middlesbrough.

"Some say George is as fit as a fiddle but I think he looks more like a cello'" - Lou Duva, Evander Holyfield's manager on George Foreman.

"I intend to have it floodlit and heated" - Laurent Charvet on his Tyneside petanque court.

"Our supporters may see this game and say, 'Better we stay in the First Division'"- Graham Taylor after Watford lost 5-2 to Spurs in the 1998/9 F.A. Cup.

"Our groundsman is fitter than some of my players." - Swindon's Jimmy Quinn.

"Our budget for the whole year including everything is only $8m." - journalist Alexandr Prosvetov talking about Spartak Moscow's finances in 1998.

"In 30 fights, I've never had one-to-one tuition as a world champion. I've gone into the gym and done a set routine like any other kid. The truth is that I've never had a proper trainer." - Naseem Hamed following a split with trainer Brendan Ingle.

"I predict that within 10 years we will be among the 10 wealthiest clubs in this country." - Michael Knighton, Carlisle chairman in 1994.

THE THINGS THEY SAID

"When my players get the team sheet and see Mr. Reid's name they think they are playing against 12 men." - Gérard Houllier on referee Mike Reid.

"I was disappointed not to play in a World Cup competition." - George Best in 1999.

"Last time I fought in Manchester I knocked out Billy Hardy in 91 seconds. It could be the same again." - Naseem Hamed on his fight against Paul Ingle in Manchester in 1999.

"They've only just gone to secondary school but each of them could bend down, pick me up and break me like a twig." - Barry John on Craig and Scott Quinnell.

"Beckham is the best crosser of the ball I've ever seen." - Alan Shearer.

"Right now we're on a par with Albania and Moldova." - German footballer Paul Breitner after his country's 3-0 defeat by the U.S. in 1999.

"There's no confidence in the bank." - Nick Faldo at the 1999 Players' Championship at Ponte Vedra.

"If things carry on like this, I will seriously think about chucking it all out at the end of the season." - Stephen Hendry in 1998 following his exit in the German Masters.

"When you win London you become the best runner in the world." - Antonio Pinto on the London Marathon.

"It's amazing what happens when a putt finally goes in." - Colin Montgomerie at the 1999 Bell South Classic.

"I drew Hendry last year. They'll probably dig up Joe Davis for me this time."- Jimmy White in advance of the draw for the Embassy World Snooker Championship in 1999.

THE THINGS THEY SAID

"The flipper has gone, so has the drift." - anonymous Australian speaking in April 1999 on the decline of Shane Warne.

"I twitched on the blocks and went back on my heels and for the first few strokes I was thinking that they might take me out." - Swimmer Mark Foster.

"I can't blame the surface. I can't blame the balls. I can't blame the crowd." - Tim Henman on losing to Jim Courier in the 1999 Davis Cup.

"I am calm. I am going to jail. This brings to a close the campaign against me." - Atletico Madrid president Jesus Gil on being sent down in 1999.

"What does this Frenchman know about football? He wears glasses and looks like a schoolteacher. He's not going to be as good as George. Does he even speak English properly?" - Tony Adams on new boss Wenger.

"I think it should be mandatory for all fighters to retire at 65." - George Foreman.

"We had Y.T.S. boys on the bench today." - John Gregory after Aston Villa's 2-1 defeat at Newcastle in January 1999.

"I haven't seen any surprises. It was quite the same as when I left." - Ruud Gullit on his old club Chelsea after they played Newcastle in January 1999.

"How much do you get on the dole these days?" - Dominic Cork in 1997 on being left out of the West Indies tour.

"There are two teams out there and one of them is trying to play cricket." - W.M. Woodfull, Australian captain on the January 1933 Adelaide Test against England.

THE THINGS THEY SAID

"I don't like foreigners coming in and moaning and saying the league is too long." - former Lazio and Rangers paragon Paul Gascoigne in 1999.

"He's a dinosaur. We book him in training." - Dave Jones, Southampton boss on Mark Hughes.

"What you sow you reap." - Glenn Hoddle, prior to being turned over by the media.

"A nine-goal thriller." - Nottingham Forest boss Ron Atkinson's assessment of their 8-1 home defeat by Manchester United in 1999.

"I am so impressed with him, he loves playing football." - Harry Redknapp on Paulo Di Canio.

"I used to write his name on the back of my shirts." - Rigobert Song on Ronald Koeman.

"I think he can play where he wants, can't he?" - West Ham's John Moncur on being asked what Marc-Vivien Foe's best position might be.

"If you go through their team sheet you could frighten yourself." - Lydney rugby player Nick Nelmes on Saracens, their opponents in a Tetley's Bitter Cup game in 1999.

"You never feel at home in front of the cameras - but I've always seen myself as an entertainer." - Linford Christie on his new career in television.

THE THINGS THEY SAID

"If I could take two out of the United side it would be Keane and Giggs." - Bryan Robson on his former club Manchester United.

"He is undoubtedly a highly gifted lad, is David, and down to earth with it; no 'side'." - Tom Finney on Preston North End boss David Moyes.

"Black bears can do 30 miles per hour. I would never outrun one." - athlete Jon Brown on training in a forest in Canada.

"I'm on a diet of bananas and seaweed. It doesn't make me a better player but I'm a better swimmer." - culinary guru Gordon Strachan.

"If my footballers were bricklayers, the house they built would fall down." - Alan Ball in 1998.

"It's not humane. We are playing again in 48 hours. They laugh at us abroad." - Brian Kidd in 1998.

"I was never worried. I knew we couldn't make the runs." - I.W. Johnson, Australian bowler on their unlikely one wicket victory over West Indies in 1952.

"Since 776 B.C." - Craig Masback, Chief Executive Officer of U.S.A. Track and Field when asked by a potential sponsor how long his sport had been in the Olympic Games.

"This is the big one, a big jump for me. This was some magic." - Mika Hakkinen after winning the 1999 Montreal Grand Prix.

"I usually make one mistake a year." - Michael Schumacher after retiring from the 1999 Montreal Grand Prix.

"I'm not in the mood for quirk." - Colin Montgomery in jovial mood at the 1999 Bay Hill Invitational.

THE THINGS THEY SAID

"That dream was never going to happen, but there were five or six when I went there. So there was half a dream." - Keith Gillespie on Sir John Hall's dream of a Newcastle team composed of Geordies.

"Personally I need to start winning races." - David Coulthard after the 1999 Spanish Grand Prix.

"I appreciate other drivers have got their own races to run but I think they should have been prepared to lose a second or so to let the leaders past." - David Coulthard after losing the 1999 San Marino Grand Prix by under 5 seconds.

"Marcello Lippi, the best coach in the world, packed it in at Juventus last week because he couldn't figure out football, so there's no point at all in asking me what went on today." - Gordon Strachan after Coventry's 2-1 defeat by Everton in 1999.

"The club is unfulfilled, not just me." - Alan Shearer on Newcastle United.

"I watched him hit a few shots on Saturday and went home with a bad back." - Ray Floyd on John Daly.

"This has opened a real can of worms." - Ian Rush on the decision to replay the 1998/9 Arsenal-Sheffield United F.A. Cup tie after Marc Overmars scored an 'ungentlemanly' winner.

"I don't think I've ever been so nervous going for a win in my life as I have been today."- Colin McRae after winning the 1999 Safari Rally.

"He sweats and I get the glory." - Eddie Irvine joking about Michael Schumacher's role after Irvine won a Grand Prix in 1999 at the 82nd attempt.

"I thought the game was over, but suddenly the gears came back and I was able to keep going." - Mika Hakkinen after winning the 1999 Brazilian Grand Prix.

SPORTING ASSORTMENT

SPORTING ASSORTMENT

England badminton coach Ray Stevens is a cousin of England player Darren Hall.

Ray Mercer became W.B.O. heavyweight boxing champion in January 1991.

The Dallas Stars and the Buffalo Sabres contested the 1999 Stanley Cup final in ice hockey.

A rubber cube was originally used instead of a ball in hockey.

Graciano Rocchigiani lost the W.B.C. light-heavyweight title in 1998 for not fighting Roy Jones.

Italy's Francesco Casagrande won the 1999 Tour of Switzerland, his first title since a nine month drug ban.

England men's hockey team lost 4-0 in the 1999 Champions Trophy to the Netherlands. It was their 12th successive defeat.

First prize for the 1998 Olympia Grand Prix in equestrianism was £16,000.

Mauro Galvano beat Dario Matteoni in December 1990 to take the vacant W.B.C. supper-middleweight title.

Chris Eubank beat Nigel Benn in 1990 to take the W.B.O. middleweight title.

SPORTING ASSORTMENT

1996 European lightweight judo champion Danny Kingston was forced to enter the light-middleweight category at the 1998 British championships as he was 3.3lb overweight.

After Swedish ice hockey player Karl Oberg hit Canadian coach Father David Bauer over the head with his stick at the 1964 Winter Olympics, the referee was suspended for two games for not penalising him.

Joe DiMaggio, the famous baseball player who had an affair with Marilyn Monroe, was buried in March 1999 in Holy Cross Cemetery, Colma, California.

Peter Nicol, the world's former No. 1 squash player, was born in Inverurie in Scotland.

The International Olympic Committee paid out $204,000 in 1998 to cover Juan Antonio Samaranch's living expenses at the Palace Hotel in Lausanne.

The prize for winning the 1999 Greyhound Derby was £50,000.

Squash player Amjad Khan is the nephew of Jansher Khan.

Canada's Jonathan Power became squash's No. 1 in May 1999.

The TVM team were banned from the 1999 Tour De France race because of possible drugs links.

SPORTING ASSORTMENT

Hockey was first played at the Blackheath Club in 1861.

Monsanto, the firm linked to GM foodstuffs, made the artificial turf for the 1976 Montreal Olympics hockey tournament.

The New York Mets' baseball manager Bobby Valentine received a two match ban after attempting to retake his seat on the bench in a game against the Toronto Blue Jays after having been sent off for arguing too fiercely. He disguised himself in a cap, sunglasses and false moustache but was spotted by TV cameras.

Graham Bell became British skiing's director of performance in 1998.

The first set of ice hockey rules were drawn up in 1865.

Joshua West, at 6' 9", became the tallest rower to take part in the University Boat Race in 1999.

SPORTING ASSORTMENT

Sumner, Bramich and McKee are all types of hares used in greyhound racing.

The Phillie Phanatic, the Philadelphia Phillies' baseball team mascot, is a seven feet tall green bird.

Dick Tiger was Ring Magazine fighter of the year in 1962 & '65.

Boxer Chatchai Sasakul represents Thailand.

The head of the French Cycling Federation is Daniel Baal.

Nick Pert and Ruth Sheldon won the boys' and girls' Under-18 world championships in chess in November 1998.

Of the 25,000 birds entered into the 1,000km International Barcelona pigeon race in 1997, over 12,000 were Belgian.

The Stanley Cup in ice hockey is named after Lord Stanley of Preston, a former governor-general of Canada.

The dog Spin won the first race at Wembley Stadium dog track on December 10, 1927.

Jessie Gilbert became the world's youngest winner of an adult world chess title at the age of 11 in January 1999, when she took the women's gold medal at the World Amateur Championships in Hastings.

SPORTING ASSORTMENT

The standard size of a clay pigeon is 120mm in diameter with a 26mm breadth.

Thomas Hearns beat Virgil Hill in 1991 to take the W.B.A. light-heavyweight title.

The San Antonio Spurs won their first N.B.A. championships basketball title in 1999.

George Ligowsky invented the clay pigeon in the 1880s.

In a May 1999 W.B.A. super-bantamweight fight, holder Nestor Garza retained his title.

The original basket in basketball as invented by James Naismith in 1891 was a peach basket.

Australian Rules Football star Peter Everitt donated £7,500 to an Aboriginal community scheme after admitting racially abusing Melbourne opponent Scott Chisholm in a game in 1999.

Baseball player Orlando Hernandez escaped from Cuba to the U.S. on a raft and signed a $6.6m contract with the New York Yankees.

The Cambridge University cox in the 1999 University Boat Race, Vian Sharif, is 5ft tall.

Baseball legend Hank Aaron's charity 'Chasing the Dream' provides financial assistance to young people with limited abilities.

SPORTING ASSORTMENT

A last-second shot by Terrell Myers for the Sheffield Sharks basketball team won them the 1999 Budweiser League title.

Magnus Gustafsson won the 1998 Copenhagen Open singles tennis title.

Escrima is a Philippine martial art using sticks, knives and hands.

Rugby league player Steve Prescott scored 22 points for England against France at Gateshead in 1996.

Opening Day in the 1999 baseball season in the U.S. was staged in Monterrey, Mexico - the first time it had been held outside the U.S.

Snooker player Stephen Lee departed from the British Open in 1999 after damaging a muscle when answering the telephone.

Gloucester rugby union player Simon Mannix played for the Petone club in New Zealand.

Rugby League team Barrow Border Raiders had four players sent off in the 1998 league.

Multum in Parvo won the 1990 Mackeson Gold Cup.

Goalkeeper Dave Beasant was once out of action after dropping a jar of salad cream on his foot.

SPORTING ASSORTMENT

Footballer-turned-coach David Platt owns the horse Handsome Ridge.

Tim Brookshaw was National Hunt Champion jockey in 1958/9.

Four Scots contested the snooker semi-finals of the 1999 China International Tournament.

C.L. Cairns took 15-83 for Nottinghamshire against Sussex at Arundel in the 1995 county championship.

Ashley Crawford became British light-heavyweight boxing champion in June 1991.

British tennis rivals Tim Henman and Greg Rusedski share the same birthday.

Stirling Moss never won the motor racing World Drivers' Championship, but was runner-up four times.

Ron Dennis is team manager for Formula 1 racing team McLaren.

Paul Lawrie had three European Tour victories under his belt before his victory in the 1999 British Open Championship in Carnoustie.

Ellery Hanley played rugby league for Bradford, Wigan and Leeds.